Date Due

DEMCO NO. 38-298

D1261272

PRINCIPLES

& METHODS OF

Chemical Analysis

PRINCIPLES & METHODS OF

HAROLD F. WALTON

Department of Chemistry
University of Colorado

Chemical Analysis

158 18

PRENTICE-HALL, INC.

New York

PRENTICE-HALL CHEMISTRY SERIES

WENDELL M. LATIMER, PH.D., *Editor*

Library of Congress Catalog Card Number: **52-9945**

First printing . . . . *August, 1952*
Second printing . . . . *May, 1955*

CHEMISTRY

Preface

THIS BOOK surveys the field of non-instrumental analysis, with emphasis on the basic principles of analytical processes. Individual procedures and determinations are used to ensure an understanding of these principles, although generally not described in detail.

Important recent advances in conventional gravimetric and volumetric analysis are explained. The field of conventional analysis is consolidated, thereby placing its methods in proper orientation with the methods used in instrumental analysis. The book also emphasizes that analytical chemistry involves the utilization of all other branches of chemistry to a particular end; that it is *not* a "cookbook" or mechanical "button-pushing" kind of subject.

Although primarily intended for senior undergraduate and graduate students, this volume will also be helpful to the practicing chemist as a reference handbook. A knowledge of physical chemistry is assumed. The approach is somewhat like that of T. B. Smith in "Analytical Processes: A Physico-Chemical Interpretation," a book to which I am greatly indebted, having known it since my undergraduate days. My discussion in Chapter 13 is largely patterned on that book.

I am deeply grateful to my wife, Sadie Goodman Walton, for her devoted application during the preparation of the manuscript. Hers was the onerous job of typing and copy-editing the manuscript, as well as nudging me along the way until the writing was completed. My sincere thanks and appreciation also to the staff of Prentice-Hall for their cooperation; to Professor Stanley J. Cristol, of the University of Colorado, for pertinent criticism; and to Mr. M. Payne for drawing of the illustrations.

HAROLD F. WALTON

Boulder, Colorado

Table of contents

1

Introduction

ANALYTICAL CHEMISTRY was once considered a craft rather than a science, a dull but necessary prerequisite to more interesting fields of activity. This attitude has changed in recent years. We deem it a fit subject for graduate study and no longer expect a college student to master analytical chemistry in his second year, for we recognize that the analytical chemist of today must also be a physical, inorganic, or organic chemist, and if possible, all three. In particular, he must know the fundamentals of physical chemistry.

The main reason for this change in emphasis is the spectacular growth of physical or "instrumental" methods of analysis over the last twenty years. Examples of these methods are emission and absorption spectroscopy, mass spectroscopy, polarography, and x-ray diffraction. By these methods, analyses which formerly required hours can be performed in minutes, trace constituents can be detected and determined whose presence was formerly unsuspected, and mixtures can be analyzed whose components could hardly be differentiated in any other way; for example, the various crystalline forms of alumina or the differently linked polymers in synthetic rubber. It is no wonder that the impression has spread among chemists that the older methods of gravimetric and volumetric analysis would soon be obsolete. Yet this is a great error, as anyone who is active in analytical chemistry knows. The instruments we have mentioned do not "analyze" in the true sense of the term; that is, they do not separate a complex body into its individual, simple components; when used for quantitative determinations, they are all relative, and need calibration, sometimes extensive calibration, by the slower but more nearly absolute classical procedure. Instruments are cumbersome, and it need hardly be added that they are expensive.

Thanks to physical methods, more analyses are being made than ever before, but they have supplemented the older methods rather than displaced them. H. V. Churchill, of the Aluminum Corporation of America, reported recently that 53% of the analytical laboratory man-hours in his organization were used to make 9% of the determinations by strictly chemical means, while the remaining 91% of the determinations were made by 47% of the labor by various physical methods. The more efficient the instrumental techniques, he said, the greater the demands on fundamental analytical chemistry to evaluate and calibrate the instruments [1]

Along with the growth of instrumental methods there have been less spectacular, but perhaps equally important advances in gravimetric and volumetric analysis and in the general techniques of chemical separations. New reagents, such as organic precipitants, complex-formers and indicators, and new techniques, such as ion exchange and titration in nonaqueous solvents, have been steadily coming into use. The analyst has a vast array of tools at his disposal and he must know what they are, what each will do, and above all, how each works, so that he can select the right tool for the problem at hand.

Every new analysis presents a new problem, the answer to which is seldom to be found in compendia of standard procedures. Interfering elements may be present which the standard procedure does not mention. The size of the sample is another variable, and so is the concentration in the sample of the constituent to be determined. Whether such methods as colorimetry or potentiometric titration are to be employed depends on the facilities available, and whether it is worth while calibrating an instrument or standardizing a solution depends on the number of determinations to be made. Always there is the choice to be made between accuracy and speed; in some cases ten analyses with an accuracy of 1% are of more value than one with an accuracy of 0.1%, in other cases the reverse is true. The method chosen will depend on the particular requirements.

This book attempts to describe the "noninstrumental" methods of chemical analysis, though it is hard to say where "noninstrumental" methods leave off and "instrumental" methods begin. The balance and the buret are instruments, and every quantitative chemical analysis depends on a physical measurement, whether of mass, vol-

[1] *Chem. Eng. News,* **28,** 688 (February 27, 1950).

ume, pressure, or optical density. It seems illogical to discuss complex ions and the compounds of organic reagents with metals and not mention that some of these are colored and adapted to photometric determination, but the experimental techniques of photometry (or colorimetry) are not discussed. Under "gravimetric analysis" it was obviously necessary to include analysis by electrodeposition and, having introduced this subject, it would have been foolish to omit coulometric titration. Under "volumetric analysis," the theory and practice of potentiometric titration are discussed, because they are basic to titrations of all kinds. An account of conductometric titration is given, but amperometric titration and high-frequency titration are omitted, save for a brief mention.

The organization of the book is in two parts. The first deals with those methods in which a constituent is quantitatively separated from the other substances present, and includes gravimetric analysis as well as such general separation methods as distillation, solvent extraction, and complex ion formation. Gravimetric analysis is the most fundamental form of analysis, for one or more of the components of the mixture is quantitatively separated in pure form, or in the form of a pure compound of known composition, and weighed. The balance is the most accurate of all the instruments in the analytical laboratory, and gravimetric analysis is potentially the most accurate, as well as the most reliable means of chemical analysis. Moreover, it is the most versatile, being applicable to every element in every combination. Its drawbacks are that it is often long and tedious compared to other methods, and that the requirement of quantitative separation as a pure compound may be difficult to fulfill.

Volumetric methods are covered in the second part of the book. These are faster than gravimetric procedures, once the necessary standard solutions are prepared, and often nearly as accurate. Their theory is much more complicated than that of gravimetric analysis, and considerable space has therefore been given to a discussion of the four basic types of chemical reactions used in titrations; namely, acid-base, oxidation-reduction, precipitation, and complex-forming reactions, as well as to the theory of indicators.

The physical properties of precipitates

PRECIPITATES are all-important in gravimetric analysis. They are not just finely divided solids, but have their characteristic, individual properties, some being crystalline, some curdy, some gelatinous, some slimy, and all containing more or less occluded water and contaminating salts. These characteristics all depend on the conditions of precipitation as well as on the intrinsic properties of the materials precipitated. A material can be curdy under some conditions, crystalline under others, depending on the particle size; particle size, in turn, depends in part on the solubility of the precipitated material. Particle size and solubility are two of the physical properties we shall discuss in this chapter. Both can be regulated within certain limits by controlling the conditions of precipitation.

Solubility

Most of the precipitates formed in gravimetric analysis are sufficiently insoluble that the errors caused by incomplete precipitation or by dissolving of the precipitate in the wash liquid are insignificant compared with other errors in the analysis. However, analytical precipitates vary widely in solubility. At one extreme is hydrous ferric oxide, one of the most insoluble substances known, and at the other is the triple acetate, $NaZn(UO_2)_3(CH_3COO)_9 \cdot 6H_2O$, in which form sodium is usually separated and weighed. The solubility of this salt in pure water is 58.5 grams, or 0.038 mole, per liter at 21°C, which is so high that special precautions are needed to avoid incomplete precipitation and the loss of material before weighing. The volume of the sample must be kept small, a large excess of reagent must be used, and the reagent must be previously saturated with the sodium salt at the room temperature at which it is to be used. This temperature should preferably be low, and it must remain constant during the precipitation. The precipitate must be washed with 95% ethyl alcohol which has been saturated with the triple acetate.[1] When these precautions are taken, good accuracy is possible despite the high solubility of the precipitate. Similar precautions are needed in determining potassium as its dipicrylamine salt.

These cases are exceptional, but often a careful control of precipitation and washing is necessary to avoid undue solubility losses. On the other hand, a precipitate which is too insoluble may separate in an undesirable, finely divided form. Solubility control during precipitation is therefore of prime importance.

Solubility product. Basic to the study of the solubility of electrolytes is the solubility product relation. For any binary compound, A_xB_y, which gives the ions A^{+y} and B^{-x} in solution:

$$A_xB_y \text{ (solid)} \rightleftharpoons xA^{+y} + yB^{-x} \text{ (solution)},$$

the concentrations of the dissolved ions which are in equilibrium with the undissolved solid are related approximately by the equation

$$[A^{+y}]^x \cdot [B^{-x}]^y = \text{a constant}, \tag{1}$$

where $[A^{+y}]$, $[B^{-x}]$ are the molar concentrations of the ions A^{+y} and B^{-x}. For example, in saturated solutions of AgCl, Ag_2CrO_4, and $Co(NH_3)_6Cl_3$,

$$[Ag^+][Cl^-] = 1.6 \times 10^{-10}.$$

$$[Ag^+]^2[CrO_4^=] = 9 \times 10^{-12}.$$

$$[Co(NH_3)_6^{+++}][Cl^-]^3 = 1.2 \times 10^{-1}.$$

The constant in equation (1) is called the *solubility product*. The equation tells us that if the concentration of one of the ions is raised, the concentration of the other must fall to maintain equilibrium; or

[1] H. H. Barber and I. M. Kolthoff, *J. Am. Chem. Soc.*, **50**, 1625 (1928); E. G. Ball and J. F. Sadusk, *J. Biol. Chem.*, **113**, 661 (1936); I. M. Kolthoff and E. B. Sandell, *Quantitative Inorganic Analysis*, 2d ed., New York, Macmillan, 1943, p. 416.

if we wish to depress the concentration of one of the ions, we may do so by raising the concentration of the other. Thus the solubility of silver chloride is depressed by adding sodium chloride to the solution. This effect is known as the *common ion effect*. According to the solubility product relation, the solubility of silver chloride in pure water is $\sqrt{1.6 \times 10^{-10}} = 1.25 \times 10^{-5}$ mole per liter, but in 0.01 M sodium chloride it is only 1.6×10^{-8} mole per liter. The solubility product relation tells us, incidentally, that the common ion effect will be greater, the more abundant the added ions are relative to the other ions in the precipitate. Doubling the chloride ion concentration halves the silver ion concentration in equilibrium with solid AgCl, but it divides the concentration of $Co(NH_3)_6^{+++}$ in equilibrium with solid $Co(NH_3)_6Cl_3$ by eight.

The use of solubility products in numerical calculations is treated extensively in elementary texts.

Activity. Equation (1), we noted, is only approximate. A rigid relation is

$$(a_{A^{+y}})^x \cdot (a_{B^{-x}})^y = \text{a constant.} \tag{2}$$

This is true so long as the solid is pure and the temperature is constant. (Pressure affects the constant slightly, but this effect is negligible for our purpose.) The a's in equation (2) represent *activities*. To relate activities to concentrations, *activity coefficients*, represented by the symbol f, are used:

$$a_{A^{+y}} = f_{A^{+y}} \cdot [A^{+y}]. \tag{3}$$

In very dilute solutions activity coefficients are close to unity, and for rough calculations activities and concentrations may be used interchangeably, but in concentrated salt solutions, f may be as low as 0.05 or as high as 3.[2]

Activity is defined thermodynamically by two equations. The first defines the ratio of the activities of a substance in two different environments (or concentrations) in terms of the work which must be done to transfer a mole of the substance from one environment to the other:

$$\Delta F_{12} \equiv RT \ln \frac{a_2}{a_1} \tag{4}$$

[2] For a comprehensive table of activity coefficients in concentrated salt solutions, see R. A. Robinson and R. H. Stokes, *Trans. Faraday Soc.*, **45**, 612 (1949).

where ΔF_{12} is the increase in free energy of a substance when a mole of it is transferred at constant temperature and pressure from one solution, or environment, denoted by the subscript 1, to another solution, or environment, denoted by the subscript 2. Or, ΔF_{12} is the work needed to effect this transfer under reversible conditions.

If the two "environments" were two ideal dilute solutions having concentrations c_1 and c_2, ΔF would equal $RT \ln (c_2/c_1)$. The more dilute a solution is, the more nearly ideal it becomes, and the more closely activities parallel concentrations. It is therefore appropriate, since equation (4) defines only the *ratio* of two activities and leaves their units unstated, to make activities arbitrarily equal to molar concentrations in infinitely dilute solutions. Mathematically,

$$\operatorname*{Lim}_{c \to 0} \frac{a_1}{c_1} = \operatorname*{Lim}_{c \to 0} f_1 = 1. \tag{5}$$

Equations (4) and (5) define the activity of a dissolved substance completely.

The activity coefficient f of an ionized substance in solution is generally less than 1. This is due to two main reasons, namely:

(a) Interionic attraction.

(b) Association of ions with one another or with neutral molecules. Where f is greater than 1, as in a concentrated lithium chloride solution, there is a breakdown of the structure of water by the electric fields of the dissolved ions.

Activity and interionic attraction. The effect of interionic attraction upon activity is the easiest of these effects to interpret and has been extensively studied both theoretically and experimentally. Unlike charges attract one another, while like charges repel. In an ionic solution, therefore, the positive ions have more negative ions than positive ions in their immediate neighborhood, and the negative ions, in turn, have an excess of positive ions around them. The more concentrated the solution, the closer is this clustering of ions of opposite charge. The attraction of unlike charges for one another has the effect of lowering the potential energy; that is, it is easier to move a mole of salt from a dilute solution into a more concentrated solution than one would expect from the dilute solution laws. It is also easier to move a mole of a sparingly soluble salt from the solid crystals into a solution containing an indifferent electrolyte, that is, one with no ions in common with the solid, than it is to move it into pure water.

In other words, the solubility of a sparingly soluble salt is raised by the presence of an indifferent electrolyte. This is sometimes called the "diverse ion effect," to distinguish it from the "common ion effect" which is the lowering of solubility by the addition of a salt having an ion in common with the solid, in accordance with Equation (1).

The activity coefficient of an ion in solution is lowered by the presence of other ions in the same solution, regardless of what kinds of ions these are. A quantitative relationship between activity coefficient and ionic concentration was worked out by Debye and Hückel,[3] who considered the clustering of ions around those of unlike charge to be the resultant of electrostatic attraction (which favors clustering) and thermal agitation (which favors random mixing). For the simple case in which the ions are treated as point charges, and the solvent as a continuous medium of uniform dielectric constant, they derived the equation

$$\ln f_{\pm} = -A z_A z_B \sqrt{\mu} \tag{6}$$

where: $f_{\pm}$ = mean activity coefficient of a salt AB = $(f_A{}^x f_B{}^y)^{1/(x+y)}$.

$$A = \left[\frac{2\pi N \epsilon^6}{1000(DkT)^3} \right]^{1/2}.$$

z_A, z_B = charges on the ions = y and x in the above example, taken without regard to sign.

N = Avogadro's number.

ϵ = charge on the electron.

D = dielectric constant of the medium.

k = Boltzmann constant.

T = absolute temperature.

The factor A, divided by 2.303 for use with common logarithms, is 0.5065 in water at 25°C.

The quantity μ is very significant. It is called the *ionic strength,* and is defined by

$$\mu = \frac{1}{2} \sum_i c_i z_i^2 \tag{7}$$

---

[3] P. Debye and E. Hückel, *Physik. Z.*, **24**, 185, 305 (1923). See textbooks of electrochemistry or of physical chemistry, e.g., W. Moore, *Physical Chemistry,* New York, Prentice-Hall, 1950, Chap. 15.

where c_i is the molar concentration of an ion i, and z_i is its charge. The terms $c_i z_i^2$ are summed over *all the ions in the solution*. That is to say, the activity of a dissolved salt—say silver chloride—depends not only on the concentrations of its own ions, but on the concentrations of all the ions in the solution. This is reasonable, of course. The cluster of negative ions surrounding a silver ion will contain not only chloride ions, but nitrate ions, sulfate ions, acetate ions—any negative ions that happen to be in the solution. All will cooperate to depress the activity of the silver ion, and all the positive ions present will cooperate to depress the activity of the chloride ion. The result will be to raise the solubility of silver chloride, for the product $f_{Ag^+} f_{Cl^-} \cdot c_{Ag^+} c_{Cl^-}$ must be constant and equal to the solubility product, which is determined by the fugacity of solid silver chloride, and if the f's are diminished, the c's must rise.

A more accurate equation, which takes account of the radii of the ions and of the lowering of the dielectric constant of the solvent by the electric force between the ions, is the following:

$$\log f_{\pm} = -\frac{z_+ z_- \cdot A \sqrt{\mu}}{1 + B \sqrt{\mu}} + C\mu. \tag{8}$$

B depends on the ionic radii, and is 0.3288Å at 25°C in water, Å being the mean distance of closest approach of the two ions in Ångstrom

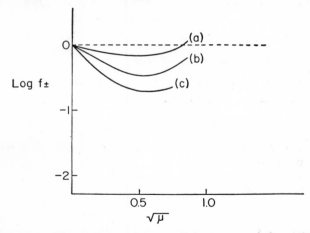

Fig. 2-1. Theoretical activity coefficient curves (schematic). (a), 1-1 valent; (b), 1-2 valent; (c), 2-2 valent.

units. C is a small constant which depends on the salt as well as on the solvent. This equation gives values of the activity coefficient which are always larger than equation (6), the limiting equation, predicts. Typical theoretical graphs of $\log f_{\pm}$ against $\sqrt{\mu}$ are given in Figure 1. It will be noted that the activity coefficients are smaller, the greater the charges on the ions concerned. Thus the solubility of $BaSO_4$ will be affected more by added salt than that of $Mg(OH)_2$, and that of $Mg(OH)_2$ more than that of $AgCl$, and the added salt will have more effect on the solubility, the greater the charges on the ions of which it is composed.

Electrostatic effects between ions may raise the solubilities of

TABLE I

SOLUBILITY OF BaSO₄ IN SALT SOLUTIONS

Added salt	Ionic strength	$BaSO_4$ solubility, moles/liter $\times 10^5$
None	3.93×10^{-5}	0.957
KCl	$2.5 \ \times 10^{-3}$	1.274
KCl	$3.6 \ \times 10^{-2}$	2.355
$Mg(NO_3)_2$	$1.2 \ \times 10^{-2}$	2.458
$LaCl_3$	$4.3 \ \times 10^{-3}$	2.394

Reference: E. W. Neumann, *J. Am. Chem. Soc.*, **55**, 879 (1933).

TABLE II

SOLUBILITY OF MgNH₄PO₄·6H₂O IN SALT SOLUTIONS

Added salt	Ionic strength	Solubility, moles/liter $\times 10^4$
None	about 0.003	5.84
KCl	0.10	7.83
KCl	0.50	11.0
K_2SO_4	0.15	9.12
K_2SO_4	0.75	14.3
NH_4Cl	0.10	8.0
NH_4Cl	0.50	16.0
$Na_2C_2O_4$	0.15	28.5
$Na_2C_2O_4$	0.75	79.5

Reference: R. F. Uncles and G. B. L. Smith, *Ind. Eng. Chem., Anal. Ed.*, **18**, 699 (1946).

sparingly soluble salts several fold. Figure 1 indicates the effects expected theoretically, and Tables I and II show some typical experimental data. To these we shall add, as a further example, the data of Näsänen[4] on $Mg(OH)_2$. The apparent solubility product of $Mg(OH)_2$ is six times as great in 0.8 M NaCl solution as it is in water, that is, the product $f_{Mg} \cdot f_{(OH^-)}^2$ is 1/6.

In nonaqueous solutions the dielectric constant is usually less than in water, and the electrostatic effects are therefore greater. A recent publication describes the precipitation of sulfate as $[Co(NH_c)_6]BrSO_4$, which is then redissolved and determined colorimetrically. This salt is too soluble in water for quantitative separation, so it is precipi-

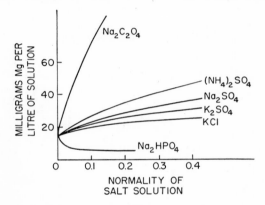

Fig. 2-2. Solubility of $MgNH_4PO_4 \cdot 6H_2O$ in salt solutions. Data of Uncles and Smith, *Ind. Eng. Chem., Anal. Ed.*, **18**, 699 (1946).

tated in 66% acetone (dielectric constant = 43). It was found that if this solution was 0.023 M in $MgCl_2$, the solubility of the sulfate was raised from almost zero to 0.8 mg. (as $SO_4^=$) in 150 ml.[5]

Association and activity. The effects of interionic attraction upon solubilities are large enough to be of some consequence in analytical chemistry, but in aqueous solutions their importance is not as great as the figures just quoted might indicate, because, first, the solubility error is usually small compared to other errors in gravimetric analysis, and second, true solubility equilibrium is approached very slowly with sparingly soluble salts, and analytical procedures

[4] R. Näsänen, *Z. physik. Chem.*, **A, 190**, 183 (1942).
[5] C. Mahr and M. Krauss, *Z. anal. Chem.*, **128**, 477 (1948).

are therefore adjusted where possible to give a safety factor such that even if the solubility loss were as much as ten times the theoretical, the effect on the accuracy of the analysis would still be very small.

A much more serious source of solubility loss in gravimetric precipitation is the combination of ions of the precipitate with other ions or molecules in the solution to form weakly ionized complexes. Extreme examples of such an effect are the dissolving of silver chloride in sodium thiosulfate solution to form the complex ion $AgS_2O_3^-$, or in

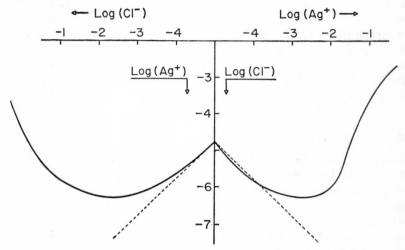

Fig. 2-3.   Solubility of AgCl in solutions of NaCl and $AgNO_3$. The dotted lines show the ideal solubility product relation.   Data of Pinkus *et al.*, *Bull. Soc. Chim. (Belg.)*, **46,** 46 (1937), **47, 304** (1938).

cyanide solutions to give $Ag(CN)_2^-$.   Other complex-forming reactions, which are more likely to cause error in gravimetric analysis because they are not so obvious, are the association of lead ions with acetate ions, which makes lead sulfate more soluble in acetate solutions than in water, and of magnesium ions with oxalate ions, which causes the solubility of magnesium ammonium phosphate to be raised significantly by even small amounts of oxalate, with formation of the ions $Mg(C_2O_4)_2^=$ (see Table II).   This sort of complex formation is extremely common with metals other than the alkali and alkaline earth metals, as will be seen in Chapter 7.   It is not generally known, for example, that silver chloride is much more soluble in 1 N sodium chloride or 0.1 N silver nitrate than it is in water. Figure 3 shows the very great deviation of silver chloride from the simple solubility product relationship. The abnormal solubility is due to ions such as $AgCl_2^-$, Ag_2Cl^+ and $Ag(NO_3)_2^-$. Effects like these can cause great errors in analyses performed in concentrated salt solutions.

Solubility and pH. A very important kind of association, in fact the commonest, which affects the solubility of sparingly soluble salts is that between protons and the anions of weak acids. This is the reason that sparingly soluble salts of weak acids dissolve in solutions of strong acids while sparingly soluble salts of strong acids do not. Barium carbonate, calcium oxalate, barium sulfate, and silver chloride all have about equal solubility products, yet only the first two dissolve to any great extent in dilute acid. Calcium oxalate, for example, dissolves because of the reactions

$$C_2O_4^= + H^+ \rightleftharpoons HC_2O_4^-$$

and
$$HC_2O_4^- + H^+ \rightleftharpoons H_2C_2O_4$$

which cut down the concentration of oxalate ions. In a case such as this the solubility of the salt can be varied over a very wide range simply by changing the pH. With the help of ionization constants and solubility products, one can calculate the effect of pH on the solubility of salts of weak acids. Such calculations are extremely useful in analytical chemistry, and we shall illustrate them with calcium oxalate as an example.

The necessary equilibrium constants are:

$$[Ca^{++}][C_2O_4^=] = K_{sp} = 2.0 \times 10^{-9}$$

$$\frac{[H^+][HC_2O_4^-]}{[H_2C_2O_4]} = K_1 = 6.5 \times 10^{-2}$$

$$\frac{[H^+][C_2O_4^=]}{[HC_2O_4^-]} = K_2 = 6.1 \times 10^{-5}.$$

These are thermodynamic constants in which activities should be used and not concentrations, but we shall approximate and consider the activity coefficients to be unity for the time being.

Let us calculate the calcium ion concentration in a solution of pH 3.0 and of total or "formal" oxalate concentration, $[H_2C_2O_4] + [HC_2O_4^-] + [C_2O_4^=]$, equal to 0.05. The first step is to calculate the proportions of the different oxalate species. Let one of these concentrations equal 1; for example, $[HC_2O_4^-]$. (This is chosen because inspection of the ionization constants shows that $HC_2O_4^-$ is the most abundant species at pH 3.0, but either of the other species could have been chosen instead; we need only the ratios.) From the ionization constants and the pH,

$$\frac{[H_2C_2O_4]}{[HC_2O_4^-]} = \frac{[H^+]}{K_1} = \frac{1.0 \times 10^{-3}}{6.5 \times 10^{-2}} = 0.015,$$

$$\frac{[C_2O_4^-]}{[HC_2O_4^-]} = \frac{K_2}{[H^+]} = \frac{6.1 \times 10^{-5}}{1.0 \times 10^{-3}} = 0.061.$$

The ratio of concentrations, $[H_2C_2O_4] : [HC_2O_4^-] : [C_2O_4^=]$, is 0.015 : 1 : 0.061; the fraction of the total oxalate which is $C_2O_4^=$ is therefore $0.061/(0.015 + 1 + 0.061) = 0.058$. The total oxalate concentration is 0.05; the concentration of $C_2O_4^=$ is therefore $0.05 \times 0.058 = 0.0029$. To obtain the calcium ion concentration which is in equilibrium with solid calcium oxalate and this solution, we substitute this value into the solubility product of calcium oxalate:

$$[Ca^{++}] = \frac{2.0 \times 10^{-9}}{2.9 \times 10^{-3}} = 6.9 \times 10^{-7}.$$

Figure 4 shows the results of such calculations made at different pH values. Figure 4(a) shows the proportions of the different oxalate species, and Figure 4(b) shows, by a logarithmic plot, the equilibrium concentrations of calcium ions for a total oxalate concentration of 0.05 molar. We note in passing that according to these calculations calcium oxalate is quantitatively precipitated at a pH considerably lower than the pH usually recommended for this precipitation, which is pH 5.0–5.5, the change point of methyl red.

In these calculations we have neglected the activity coefficients. The easiest way to take these into account is to calculate "practical" ionization constants and solubility products, using the extended Debye-Hückel equation [Equation (8) above], inserting the appropriate value for the ionic strength and the mean interatomic distance, Å. Thus the "practical" second ionization constant of oxalic acid would be

$$K_2' = \frac{a_{H^+} \cdot [C_2O_4^=]}{[HC_2O_4^-]} = \frac{a_{H^+} \cdot a_{C_2O_4^-}}{a_{HC_2O_4^-}} \cdot \frac{f_{HC_2O_4^-}}{f_{C_2O_4^-}} = \frac{K_2 \cdot f_{HC_2O_4^-}}{f_{C_2O_4^-}}, \quad (9)$$

K_2 being the true, or thermodynamic, constant. We leave the hydrogen ion activity as such, and make no attempt to introduce the hydrogen ion *concentration*, because potentiometric pH measurements give hydrogen ion activities directly (subject to certain assumptions; see Chapter 13).

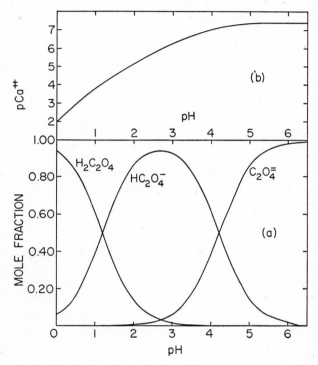

Fig. 2-4. (a) Proportions of the different oxalate species as a function of pH; (b) negative logarithm of calcium ion concentration in equilibrium with solid calcium oxalate and 0.05 M dissolved oxalate.

Converting to logarithms, and introducing equation (8) in the form for single ion activities, namely:

$$\log f_i = -\frac{z_i^2 \cdot A\sqrt{\mu}}{1 + B\sqrt{\mu}} + C\mu, \tag{8a}$$

and simplifying by taking the constant C as zero, equation (9) becomes

$$\log K_2' = \log K_2 + \frac{3A\sqrt{\mu}}{1 + B\sqrt{\mu}}.$$

For most ions, the effective diameter is of the order of 3 Ångstrom units, and B, which is 0.3288 Å, is close to 1. A is 0.5065 in water at 25°C. Letting the ionic strength μ be 0.2 as an example,

$$\log K_2' = \log K_2 + 0.47; \quad K_2' = 2.3 \times 10^{-4}.$$

By similar reasoning the "practical" solubility product of calcium oxalate, the product of the molar concentrations of the two ions, is 3.5×10^{-8}. Using these values instead of the thermodynamic constants, we calculate that in a solution of pH 3.0 which is 0.05 M in total oxalate and contains additional salts to bring the ionic strength up to 0.2, the calcium ion concentration in equilibrium with solid calcium oxalate is 3.7×10^{-6} mole per liter, more than five times the value calculated without considering interionic attraction.

The precipitation of calcium oxalate has been considered in some detail because it is a typical sparingly soluble salt of a weak acid, and sparingly soluble salts of weak acids are very common and important in analytical chemistry. Consider, for example, the phosphates. All phosphates are sparingly soluble except those of sodium, potassium, rubidium, cesium, and ammonium. They are seldom used as gravimetric weighing forms, because when precipitated they are nearly always a mixture of two or more salts. Precipitated calcium phosphate, for example, may contain $CaHPO_4$, $Ca_3(PO_4)_2$, or $Ca_5(PO_4)_3OH$ (hydroxyapatite), and its uncertain composition makes it quite useless as a gravimetric weighing form. Nevertheless it is important to know the conditions under which metallic phosphates precipitate, since their precipitation may interfere with other analytical determinations. All phosphates dissolve in acid, since $PO_4^{\equiv}$ ions are converted to $HPO_4^{\equiv}$, then to $H_2PO_4^-$, and finally to H_3PO_4. The more insoluble the metal phosphate, the greater the hydrogen ion concentration needed to bring it into solution. Table III gives the approximate pH ranges in which different phosphates precipitate from 0.01 M solutions of the metallic ions. They are only a rough guide, for the pH of precipitation depends on the phosphate concentration and on the complex-forming ability of other ions present. The table also gives the pH ranges for precipitation of metallic oxides and hydroxides.

TABLE III

PRECIPITATION OF HYDROXIDES AND PHOSPHATES

pH range	Hydroxides and hydrous oxides precipitated	Phosphates precipitated
0–2	Ti, Zr, Sn(IV)	Bi, Zr, rare earths
2–4	Fe(III), Al, Th	Fe(III), Al, Be, Th
4–6	Cu, Be, Cr(III)	Zn
6–8	Zn, Fe(II), Co, Ni rare earths	Mn, Ca, most divalent metals
8–10	Ag, Mn	Mg
Over 10	Mg	...

Most of these data are taken from H. T. S. Britton, *Hydrogen Ions*, 3d ed., London, Chapman and Hall, 1942, Vol. II, p. 122.

Double *ammonium* phosphates, such as $MgNH_4PO_4 \cdot 6H_2O$ and $ZnNH_4PO_4 \cdot 6H_2O$, can be precipitated in sufficient purity for gravimetric determinations and hence are important analytically. Generally they are ignited to the pyrophosphates, e.g., $Zn_2P_2O_7$. Magnesium ammonium phosphate precipitates above pH 9, but the pH must not be too high, or magnesium hydroxide may coprecipitate; zinc ammonium phosphate precipitates above pH 5.5, but dissolves again above pH 8, owing to formation of the zinc ammonia complex cation.

Sulfuric acid is not generally considered a weak acid, but its second ionization constant, $[H^+][SO_4^=]/[HSO_4^-]$, is only 1.0×10^{-2}. The result is that barium sulfate is quite appreciably soluble in strongly acid solutions, sufficiently so to cause an error in gravimetric sulfate determinations. Let us calculate the solubility of barium sulfate in 2 *M* hydrochloric acid, for example, neglecting activity coefficients. If

$$[H^+] = 2.0, \quad \text{then} \quad \frac{[SO_4^=]}{[HSO_4^-]} = 0.005.$$

If the solution contains no sulfate other than that which comes from the barium sulfate,

$$[Ba^{++}] = [HSO_4^-] + [SO_4^=] \doteq [HSO_4^-] \text{ approximately.}$$

Thus $[SO_4^=] = 0.005[HSO_4^-] \doteq 0.005[Ba^{++}]$,

and since

$$[Ba^{++}][SO_4^=] = K_{sp} = 1.0 \times 10^{-10},$$

$$0.005[Ba^{++}]^2 = 1.0 \times 10^{-10}, \quad [Ba^{++}]^2 = 2.0 \times 10^{-8},$$

and $B[a^{++}] = 1.4 \times 10^{-4}$.

In other words, barium sulfate is fourteen times as soluble in 2 N hydrochloric acid as it is in pure water. When activity effects are taken into account, the solubility is even greater.

The increased solubility of barium sulfate in presence of acids may lead to significant error if the acid concentration is high, but a moderate concentration of acid is beneficial. Standard procedures for the precipitation of barium sulfate in analysis always call for the addition of a little hydrochloric acid. By raising the solubility somewhat, this promotes "ripening" or recrystallization of the precipitate (see Chapter 3).

Particle Size

Next in importance to the solubility is the particle size of a gravimetric precipitate. This determines the ease with which the precipitate can be separated and washed, and in large measure it determines its purity.

Beginning courses in gravimetric analysis almost always include the precipitation of barium sulfate, silver chloride, and hydrous ferric oxide.[6] These illustrate the three types of precipitate: crystalline, curdy, and gelatinous. These differ primarily in particle size, as the electron micrographs in Figure 5 show. Crystalline precipitates have the largest particles, about 0.1 to 1 micron in diameter. The particles of curdy precipitates are smaller, and those of gelatinous precip-

---

[6] "Hydrous oxide" is a term introduced by H. B. Weiser to describe colloidal oxides which hold water firmly by surface forces without forming any recognizable compounds.

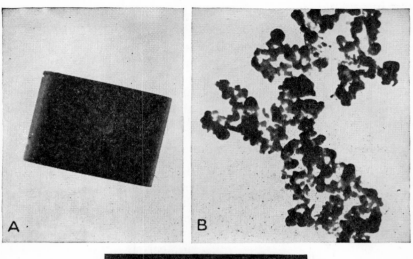

Fig. 2-5. Crystalline, curdy, and gelatinous precipitates. Electron micrographs of (a) $BaSO_4$, (b) $AgCl$, (c) hydrous Fe_2O_3. By courtesy of Professor R. B. Fischer.

itates very small indeed (0.02 micron or less). The particles of curdy and gelatinous precipitates are fine enough to pass through the ordinary analytical filter media, and are retained by filters only if they coagulate to form large secondary aggregates ("curds" or "flocs"). These are held together by weak cohesive forces and are easily dispersed again, or "peptized." To prevent such peptization, they must always be washed with an electrolyte solution, never with pure water. Very fine crystalline precipitates such as cuprous thiocyanate or improperly precipitated barium sulfate present a problem. The particles are too large to coagulate as do colloidal particles, yet they

Fig. 2-6. Electron micrograph of precipitated nickel dimethylglyoxime. By courtesy of Professor R. B. Fischer and the American Chemical Society.

are small enough to pass through the filter or else get into its pores and clog them.

The particle size is not the only factor which determines the physical character of a precipitate. The electric charge on the particles is important, and so too is their shape. The needlelike form of crystals of precipitated nickel dimethylglyoxime (Figure 6) accounts for the light, voluminous character of this precipitate. Nonetheless, particle size is an extremely important property, and it is very desirable to know how to control it. We shall therefore discuss next the factors which influence the particle size of precipitates.

Particle size and speed of precipitation; von Weimarn's rule. It is a general rule that the more slowly a precipitate forms, the larger are its particles. Slow crystallization gives large crystals because the ions or molecules have time to arrange themselves in an orderly manner upon the faces of crystals which are already there. In very rapid crystallization, however, the ions or molecules cannot build on to existing crystals fast enough, and so they form new nuclei, and we get many small crystals instead of a few large ones. The speed of crystallization or precipitation of a substance is greater, the greater the concentration of the substance in solution, and it depends on the solubility of the substance. Obviously a solution will not deposit crystals if it is unsaturated. A very useful rule was given by von Weimarn[7] in the form of an equation:

$$\text{speed of precipitation} = K \cdot \frac{Q - S}{S},$$

where Q = momentary concentration of supersaturated solution formed by mixing the reactants.

S = solubility.

K = a constant.

The numerator $Q - S$ expresses the force favoring precipitation, the denominator S the force opposing precipitation. The equation is of course only approximate, and it fails for low values of $Q - S$. If the degree of supersaturation is slight, precipitation may not occur for weeks or months. This fact was observed by von Weimarn and others, and has recently been confirmed by Davies[8] and La Mer.[9] For precipitation to occur "instantaneously," i.e., within a minute or so, there must be a certain minimum degree of supersaturation. Barium ions and sulfate ions must be mixed in sufficient concentrations to exceed the solubility product of barium sulfate by a factor of 400, silver ions and chloride ions must be mixed so as to exceed the solubility product of silver chloride by a factor of two[8] to six.[9] The ratio of the two ion concentrations is also significant.[8] The difference between these two salts is probably connected with their surface tensions, for their solubility products are nearly equal. Strontium sulfate, which is much more soluble, needs less supersaturation than

[7] P. P. von Weimarn, *Die Allgemeinheit des Kolloidzustandes*, Leipzig, Steinkopff, 1925. See also J. W. McBain, *Colloid Science*, Boston, Heath, 1950, Chap. 5.

[8] C. W. Davies and A. L. Jones, *Faraday Soc. Discussions*, **5**, 103 (1949). This number of the *Discussions* deals with the general subject of crystal growth.

[9] V. K. La Mer and R. H. Dinegar, *J. Am. Chem. Soc.*, **73**, 380 (1951).

barium sulfate. La Mer has proposed an explanation of these facts, based on the theory of fluctuations and upon the idea that an embryo crystal of a certain size must form before the probability of its growth exceeds that of its dissolution.

The concentrations encountered in most analytical precipitations are high enough to avoid prolonged supersaturation, but the last stages of precipitation, before equilibrium is reached between solution and precipitate, may be extremely slow. Hence the long period of standing needed in certain precipitations, for example that of magnesium ammonium phosphate.

Von Weimarn's rule tells us that we can slow down the precipitation, and thereby increase the particle size, by lowering the concentrations of the reactants and raising the solubility of the precipitate. Thus silver chloride can be obtained in relatively coarse crystals instead of the usual curdy form by slowly running dilute solutions of silver nitrate and sodium chloride into a fairly concentrated ammonia solution. Von Weimarn obtained barium sulfate as a colloidal, gelatinous precipitate by mixing 7 N solutions of barium thiocyanate and manganous sulfate, and it can be obtained in coarse crystals, several microns across, by mixing 0.001 N solutions of a barium salt and a sulfate. In precipitating barium sulfate in gravimetric analysis, Q is kept as low as is practicable by mixing dilute solutions of barium salt and sulfate, while S is raised by using hot solutions and adding a little hydrochloric acid, which raises the solubility by combining with the sulfate ion:

$$SO_4^= + H^+ \rightleftharpoons HSO_4^-.$$

The solubility is raised sufficiently to give the desired larger particles, but not so much as to cause error through incomplete precipitation.

Gravimetric analysis provides many examples of particle size control through control of solubility. An interesting case is the precipitation of zinc sulfide, by which zinc is separated from iron, manganese, and other metals. In qualitative work zinc sulfide is generally precipitated from weakly alkaline solution as a slimy precipitate which is very hard to filter. The particles are extremely small and may even remain in colloidal suspension. This can be remedied by precipitating from a more acid solution, for as the hydrogen ion concentration is raised, the sulfide ion concentration falls; in presence of a constant hydrogen sulfide concentration, $[S^=]$ varies inversely as

$[H^+]^2$. As the sulfide ion concentration falls, the solubility of zinc sulfide rises. It should therefore be possible to adjust the acidity to a point at which the solubility of zinc sulfide is high enough to give filterable particles, yet not so high that incomplete precipitation causes error. In practice the acidity must be controlled within rather close limits (pH between 2.0 and 3.0), which is not surprising, since the solubility of sulfides increases with the *square* of the hydrogen ion concentration. To keep the acidity within these limits, a rather concentrated buffer of formic and citric acids plus their sodium salts is used. Good buffering is essential, since the reaction between hydrogen sulfide and zinc ions liberates hydrogen ions. Precipitation is done by passing hydrogen sulfide gas into the hot solution. A granular precipitate of zinc sulfide results which settles quickly, is easily filtered and washed, and is free from iron.[10]

This example shows the value of pH control in precipitating salts of weak acids. Not only does it help to control particle size, but it also makes the process more selective by avoiding the precipitation of other substances. Another and more familiar example of pH control in gravimetric work is the precipitation of calcium oxalate. Here we usually start with a calcium solution which is too acid to give a precipitate, and add, first oxalic acid, then ammonia dropwise to the hot solution. The pH rises slowly and the calcium oxalate forms at first under conditions of high solubility, ideal for forming large particles. More ammonia is added until the solubility is lowered so much that the amount of calcium in solution is negligible. The solid formed in the later stages of precipitation will deposit on the crystals which are already there instead of forming fresh nuclei, and large easily filtered particles result. By adding the ammonia slowly with stirring, the pH never gets very high, and precipitation of unwanted substances, such as calcium phosphate, is avoided.

It is always good practice to form a precipitate first under conditions of high solubility and then reduce the solubility gradually until the precipitation is "quantitative." A very delicate way of doing this is the method of "precipitation from homogeneous solution," which will be discussed in the next chapter.

Particle size, surface energy and solubility: Ostwald ripen-

[10] H. A. Fales and G. M. Ware, *J. Am. Chem. Soc.*, **41**, 487 (1919). For a full discussion see T. B. Smith, *Analytical Processes*, London, Arnold, 1940, Chap. 14.

ing. It is common knowledge that many precipitates become coarser if they are digested for a while in contact with their mother liquor. During digestion the smallest particles disappear entirely, while material from them deposits on the larger particles. This effect is known as "Ostwald ripening."

The driving force causing this effect is that of surface energy. Every surface or phase boundary is associated with a certain *surface energy*, which is defined by

$$\gamma = \left(\frac{\partial F}{\partial \sigma}\right)_{T,P}$$

where F is the free energy, σ the surface area. The surface energy γ is the same thing as the surface tension in a liquid-gas or liquid-liquid interface. Since any process is spontaneous which produces a decrease in free energy at constant temperature, all surfaces tend to become as small as possible. This applies to the surface of solid precipitates as well as to that of soap bubbles. The solid can reduce its surface area by aggregating to form larger particles, since small particles have more surface area per unit mass than large ones; but since a solid is rigid, the only way this can happen as a rule is for material to go into solution from the small particles and redeposit on the large particles.

This tendency is reflected in the fact that small particles are more soluble than large ones. An equation for the solubility of spherical particles in terms of their particle size is obtained as follows.

Consider a spherical particle of radius r, surface $\sigma = 4\pi r^2$, surface energy γ, and solubility S moles per liter. Let it be placed in a solution of concentration S, that is, one which is saturated with the material of the particle and in equilibrium with it. Let the molecular weight be M, and the density of the particle be ρ. For simplicity let us suppose that the substance is not ionized.

Let dn moles of substance separate from the solution on to the surface of the particle, whose radius is thereby increased by dr. The total free energy increase is

$$dF = dn\,(F_{solid} - \bar{F}_{solution}) + \gamma\,d\sigma$$

$$= dn\,(F_{solid} - RT \ln S) + \gamma \cdot 8\,\pi\,r\,d\,r = 0,$$

since we have equilibrium. (It is understood that free energies are referred to a solution of unit activity as standard.) Now the increase in volume of the sphere is $4\pi r^2 \, dr = \dfrac{M}{\rho} \, dn$; therefore

$$dn \, (F_{solid} - RT \ln S) = - \frac{2M\gamma}{\rho r} \cdot dn.$$

The expression dn cancels, and if $r = \infty$, then $F_{solid} = RT \ln S_0$, if S_0 is the solubility of a very large particle.   Hence

$$RT \ln \frac{S}{S_0} = \frac{2\gamma}{r} \cdot \frac{M}{\rho}.$$

From this we see that the greater the surface energy of the solid, the greater is the effect of particle size on its solubility.   Unfortunately we have no independent means of measuring the surface energy of a solid; we can measure only the solubility of different-sized particles and estimate the surface energy from solubility data. Such measurements have been made by Dundon and Mack.[11]   They indicated that barium sulfate, for instance, has a surface energy of about 4000 ergs per square centimeter while lead iodide, a much softer material, has a surface energy of only 130 ergs per square centimeter.   For barium sulfate, S/S_0 is 1.1 for $r = 1.4$ microns. So we can generalize and state that particle size has very little effect on solubility above 1 to 2 microns, and that the effect is greater with hard substances than with soft ones.

With many precipitates the most important change occurring during digestion is not the dissolving of small particles and redeposition of material on large ones, but an "internal Ostwald ripening" in which particles which are originally very irregular become more compact by material dissolving at the corners and edges and redepositing in the hollows.   Thus both the microscopic observations of Balarew[12] and the adsorption and exchange studies of Kolthoff[13] show that freshly precipitated barium sulfate and lead sulfate consist of feathery particles, like snowflakes, with an enormous surface area; on standing in contact with the solution, the crystals become more compact and perfect, with accompanying reduction in area (see Figure 7).   For this internal perfection the solubility of the solid in

[11] M. L. Dundon and E. Mack, *J. Am. Chem. Soc.*, **45**, 2479 (1923); Dundon, *J. Am. Chem. Soc.*, **45**, 2658.
[12] D. Balarew, *Kolloid-Beihefte*, **30**, 249 (1930).
[13] I. M. Kolthoff and C. Rosenblum, *J. Am. Chem. Soc.*, **56**, 1264, 1658 (1934); **57**, 597 (1935).

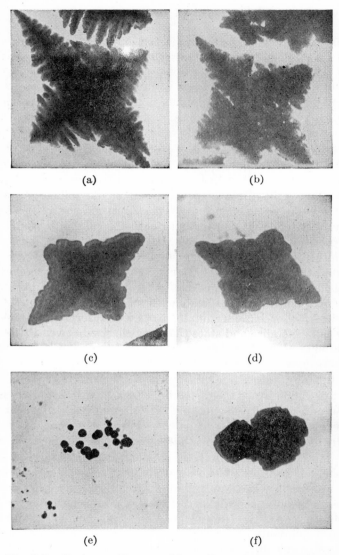

Fig. 2-7.   Barium sulfate particles: effect of concentration and room temperature aging.   Ba^{++} solution 0.1 M and in excess. SO$_4^=$ solution, top row, 0.01 M; middle row, 0.001 M; bottom row, 0.0001 M; left-hand column, immediately after precipitation; right-hand column, four days after precipitation.   Reproduced from *Anal. Chem.*, **23,** 1669 (1951), by courtesy of Professor R. B. Fischer and the American Chemical Society.   See original publication for other electron micrographs.

the layer of solution immediately next to it, which contains adsorbed salt, is more important than the solubility in the solution in bulk.[14] Internal perfection may even occur without material dissolving at all, simply by diffusion of atoms within the solid.   This apparently happens with the silver halides, although the extent of perfection is not enough to make much difference to their analytical properties.[15]

Following such "internal Ostwald ripening" the particles may aggregate, like the particles of a colloid, and become cemented together by the deposition of solid between them.[14]   This may have as much or more to do with the improved filterability after digestion as the type of ripening described at the beginning of this section.

It remains to explain why colloidal precipitates such as silver chloride and hydrous ferric oxide remain colloidal after long digestion and do not seem to "ripen."   In the case of silver chloride the reason may be that the surface energy is too small.   Otherwise we would expect silver chloride to precipitate in the same form as barium sulfate, for the solubility products are the same.   In the case of hydrous ferric oxide and hydrous oxides in general, the solubility is altogether too small to permit the growth of larger particles at any significant rate.   A certain amount of crystal growth or crystal perfection does occur in hydrous ferric oxide on standing, as shown by the sharpening of its x-ray diffraction pattern, but this is not enough to improve the filterability of the precipitate.

In some cases the electric charge on the particles of the precipitate may hinder Ostwald ripening.   Thus very finely divided particles of barium sulfate are sometimes unexpectedly stable in water, and this is believed to be due to the high electrokinetic potential of the particles.

Perhaps the best example of digestion causing Ostwald ripening is given by calcium oxalate.   Instead of proceeding as outlined on page 23, we can do just the reverse, that is, precipitate first under conditions of very low solubility, then digest under conditions of increased solubility.   Kolthoff and Sandell [16] mixed concentrated solutions of calcium chloride and ammonium oxalate (pH about 5) and obtained a very fine precipitate which was impure.   Water was then added and the solution and precipitate kept at 100°C for 20

[14] I. M. Kolthoff, *Science*, **84**, 376 (1936).
[15] I. M. Kolthoff and A. S. O'Brien, *J. Am. Chem. Soc.*, **61**, 3409, 3414 (1939).
[16] I. M. Kolthoff and E. B. Sandell, *J. Phys. Chem.*, **37**, 443, 459 (1933).

hours.   During digestion large, easily filtered particles were formed, and nearly all the impurities originally absorbed from the solution were released.

PROBLEMS

1. Plot a graph similar to Figure 4(a) to show the mole fractions of H_3PO_4, $H_2PO_4^-$, $HPO_4^=$, and $PO_4^{\equiv}$ in phosphate solutions as a function of pH.

2. Plot a graph similar to Figure 4(b) to show log $[Mg^{++}]$ as a function of pH for solutions which are 1.0 M in NH_4^+, 0.10 M in total phosphate, and in equilibrium with (1) $MgNH_4PO_4$, (2) $Mg(OH)_2$. Cover the pH range from 8.0 to 11.0, and draw conclusions regarding the correct pH for precipitating $MgNH_4PO_4$.

3. Why is $MgNH_4PO_4$ less soluble in ammonia solution than in pure water? Why is it more soluble in ammonium chloride solution than in water?

4. Calculate the activity coefficient of $BaSO_4$ in 0.02 M $MgCl_2$ solution, first using the ideal law [Equation (6)], then using the extended Debye-Hückel equation [Equation (8)] with $\overset{\circ}{A} = 4.0$ and $C = 0$.

5. Calculate the solubility of $BaSO_4$, in milligrams per liter, in 0.2 M $HClO_4$, without regard for activity coefficients, and compare it with the solubility in pure water.

6. How will interionic attraction affect the ionization of HSO_4^-?   (See Chapter 14.)

7. Plot a graph of the logarithm of the molar concentration product, $[Ag^+][Cl^-]$, in equilibrium with solid AgCl, i.e., the molar solubility product, against the ionic strength of the solution from 0 to 0.5 at 25°C, using Equation (8) with $\overset{\circ}{A} = 4.0$, $C = 0$, and taking the thermodynamic solubility product to be 1.6×10^{-10}.   What is the ionic strength of a saturated solution of AgCl in water at 25°C?

8. Repeat Problem 7 for Ag_2CrO_4. taking $\overset{\circ}{A} = 5.0$, $C = 0$, and the thermodynamic solubility product = 9.0×10^{-12}.

9. Dundon estimated the surface tension of solid CaF_2 to be 2500 dynes/cm. Its density is 3.18 grams/ml.   Calculate the ratio of solubility of particles of 2 microns diameter to that of large particles.   (Note that CaF_2 dissociates into *three* ions.)

10. Discuss the various types of changes that take place in precipitates when they are digested with their mother liquor.

3

Impurities in precipitates

IMPURE PRECIPITATES constitute the greatest source of error in gravi-metric analysis. Precipitates nearly always carry down weighable amounts of soluble impurities from the solution in which they are formed, and these impurities are not always removed by washing.

Coprecipitation

The process by which soluble impurities become incorporated into precipitates during their formation is known as *coprecipitation*. Co-precipitation may happen in two ways. One is by the formation of a solid solution, in which the impurity actually enters the crystal lattice of the precipitate; the other is by surface adsorption, which is followed, usually, by an occlusion or imprisonment of the absorbed substance as the particles of the precipitate grow. Surface adsorption is by far the more common cause of coprecipitation, but, since solution formation is simpler, we shall deal with this first.

Solid solutions. The condition for equilibrium between a solid substance and a solution of that substance is that the activities of the solid and of the dissolved substance shall be equal. In Chapter 2 we considered factors which reduced the activity of the dissolved substance, and therefore increased the solubility, provided that the solid phase was pure solute. Now if the activity of the solid solute is reduced through the formation of a solid solution with another substance, the activity of the dissolved solute must also fall to main-tain equilibrium; that is, the solubility is decreased.

An example of coprecipitation caused by solid solution formation

is the coprecipitation of barium chromate with barium sulfate.[1]
Barium chromate and barium sulfate are isomorphous and form
mixed crystals, or solid solutions, over a restricted range of compositions.   If barium chloride is added to an 0.02 M chromate solution
which is 0.1 N in hydrochloric acid, no precipitation of barium occurs,
because there is not enough chromate ion to exceed the solubility
product of barium chromate; the reactions $CrO_4^= + H^+ \rightarrow HCrO_4^-$
and $2HCrO_4^- \rightarrow H_2O + Cr_2O_7^=$ cut down the $CrO_4^=$ concentration.
If, however, barium chloride is added to a similar solution, which is
0.02 M in sulfate as well as chromate, the resulting barium sulfate
contains 5% by weight of barium chromate.   The concentration of
dissolved $CrO_4^=$ *is* sufficient to precipitate $BaCrO_4$ if the latter is
"diluted" through solid solution formation with $BaSO_4$.

As this example shows, coprecipitation due to solid solution formation may cause very serious error in analysis.   Fortunately, this type
of coprecipitation is rare, because the conditions for solid solution
formation are stringent.   To be able to dissolve in one another and
give a mixed crystal lattice, two solids must not only be isomorphous,
but the radii of their ions of like sign must not differ by more than
10%.   Important examples of error in gravimetric analysis caused
by solid solution formation are the partial replacement of NH_4^+ by
K^+ in $MgNH_4PO_4 \cdot 6H_2O$, of Ba^{++} by Pb^{++} in $BaSO_4$,[2] and of Br^- by
Cl^- in $AgBr$.   As a rule, solid solution formation, where it occurs, is
so bad as to render the precipitation analytically useless; thus, it is
futile to try to separate Cl^- from Br^- by fractional precipitation with
silver nitrate, or to separate $PO_4^{\equiv}$ from $AsO_4^{\equiv}$ by precipitation of
their magnesium ammonium salts.   It is possible, though not very
easy, to precipitate pure AgI in presence of chloride ions, because
AgI and $AgCl$ have different crystal lattices, body-centered cubic
and face-centered cubic, respectively.

It will be recalled that in fresh precipitates the crystalline form
may be very imperfect.   The crystal lattice is not as orderly as in a
fully developed crystal, and is more easily strained.   Therefore foreign ions can enter the lattice more easily.   Barium sulfate, in the
example quoted,[1] contains more barium chromate immediately after
precipitation than it does after digesting for an hour or two.   During

[1] W. B. Meldrum, W. E. Cadbury, and C. E. Bricker, *Ind. Eng. Chem., Anal.
Ed.*, **15**, 560 (1943).
[2] I. M. Kolthoff and G. E. Noponen, *J. Am. Chem. Soc.*, **60**, 197, 508 (1938).

digestion, recrystallization takes place with perfection of the crystal form, and at the same time some of the impurity is expelled. The greater part of the impurity remains, however. The only cure for coprecipitation due to mixed crystal formation is to convert the contaminating substance into another form before precipitation. Thus chromate could be reduced to chromic ion, or arsenate to arsenite.

Surface adsorption: crystalline precipitates Freshly formed precipitates often have very large surface areas, either because their particles are very small, as in the hydrous oxides, or because the crystals are imperfect and "feathery," as in barium sulfate. At any surface, adsorption may take place, and even though the adsorbed

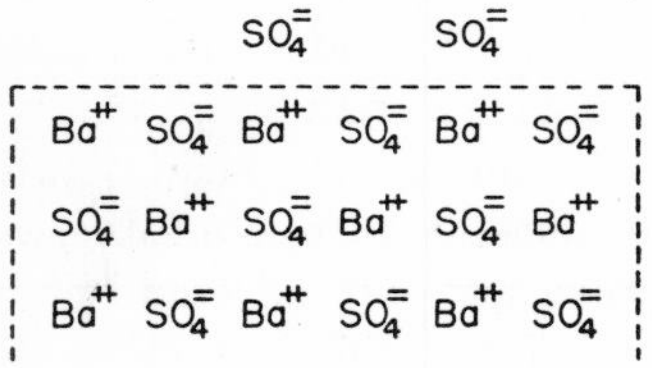

Fig. 3-1. Barium sulfate crystal lattice with absorbed sulfate ions.

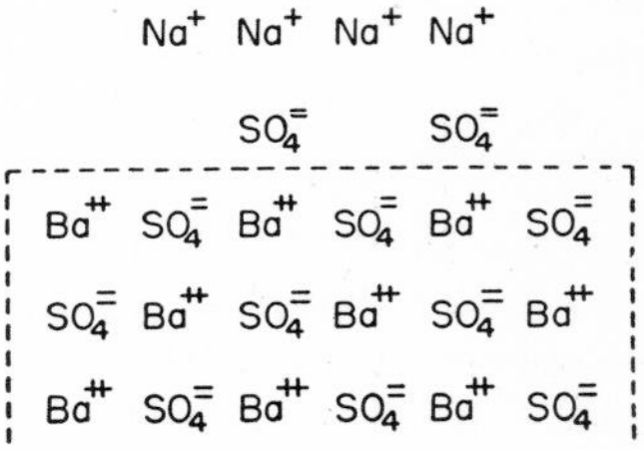

Fig. 3-2. Barium sulfate lattice with sodium ions held by secondary adsorption.

layer may be only one molecule deep, the quantity of adsorbed material will be significant if the surface is large enough.

In ionic solutions, such as are encountered in inorganic analysis, such adsorption is primarily electrical in origin. The surface somehow acquires a charge, and then it attracts oppositely charged ions to it from the solution. The course of this adsorption process differs somewhat in the gelatinous hydrous oxides from that in crystalline precipitates, such as barium sulfate. We shall consider barium sulfate first, for it is characteristic of crystalline precipitates and its coprecipitation phenomena have been thoroughly investigated.

Barium sulfate is an ionic substance, and its crystal lattice consists of barium ions and sulfate ions arranged alternately. When solid barium sulfate is placed in a sodium sulfate solution, the lattice tries to grow by adding sulfate ions, as shown in Figure 1. Since there are no barium ions in the solution, the sulfate ions remain in excess on the surface of the solid and give this a negative charge. This charge attracts sodium ions from the solution (Figure 2); the barium sulfate now carries an adsorbed layer of sodium sulfate. This is the state of affairs while barium chloride is being added to a sulfate solution. The precipitate forms in the presence of an excess of sulfate, and so adsorbs the sulfates of foreign cations. If sodium sulfate is added to a barium salt solution, barium ions are in excess during the formation of the precipitate; the latter is now positively charged and adsorbs the barium salts of foreign anions. The order of mixing therefore influences the type of foreign ions which are coprecipitated. Examples to illustrate this are given in Table I.

TABLE I

COPRECIPITATION IN BARIUM SULFATE AT 30°C

Contaminating ion	Contamination, moles/100 moles BaSO₄		Solubility of contaminating salt, moles/1000 g. water
	(a) Ba added to SO₄	(b) SO₄ added to Ba	
I⁻	0.005	0.032	5.64
Br⁻	0 35	1.65	3 55
Cl⁻	0 45	2.7	1 83
ClO₃⁻	2.7	9.8	1.37
NO₃⁻	5.4	19 6	0 46
Na⁺	9 9	4.1	3.0
Ca⁺⁺	15 9	3.6	0.02

Note: All data except for Ca⁺⁺ taken from F. Schneider and W. Rieman, J. Am. Chem. Soc., 59, 354 (1937). Ca⁺⁺ data from experiments by the author. See also H B Weiser and J. L. Sherrick, J Phys. Chem., 23, 205 (1919); M. L. Nichols and E. C. Smith, J. Phys. Chem., 45, 411 (1941)

The coprecipitation of anions is less when sulfate ions are in excess than when barium ions are in excess, but it is not zero. This is because there is always a part of the zone of mixing, where the barium salt is poured into the solution, where barium ions are in excess; precipitates formed in this region will carry a positive charge   Another point to be borne in mind is that barium ions and sulfate ions are not bound equally strongly by the precipitate   Barium sulfate suspended in pure water carries a positive charge due to preferential solution of the sulfate ions.[3]   An appreciable excess of sulfate ions—

[3] A. S. Buchanan and E. Heymann, J Colloid Sci., 4, 137 (1949).

about 10^{-3} mole per liter—must be added before the precipitate becomes negatively charged.

Table I illustrates an important factor in coprecipitation; namely, that the coprecipitation is greater, the less soluble the coprecipitated salt. There is no quantitative relationship, however; other factors enter in, such as the hydration of the ion and its deformability. The magnitude of the charge of the coprecipitated ion seems to have little effect; ferrocyanide is less coprecipitated than chloride. It is suggested that the large coprecipitation of barium nitrate shown in Table I is due to solid solution formation, for x-ray diffraction shows the lattice of barium sulfate to be expanded by coprecipitated barium nitrate.[4]

It must be emphasized again that in none of these experiments was the solubility product of the coprecipitated salt exceeded or even closely approached. These substances would not have been precipitated had the barium sulfate not been there. Of course, the more nearly the solubility product of an impurity is approached, the more liable that impurity is to be coprecipitated. Calcium oxalate carries down appreciable amounts of calcium hydroxide if the pH of precipitation exceeds 7, even though the solubility product of calcium hydroxide is as large as 3×10^{-5}.

Once coprecipitation has taken place in a crystalline precipitate, such as barium sulfate or calcium oxalate, the impurity cannot be washed out. From the crystal habit and growth of barium sulfate precipitates (see Chapter 2) this is not surprising. The crystal forms first of all as a feathery skeleton, but as it grows, the arms of crystal interlace and grow together, enclosing any adsorbed impurity. The "internal Ostwald ripening," or the process of perfection which occurs on standing with the mother liquor, has the same effect. These processes are faster, the higher the temperature, which accounts for the fact that precipitates of barium sulfate and calcium oxalate are often more heavily contaminated when formed in hot solution than when they are formed in the cold.[5]

Even the very large particles of precipitate which are obtained by the method of "extreme dilution"—adding solutions of the two reac-

[4] G. H. Walden and M. U. Cohen, *J. Am. Chem. Soc.*, **57**, 2591 (1935).

[5] I. M. Kolthoff and E. B. Sandell, *J. Phys. Chem.*, **37**, 443, 459 (1933); *Textbook of Quantitative Inorganic Analysis*, 2d ed., New York, Macmillan, 1943, Chap. VIII.

tants slowly and simultaneously to a large volume of water—are often heavily contaminated because of imprisonment of impurities by the growing crystals.

Coprecipitated impurities are released again during true "Ostwald ripening," or the dissolving of small particles followed by redeposition of the material on the larger particles. Thus Kolthoff and Sandell (*loc. cit.*) found that they could get very pure calcium oxalate by precipitating it first in very fine particles and then allowing these to ripen; again, Kolthoff and Halversen[6] found that precipitated lead sulfate lost 94% of its coprecipitated lead nitrate after six hours' digestion with 0.01 N nitric acid at 95°C. With barium sulfate, however, which is less soluble, several days of digestion are needed to remove half the coprecipitated impurity.

Curdy precipitates. The adsorption of ions at the curdy precipitates of silver halides takes place by the same mechanism as at crystalline precipitates; that is, the charge on the surface is determined by the lattice ion (Ag^+ or halide$^-$) which happens to be in excess, and oppositely charged foreign ions are then attracted to the surface. The big difference between curdy and crystalline precipitates is that in the former the crystals do not grow beyond colloidal size. They do not, therefore, enclose impurities by growing around them as do barium sulfate particles. The adsorbed impurities can therefore be washed out. Coagulation of the particles does not prevent this, for it involves only a loose cohesion between the particles, and a wash liquid can penetrate to all parts of the "curd." The difference in

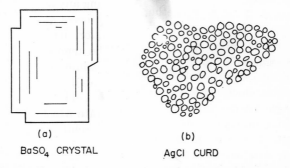

(a)   (b)
BaSO$_4$ CRYSTAL   AgCl CURD

Fig. 3-3. Contrast between crystalline and curdy aggregates.

[6] I. M. Kolthoff and R. A. Halversen, *J. Phys. Chem.*, **43**, 605 (1939).

structure between a barium sulfate particle and a silver chloride curd is shown diagrammatically in Figure 3.

It may be that a solid silver halide, with ions of charge ±1, attracts other ions less in the first place than barium sulfate, with ions charged ±2. This is not proved. It is, however, certain that some ions are bound more firmly by silver halides than others. Silver iodide adsorbs iodide ions very strongly, and cannot be made as pure as silver chloride; hence, the gravimetric determination of chloride as AgCl is more accurate than that of iodide as AgI, even though the solubility of the iodide is much less. This is partly due to the fact that the smaller solubility of silver iodide causes its particles to be finer (von Weimarn's rule). If we compare the adsorption of several different anions by silver iodide, we find again a rough parallelism between high adsorption and low solubility of the coprecipitated salt.[7]

Curdy precipitates are washed, not with water, but with a dilute electrolyte, usually nitric acid, which can afterwards be volatilized on drying. The primary purpose of this is to keep the curd from peptizing. The particles of the curd are electrically charged and therefore repel one another, but so long as their charges are sufficiently "screened" by a layer of adsorbed, oppositely charged ions, the repulsion is not sufficient to overcome the cohesive force. If these ions are washed out, the electric potential of the particles rises, and eventually their repulsion is strong enough so that the curd disperses or "peptizes." This is avoided if the contaminating ions which are washed out are replaced by other ions from the wash solution. Moreover, the removal of contaminating ions is faster and more complete if other ions can be adsorbed to take their place.

Gelatinous precipitates. The primary particles of these are extremely small, and so the surface area per gram is enormous. They adsorb considerable amounts of impurities which even prolonged washing does not remove completely.

The electric charge on these particles depends primarily on the pH. Their crystal lattices are so fragmentary that the simple mechanism of adsorption on crystalline precipitates does not apply, and the sign and magnitude of the charge are affected greatly by the presence of adsorbable ions, such as Ba^{++} or $Fe(CN)_6^{\equiv}$, but the main effect is that of pH. Hydrous ferric oxide, for example, is positively charged at pH values less than 8.5 to 8.9, and negatively charged at higher

[7] J. S. Beekley and H. S. Taylor, *J. Phys. Chem.*, **29**, 942 (1925).

pH. The isoelectric point of hydrous aluminum oxide is about pH 8, while that of hydrous silica is much lower, as would be expected from its acidic character.

The nature of the adsorbed impurities depends, therefore, on the pH. Hydrous ferric oxide precipitated in weakly acid solution adsorbs anions, such as NO_3^- and especially $SO_4^=$, very strongly, and it adsorbs cations relatively weakly. Above pH 10 the situation is reversed, and cations (even Na^+ and K^+) are strongly adsorbed, anions only weakly. The use of this knowledge in analytical separations is obvious. In the analysis of minerals, for example, where iron and aluminum are precipitated together in presence of ions such as Ca^{++} and Mg^{++}, the solution is kept on the acid side as much as possible; ammonia is added drop by drop to the hot acid solution, with constant stirring, until the hydrous oxides are first precipitated. Ferric oxide is completely precipitated at pH 3 5, aluminum oxide at a somewhat higher pH It is usual to add ammonia until methyl red indicator starts to change color (pH 5).

Gelatinous precipitates, like curdy precipitates, must be washed with electrolyte solutions to prevent peptization and to help displace adsorbed impurities. For the hydrous oxides of iron and aluminum, ammonium nitrate is the best wash. It is preferable to the chloride, because, first, nitrate ions are adsorbed much more strongly than chloride ions and so displace adsorbed ions more easily, and second, the chlorides of iron and aluminum are volatile at a red heat and a chloride wash may lead to some loss when the precipitate is heated. The nitrates of trivalent metals decompose very easily to the oxides when heated, as one would expect from the effect of charge on ionic deformation, and so, incidentally, do the sulfates; coprecipitation of sulfate, therefore, which is very bad with ferric oxide at low pH because basic sulfates are formed, causes no inaccuracy in determining iron.

Hydrous silica is washed with an acid, usually hydrochloric. This washing must be done very thoroughly, because adsorbed salts (e.g., the sodium chloride formed by sodium carbonate fusion of silicate rocks followed by neutralization with hydrochloric acid) are held extremely strongly, and a double precipitation of silica is not possible.

Reprecipitation and the adsorption isotherm An obvious way to remove some of the coprecipitated impurities from a precipitate is to dissolve the latter in acid or alkali, if this is possible, and then reprecipitate. Thus hydrous ferric oxide can be dissolved in dilute hydrochloric acid and then reprecipitated by adding ammonia; calcium oxalate and magnesium ammonium phosphate can be treated in the same way. Part of the impurity which the precipitate contained originally is left behind in solution when the precipitate is formed for the second time.

This means of purification is not as efficient as one might think, because the amount of an impurity adsorbed by a solid from a solution is not directly proportional to its concentration in the solution, but is relatively greater at lower concentrations, as Figure 4 shows.

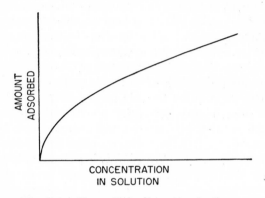

Fig. 3-4. Freundlich adsorption isotherm.

The relation between amount of adsorption and concentration is represented empirically by the Freundlich adsorption isotherm:

$$\frac{x}{m} = kC^{1/n}$$

where x/m is the amount of impurity adsorbed per unit weight of solid, C is the concentration of the impurity remaining in solution after equilibrium is reached, and k and n are constants; n is greater than 1, usually about 2. Suppose, for the sake of illustration, that the concentration of impurity in the original solution is such that the precipitate adsorbs one-tenth of the impurity present. When the second precipitation is made, the concentration of impurity in the solution is one-tenth of what it was before; the precipitate, however, adsorbs, not one-tenth of this (1% of the original impurity) but

$1/\sqrt{10}$ of this (3.2% of the original impurity); see Figure 4. In some cases the adsorption isotherm may be even less favorable. So repre-cipitation, while very useful, is not an infallible means of removing coprecipitated impurity. Moreover, many precipitates, such as barium sulfate, cannot be redissolved and reprecipitated.

The uses of coprecipitation. Coprecipitation can clearly be put to practical use. The coprecipitation of traces of radio elements with large amounts of "carriers" has become familiar in recent years, and it has been used for some time to extract radium from pitchblende; a barium salt is added and barium sulfate is precipitated, carrying with it all the radium, even though the solubility product of radium sulfate may not have been exceeded. In water conditioning, coprecipitation with magnesium hydroxide or hydrous ferric oxide helps remove un-wanted fluoride or silicate from water. In analytical chemistry, hydrous manganese dioxide has been recommended as a "carrier" to coprecipitate small amounts of antimony, bismuth, and tin, and thereby remove them quantitatively from solution.[8] Other analyti-cal applications have been proposed.

Postprecipitation

Postprecipitation is the precipitation of an impurity *after* the main precipitate has been formed. It differs from coprecipitation in the following ways:

(a) The contamination increases with time as the precipitate is left in contact with the mother liquor. With coprecipitation, the con-tamination decreases somewhat upon aging.

(b) The same degree of contamination is obtained when the impu-rity is added after the precipitate is formed as when the impurity is present during the precipitation.

(c) The contamination takes place faster, the higher the tempera-ture.

(d) The contamination may be very much greater than in copre-cipitation. It may amount to as much as 100% of the weight of the pure precipitate.

Postprecipitation is most marked with the metallic sulfides. If

[8] S. Kallmann and F. Pristera, *Ind. Eng. Chem., Anal. Ed.*, **13**, 8 (1941).

copper sulfide is precipitated at room temperature from a 0.2 M sulfuric acid solution which also contains zinc, and the precipitate is filtered immediately (within one minute), the precipitate is free from zinc. If it is allowed to stand for several minutes before filtering, it is contaminated with zinc, and the contamination is greater, the longer the precipitate stands before filtration. The same thing happens if zinc sulfide or copper sulfide is precipitated in the presence of a nickel salt, with enough acid present that the nickel salt alone would give no precipitate with hydrogen sulfide. These effects are shown in Tables II and III.

These facts are all consistent with the idea that the coprecipitated sulfide is present in *supersaturated solution* under the conditions of

TABLE II

POSTPRECIPITATION OF NICKEL SULFIDE

Initial Solution: 0.05 M in $NiCl_2$, 0.05 M in $CuCl_2$, $HgCl_2$, or $ZnCl_2$

Final HCl conc.	Time after precipitation, hours	Per cent NiS in:			
		CuS	HgS	ZnS	Blank ($NiCl_2$ only)
0.01 M	3	0	0	0	0
	12	3.0	3.5	3.0	0
	24	6.5	36	33	0
	36	13.5	54	55	0
	60	37.0	82	88	0
0.02 M	23	0.5	4.0	1.0	0

Reference: I. M. Kolthoff and F. S. Griffith, *J. Phys. Chem.*, **42**, 541 (1938).

TABLE III

POSTPRECIPITATION OF ZINC SULFIDE

Initial Solution: 0.023 M in $CuSO_4$, 0.023 M in $ZnSO_4$, 0.22 M in H_2SO_4
Time of Standing: 7 minutes

Temperature	Per cent ZnS in CuS
24°C	7
100°C	91

Reference: I. M. Kolthoff and E. A. Pearson, *J. Phys. Chem.*, **36**, 549 (1932).

precipitation, and that the function of the original precipitate is to relieve the supersaturation by providing nuclei for the new precipitate to form. The solubility products of the postprecipitated sulfides confirm this view, as Table IV shows. Evidently the sulfides of zinc, cobalt, and nickel ought by rights to precipitate with hydrogen sulfide in 0.3 N HCl. The only reason they do not precipitate is that they form supersaturated solutions, but if this supersaturation is overcome, they will precipitate. The supersaturation is probably encouraged by a high dependence of solubility on particle size, and possibly also by the temporary formation of a metastable form of sulfide or hydrosulfide.

TABLE IV

SOLUBILITY OF METAL SULFIDES

| Sulfide | K_{sp} | Metal ion concentration in equilibrium with 0.1 M H$^+$: | |
		(a) in 1 M H$^+$	(b) in 0.01 M H$^+$
FeS	1×10^{-19}	9×10^3	0.9
ZnS	7×10^{-26}	6×10^{-3}	6×10^{-7}
NiS	1.1×10^{-27}	1×10^{-4}	1×10^{-8}

The supersaturation of zinc sulfide and other sulfides can be relieved by finely divided solids such as broken glass, silica gel, and barium sulfate, but these are not nearly as efficient as other sulfides. One reason for the effectiveness of sulfides is that their particles adsorb hydrogen sulfide very strongly, so that in their immediate neighborhood the sulfide ion concentration is much larger than in the body of the solution. Some of this adsorbed hydrogen sulfide can be displaced by adding aluminum ions, and still better, by adding a sulfur compound such as cysteine, $CH_2SH \cdot CH_2 \cdot CHNH_2 \cdot COOH$. These compounds slow down considerably the postprecipitation of zinc sulfide on copper sulfide.

These data show how very careful one must be in adapting the sulfide separations of qualitative analysis to quantitative work. Acidities must be regulated very carefully, and ions which are likely to be postprecipitated should be protected by complex ion formation (cf. Chapter 2, page 12).

Postprecipitation is known in compounds other than sulfides, but fortunately it is uncommon and easily avoided where it occurs. The best-known example is the postprecipitation of magnesium oxalate on calcium oxalate; this is avoided by keeping the acidity as high as possible and filtering within an hour after precipitation.

An excellent comprehensive review of postprecipitation is given by Kolthoff and Moltzau.[9]

Precipitation from Homogeneous Solutions

We have seen that to avoid coprecipitation and postprecipitation it is often necessary to hold the pH within narrow limits during precipitation. For example, if we wish to precipitate calcium oxalate in the presence of magnesium ions or phosphate ions, the pH must be held as low as possible, consistent with having enough $C_2O_4^=$ ions to precipitate the calcium; for if the pH is too high, calcium phosphate may be coprecipitated or magnesium oxalate postprecipitated.

Another advantage of close pH control in an operation such as this is that by controlling the solubility of the precipitate, we control the speed of precipitation, and hence the particle size.

One way of obtaining the desired control in our example is to add dilute ammonia slowly, with vigorous stirring, to an acid solution which is (or becomes, by the time precipitation occurs) well buffered with ammonium salt. But even with the most careful technique, there is a zone in the solution where ammonia runs in, which has a higher pH than that desired.

This locally high concentration of ammonia can be avoided if the ammonia is not added from the outside, but is *slowly liberated within the solution* by a chemical reaction *taking place in the solution*. This is the method of "precipitation from homogeneous solution"; to liberate the precipitating ion gradually and uniformly through the body of the solution by means of a chemical reaction.

The most useful reaction for raising the pH of a weakly acid solution is the hydrolysis of urea:

$$CO(NH_2)_2 + H_2O \rightarrow CO_2 + 2NH_3.$$

[9] I. M. Kolthoff and R. Moltzau, *Chem. Rev.*, **17**, 293 (1935).

Ammonium cyanate is formed as an intermediate, but below pH 5 this does not accumulate to any appreciable extent. The rate of hydrolysis is almost independent of pH between pH 1 and pH 7, but depends strongly on the temperature.[10] At room temperature the reaction is extremely slow, but at 100°C it is fast enough to liberate enough ammonia for the average gravimetric precipitation in 1 to 2 hours. The procedure is first to make the solution just acid enough so that no precipitate appears, then to add 10–15 grams of urea to 250–500 ml. of solution and heat to boiling until the precipitation is complete. The tiny bubbles of carbon dioxide which are liberated prevent bumping.[11]

Other reactions which can be used to raise the pH in a homogeneous solution are the hydrolysis of hexamethylene tetrammine or ammonium nitrite, the reaction of hydrogen ions with thiosulfate ions, and the reaction of hydrogen ions with a mixture of iodide and iodate. The reaction with thiosulfate precipitates sulfur as a negatively charged colloid, which forms a coacervate with a positively charged colloidal precipitate such as hydrous aluminum oxide, and so makes it settle more quickly and be more easily filtered. In general, however, the urea hydrolysis is the best.

Precipitating ions may be liberated by the slow hydrolysis of esters. Thus triethyl phosphate is used to liberate phosphate ions for the homogeneous precipitation of zirconium and hafnium. Ordinarily these precipitated phosphates are very gelatinous and hard to handle, but when formed slowly by the hydrolysis of trimethyl phosphate, they are more compact, purer, and more easily filterable. Actually, these precipitates have complex compositions such as $(ZrO[OPO (OH)(OC_2H_5)]_2) \cdot 2H_2O$, but they yield the simple pyrophosphates on ignition. It is possible to separate zirconium from hafnium by fractional precipitation with trimethyl phosphate; the hafnium salt separates out first.[12]

Sulfate ions can be liberated by hydrolysis of dimethyl sulfate,[13] ethyl sulfate, or sulfamic acid, chloride ions from a chlorhydrin, and

[10] R. C. Warner, *J. Biol. Chem.*, **142**, 705 (1942).
[11] H. H. Willard and N. K. Tang, *J. Am. Chem. Soc.*, **59**, 1190 (1937); *Ind. Eng. Chem., Anal. Ed.*, **9**, 357 (1937).
[12] H. H. Willard and H. Freund, *Ind. Eng. Chem., Anal. Ed.*, **18**, 195 (1946); H. H. Willard and R. B. Hahn, *Anal. Chem.*, **21**, 293 (1949).
[13] P. J. Elving and R. E. Van Atta, *Anal. Chem.*, **22**, 1375 (1950).

oxalate ions from ethyl oxalate.[14] Hydrogen ions can be liberated by hydrolysis of any ester.

The great advantage of this technique is, of course, the purity of the precipitates which it produces. Calcium oxalate can be obtained free from phosphate or magnesium in one precipitation,[15] and barium sulfate can be precipitated practically free from accompanying calcium or iron (see Table V, also footnote 13). The particles are larger and more easily washed and filtered than those precipitated in the conventional way.

TABLE V

COPRECIPITATION OF CALCIUM WITH BARIUM SULFATE

Precipitant	Ca added, mg.	Ca in precipitate, mg.
Dilute H_2SO_4	5.4	3.4
Sulfamic acid	100	0.4
Ethyl sulfate	100	0.6

The precipitated hydrous oxides of trivalent and tetravalent metals are gelatinous whether they are formed from homogeneous solution or by conventional means. They can be made denser, however, and thus more easily filtered and washed, if they are precipitated from homogeneous solution in presence of certain anions, notably succinate, formate, and sulfate.[12] These enter into the precipitate to form amorphous basic salts of indefinite composition. These precipitates are remarkably free from coprecipitated cations, as Table VI shows. The coprecipitation is less, the lower the pH, but if the pH is too low, the hydrous oxide or basic salt may not be completely precipitated. A good procedure in such cases is to precipitate most of the metal at a low pH, then filter and precipitate the remainder at a higher pH. Iron, for instance, can be quantitately separated from copper, zinc, cobalt, and nickel by precipitating the bulk of the basic ferric formate at pH 1.8 and the remainder at pH 3.0 or higher. The small amount of precipitate forming in the second stage can be collected on the same filter as the main precipitate.[16]

[14] L. Gordon and E. R. Caley, *Anal. Chem.,* **20,** 560 (1948).
[15] H. H. Willard and F. L. Chan; see H. H. Willard and N. H. Furman, *Elementary Quantitative Analysis,* 3d ed., New York, Van Nostrand, 1940, p. 344.
[16] H. H. Willard, *Anal. Chem.,* **22,** 1372 (1950).

TABLE VI

COPRECIPITATION WITH HYDROUS ALUMINUM OXIDE

Added ion	Amount of added ion, grams	Coprecipitation, mg:	
		(a) by NH_3	(b) by urea + succinate
Mn^{++}	1.0	1.7	0.2
Cu^{++}	0.05	21.1	. . .
Cu^{++}	1.0	. . .	0.05
Zn^{++}	0.05	21.6	. . .
Zn^{++}	0.1	. . .	0.8
Zn^{++}	1.0	. . .	1.4

Notes: 1. 0.1 gram of Al was precipitated.   2. Cu^{++} was reduced to Cu^+ by hydroxylamine.   3. Reference: H. H. Willard, *Anal. Chem.*, **22**, 1372 (1950).

The choice of an anion depends on the cation being precipitated, and so does the pH of precipitation.   Succinate at pH 4.4 is the best choice for aluminum, formate for ferric iron and thorium (pH 5.4), sulfate for titanium (pH 1.5–1.8), gallium, and stannic tin.   The "basic formates" of iron and thorium have a tremendous adsorptive power for silica and stick to glass tenaciously.   They are therefore best precipitated in polyethylene vessels.

Not only are hydrous oxides purer when obtained by homogeneous precipitation than when precipitated by ammonia in the usual way, but they are easier to dry.   Hydrous aluminum oxide which has been precipitated by ammonia solution must be heated to 1100°C or higher before all the water is driven off; yet the precipitate obtained by boiling with urea, urea plus succinate, or hexamethylene tetramine reaches constant weight at 650°C or less.[17]   Hydrous aluminum oxide which has been slowly precipitated at room temperature by bubbling air containing a small percentage of ammonia gas gives a precipitate which comes to constant weight at 475°C.[17]   This technique of precipitation has been little explored, possibly because it is so slow.

Sulfides can be precipitated homogeneously by thioacetamide, CH_3CSNH_2.   This is a solid, easily soluble, with only a slight odor. It is added to a cold acid solution containing the metal to be precipi-

[17] T. Dupuis and C. Duval, *Anal. Chim. Acta*, **3**, 191 (1949).

tated, which is then heated to 80°–90°; thioacetamide hydrolyzes to give hydrogen sulfide, and metal sulfides such as As_2S_3, Sb_2S_3, and HgS precipitate in a few minutes with minimum contamination by sulfur. This reagent should find wide use as a welcome substitute for hydrogen sulfide gas.[18]

PROBLEMS

1. Why is magnesium not determined gravimetrically by precipitation as $Mg(OH)_2$?

2. Fe^{+++} and Zn^{+++} are to be separated by precipitating the former as hydrous ferric oxide with addition of ammonia. The separation is helped by the fact that zinc forms a complex cation with ammonia. What procedure would you advise, and why? How much ammonium salt, if any, should be added?

3. Outline in flow sheet form a scheme for the analysis of a phosphate rock containing P, Si, F, Al, Fe, Ti, Ca. Determine each constituent gravimetrically.

4. Barium is to be determined gravimetrically in presence of a small proportion of strontium. Would you precipitate as sulfate or as chromate? Why? What procedure would you adopt?

5. How would you determine chromate in a contaminated barium sulfate precipitate?

6. What difficulties arise in determining gravimetrically (a) Fe in presence of SO_4, (b) SO_4 in presence of Fe, (c) Fe in presence of PO_4, (d) PO_4 in presence of Fe? How may the difficulties be solved?

7. A recent proposal for determining magnesium involves precipitation as $MgC_2O_4 \cdot 2H_2O$. The sample is dissolved in 85% acetic acid containing some ammonium acetate, a little ethyl oxalate is added, and the solution is heated on a hot plate for two hours.

(a) Why is 85% acetic acid used?

(b) Why is ammonium acetate added?

(c) Why is ethyl oxalate used rather than ammonium oxalate?

(d) In what circumstances might this method be preferable to the usual ammonium phosphate method of precipitating magnesium?

[18] H. Flaschka and H. Jakobljevich, *Anal. Chim. Acta*, 4, 247, 351, 356 (1950); H. H. Barber and E. Grzeskowiak, *Anal. Chem.*, **21**, 192 (1949).

4

The drying and ignition
of precipitates

THE METHOD of gravimetric analysis is to separate the constituent to be determined and then weigh it in the form of a pure compound of known composition. The last two chapters have dealt with the process of precipitation, which is the mode of separation usually employed. Before the precipitate can be weighed, it must be dried. Sometimes this is a simple matter; a silver chloride precipitate, for example, can be dried sufficiently for ordinary analytical purposes by washing with acetone and sucking dust-free air through it for a few minutes, or by heating to 110°C in an oven for half an hour, or simply by leaving it exposed to clean air for a few hours. With most precipitates, however, the removal of the associated water is not easy, and it may be accompanied by other chemical changes. Often a precipitated substance is not weighed as such, but is decomposed by heating to a high temperature, in order to get a compound which one is sure will be anhydrous and have a definite composition; for example, precipitated $CaC_2O_4 \cdot H_2O$ is often converted by heat into CaO before weighing. During this heating any adherent ammonium oxalate is destroyed.

In the pyrolysis of precipitates, as in most chemical processes, we have two factors to consider: first, the equilibria, and second, the rates of the various reactions concerned. Equilibria are easier to treat theoretically, but in practice the reaction rates may be just as important.

Water in precipitates. The first process to take place when a precipitate is heated is the loss of water. We may distinguish for convenience four ways in which water is bound by precipitates: (1)

adherent water; (2) adsorbed water; (3) occluded water; (4) water of hydration.

Adherent water is no problem. It is easily removed by washing with a volatile solvent like acetone or by heating for a short time at 100°C or below. *Adsorbed water* is held on the surface of a solid by chemical or physical forces in a layer which may be only one molecule thick, but it may be held very strongly, and if the precipitate has a large specific surface, as do the hydrous oxides, the amount of adsorbed water may be very large. Hydrous silica and hydrous alumina, for example, are notorious for the tenacity with which they retain water; they must be heated almost to a white heat before they give it all up. Such precipitates may pick up water again after ignition if they come in contact with a moist atmosphere on cooling; so special care must be taken to cool in a desiccator and weigh promptly, using a covered crucible or stoppered weighing bottle. An alternative is to use a thermobalance (see below). *Occluded water* is liquid water which has been imprisoned in the particles of the precipitate during crystal growth. In a precipitate such as barium sulfate this can easily happen (see Figure 7, Chapter 2), and even in curdy silver chloride a detectable amount of occlusion takes place, as T. W. Richards found in his work on atomic weights. Richards found that the only way to remove the occluded water was to fuse the silver chloride in a current of dry air;[1] indeed, he made a practice of fusing all his salts wherever possible, and bottling them in a dry atmosphere before weighing. Some analytical precipitates, such as barium sulfate, cannot be melted without decomposition. Some, but not all, of the occluded water in barium sulfate is lost on heating to 1000°C, probably owing to decrepitation of the particles. The last traces of water can be removed by evaporating with concentrated sulfuric acid, which dissolves the precipitate, but this practice is not recommended because spitting is difficult to avoid, and in any case, the amount of coprecipitated salts is likely to be more than that of the occluded water which remains after ignition.

Water of hydration can be driven off completely if the temperature is sufficiently high and the atmospheric humidity sufficiently low. Accurate work should never depend upon the weight of salt hydrates. Unless a thermobalance is used, it is difficult to insure that the salt contains exactly its water of hydration and no more, or that ad-

[1] T. W. Richards and R. C. Wells, *J. Am. Chem. Soc.*, **27**, 459 (1905).

sorbed or occluded water is completely driven off without decomposing the hydrate to some extent.

Phase equilibria. To understand the thermal decomposition of salt hydrates and other compounds, such as carbonates, some knowledge of the phase rule is necessary. The phase rule reads:

$$P + F = C + 2,$$

where: P = number of phases.

F = number of degrees of freedom; i.e., the minimum number of variables which must be specified in order to determine the state of the system.

C = number of components; i.e., the minimum number of the chemical substances whose proportions must be specified to define the composition of each phase.

It is assumed that temperature and pressure are the only intensive variables other than composition.

Let us apply this rule to the decomposition of calcium oxalate hydrate into calcium oxalate and water vapor:

$$CaC_2O_4 \cdot H_2O \rightleftharpoons CaC_2O_4 + H_2O.$$

The two solids are quite distinct from one another and do not form solid solutions. There are, therefore, two solid phases and one vapor phase; i.e., $P = 3$. The number of components C is 2, provided the vapor phase consists of water vapor only. Therefore

$$F = C + 2 - P = 1.$$

We may choose one intensive variable, but only one. If we specify the temperature, then the pressure is fixed; at a given temperature there is only one pressure at which $CaC_2O_4 \cdot H_2O$, CaC_2O_4, and water vapor can exist in equilibrium together. That is, for each temperature there is a definite dissociation pressure, just as a pure liquid has a definite vapor pressure at a given temperature. (These partial pressures of water vapor are altered by introducing a second gas; e.g., air, but the effect may be calculated thermodynamically and is very slight.) For exactly the same reasons, there is a perfectly definite temperature-dissociation pressure relationship for each of the reactions $CaC_2O_4 \rightleftharpoons CaCO_3 + CO$ and $CaCO_3 \rightleftharpoons CaO + CO_2$. The graph of dissociation pressure against temperature for the latter is shown in Figure 1.[2]

Theoretically, $CaC_2O_4 \cdot H_2O$ will start to lose water as soon as the temperature is high enough so that its dissociation pressure exceeds the partial pressure of water vapor in the atmosphere. At temperatures lower than this it will not decompose at all, and at higher temperatures it will decompose completely, *provided* that air is constantly circulated over the solid and that time is allowed for diffusion of water vapor from the interstices of the solid out into the free air. The higher the temperature, the faster is the decomposition. The

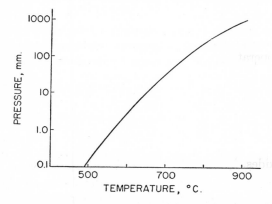

Fig. 4-1. Dissociation pressure of calcium carbonate. The ordinates give the pressure of CO_2 in equilibrium with a mixture of CaO and $CaCO_3$.

decomposition $CaC_2O_4 \rightarrow CaCO_3 + CO$ will be governed almost entirely by kinetic considerations since there is no carbon monoxide in the air. It becomes appreciable above 350°C.

The dissociation pressure of calcium carbonate reaches 0.23 mm., the partial pressure of carbon dioxide in fresh air at 515°C. It reaches 760 mm., the standard atmospheric pressure, at 882°C. Between these two temperatures the calcium carbonate will decompose, but the actual temperature at which the decomposition becomes perceptible depends on the partial pressure of carbon dioxide in the laboratory air and much more on the circulation of air within the

[2] For an excellent discussion of this system, see T. B. Smith, *Analytical Processes*, 2d ed., London, Arnold, 1940, Chap. VI.

furnace and within the crucible containing the calcium carbonate. Carbon dioxide is a heavy gas and will tend to stay in the crucible, blanketing the solid with carbon dioxide at a pressure much higher than its partial pressure in the air. This has two consequences for the analyst: first, if he wants to weigh calcium as $CaCO_3$, he has a "safety margin" and can go to 50 or 100 degrees higher than the theoretical dissociation temperature of 515°C without the decomposition being appreciable during the usual time of ignition; second, if he wants to weigh the calcium as CaO, he would better heat all the way to 882°C, so that the carbon dioxide will force its way out of the crucible against the atmosphere. Even then, most of the carbon dioxide must be swept out of the crucible before the latter is allowed to cool below 882°C; for the weight of a crucibleful of carbon dioxide is not negligible. This means that the crucible must be heated *without a cover* in a properly ventilated muffle furnace. A cover should be placed on the crucible *after* the ignition is complete, to protect the contents from carbon dioxide as the crucible cools.

If the calcium is to be weighed as carbonate, the ignition temperature is best held between 450° and 550°C. Higher temperatures may be used if the ignition is done in an atmosphere of carbon dioxide (for which operation a Rose crucible is suitable). The carbon dioxide in the crucible must, of course, be replaced by air before weighing.

We will now consider another type of phase equilibrium which is occasionally found in analytical chemistry, that in which only one solid phase exists. This is the case in the decomposition of ferric oxide at high temperatures:

$$6Fe_2O_3 \rightleftharpoons 4Fe_3O_4 + O_2.$$

The two oxides, Fe_2O_3 and Fe_3O_4, form a continuous series of solid solutions. Therefore there are only two phases, solid and gas, and by the phase rule the number of degrees of freedom is 2. We also have another variable, the composition of the solid phase. If we fix the temperature and pressure, the composition is fixed; if we fix the composition and pressure, the temperature is fixed, and so on.

When ferric oxide is ignited in air, the partial pressure of oxygen is about 150 mm., and at 1100°C, the proportion of Fe_3O_4 at equilibrium is 0.116% by weight, which means that the precipitate weighs only 0.004% less than if it were all Fe_2O_3.[3]

[3] R. B. Sosman and J. C. Hostetter, *J. Am. Chem. Soc.*, **38**, 807, 1188.

Experimental studies. Far less attention has been given to the drying and ignition of precipitates than to the processes of precipitation and washing. Until recently, the only careful experimental studies were those made in connection with atomic weight determinations and a very few others, such as the proper ignition temperature

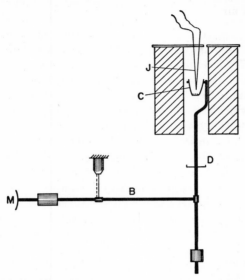

Fig. 4-2. The thermobalance: B is the balance beam, C the crucible containing the sample, D the pan for calibration weights, J the thermojunction, and M the mirror which reflects a beam of light to sensitive paper mounted on a rotating drum.

for $Mg_2P_2O_7$.[4] To correct this state of affairs, Duval and collaborators[5] have undertaken an extensive investigation of the weight-temperature relations of analytical precipitates, using a special balance designed by Chevenard[6] and called a *thermobalance*. This instrument is illustrated in Figure 2. It permits the sample to be

[4] J. I. Hoffman and G. E. F. Lundell, *J. Research Nat. Bur. Standards*, **5**, 279 (1930).

[5] For general reviews, see C. Duval, *Anal. Chim. Acta*, **2**, 432 (1948), and *Anal. Chem.*, **23**, 1271 (1951); many papers in *Anal. Chim. Acta.*, beginning with **1**, 341 (1947).

[6] P. Chevenard, X. Waché, and R. de la Tullaye, *Bull. soc. chim.*, [5], **11**, 41 (1944).

weighed while it is actually in the furnace, and provides a continuous record of weight against time; since the temperature of the furnace can be increased at a steady rate, a graph of weight against temperature is obtained.

The crucible C, containing the sample, is mounted at the upper end of a vertical quartz rod A, and is surrounded by an electrically heated muffle furnace. This furnace is partially closed at the top by a baffle, which prevents disturbing convection currents, yet permits circulation of air (or hydrogen, if desired) around the crucible. The temperature is measured by a thermojunction J, located just above the crucible. The quartz rod which carries the crucible is attached below the furnace to a horizontal duralumin rod B, which is the beam of the balance. This hangs from a bifilar suspension of tungsten wire and is suitably counterpoised; it also carries a small concave mirror M, which reflects a ray of light onto photographic paper mounted on a drum. As the weight of the crucible and contents changes, this ray of light is deflected up and down; the deflection corresponding to a given weight difference is found by placing a 50-mg. weight on the pan D, below the furnace.

The balance is sensitive to ±0.2 mg., and the temperature of the furnace can be measured and controlled to $\pm1°$ between room temperature and 1100°C. The temperature may be held constant indefinitely if desired, but more usually it is allowed to rise steadily over a period of 1–3 hours. Meanwhile the recorder drum is slowly rotated. A graph of weight against time is thus obtained, and calibration marks give the temperature at suitable intervals. The kind of record obtained is shown in Figures 3 and 4.

With continuous recording this technique does not give equilibrium conditions, but it gives something more valuable to the analyst; namely, the weight-temperature relationships in an open crucible in a ventilated muffle furnace for ignition periods up to three hours. These are a resultant of equilibrium and rate effects. Consider, for example, the pyrolysis curve for calcium oxalate shown in Figure 3. This shows that, under these conditions of ignition, the salt can be weighed as $CaC_2O_4 \cdot H_2O$ below 100°C, as CaC_2O_4 between 226° and 398°C, as $CaCO_3$ between 420° and 660°C, and as CaO above 838°C. These temperatures can be compared with those indicated by the equilibrium curves of Figure 1. They are different, but they are definite and reproducible, and they show that the dissociation of

calcium carbonate proceeded only slowly. This was probably due
to the poor removal of carbon dioxide from a crucible by a vertical
flow of air.

The magnesium oxalate curve is quite different from that of calcium oxalate. The horizontal step corresponding to $MgCO_3$ is
missing, showing that MgC_2O_4 loses CO and CO_2 simultaneously
between 400° and 480°C.

Comparing these two pyrolysis curves, we see that the recording
thermobalance may be used in certain cases for identification purposes and to analyze mixtures. Suppose we have a mixture of cal-

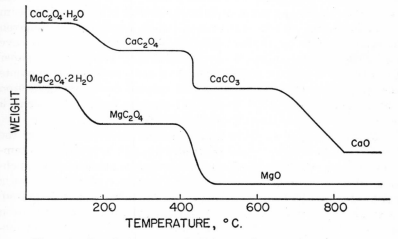

Fig. 4-3. Pyrolysis curves of calcium and magnesium oxalates.

cium oxalate and magnesium oxalate; from the weights at two temperatures, say, 500° and 900°C, we can find how much of each
component was present. The loss in weight between 500° and 900°C
is proportional to the weight of calcium, and the weight of magnesium can be found by difference from the weight of the combined
oxides recorded at 900°C. Good results were reported by Peltier
and Duval [7] for synthetic mixtures of the two oxalates, and the
amount of coprecipitated magnesium oxalate present in a calcium
oxalate precipitate was also determined. In the same way, a mixture
of silver and copper can be analyzed by converting them to their

[7] S. Peltier and C. Duval, *Anal. Chim. Acta*, **1**, 408 (1947).

nitrates and taking the pyrolysis curve. Silver nitrate and copper nitrate behave quite differently upon heating; at 400°C, the mixture consists of $AgNO_3$ and CuO; at 700°C, of Ag and CuO. The weights at these two temperatures will therefore give the proportions of silver and copper in the mixture. Yet another example, studied recently, is the analysis of a mixture of potassium, rubidium, and cesium by pyrolysis of their perchlorates. These decompose successively, the potassium perchlorate decomposing first, and the weight-temperature curve shows three distinct breaks.

In applying the thermobalance to the analysis of mixtures, however, one difficulty must always be borne in mind. If two solids form solid solutions or combine to give a double salt, their activities are no longer the same as in the pure solid phases, and therefore their dissociation pressures and pyrolysis curves are affected. From Figure 3, for example, one might think it possible to analyze a dolomite or a dolomitic limestone by means of the thermobalance, since $CaCO_3$ and $MgCO_3$ decompose at different temperatures. However, dolomite, $CaMg(CO_3)_2$, is a double salt, with its own characteristic crystal lattice; on heating in the thermobalance, it loses carbon dioxide continuously over a broad temperature range, with no level portion corresponding to undecomposed $CaCO_3$. Dolomite forms a restricted range of solid solutions with both $CaCO_3$ and $MgCO_3$, so that neither dolomite itself, nor dolomitic limestone, nor magnesite can be analyzed by simple ignition in the thermobalance.[8] The possibilities of the thermobalance for analyzing mixtures have, however, been very little explored as yet, and one may confidently expect more applications in the future.

The pyrolysis curves of a few representative precipitates are shown in Figure 4. From them we can tell the correct temperature range for ignition, and whether or not a precipitate is suitable for gravimetric analysis. Barium sulfate and magnesium ammonium phosphate are evidently good precipitates for weighing, for their weights remain constant over wide ranges of temperature. Incidentally, magnesium ammonium phosphate yields magnesium pyrophosphate at temperatures above 475°C, showing that the familiar Bureau of Standards procedure[4] of igniting to bright redness for three hours is unnecessary, except where extreme accuracy is required. Heating to

[8] C. Duval, private communication.

500°C for 15 minutes is sufficient. The magnesium complex of 8-hydroxyquinoline is evidently *not* a suitable precipitate for weighing, for its pyrolysis curve shows no flat portion, only a continuous

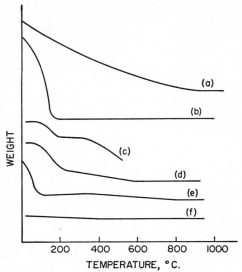

Fig. 4-4. Pyrolysis curves of typical precipitates. (a), hydrous Al_2O_3 precipitated by ammonia solution; (b), hydrous Al_2O_3 precipitated by urea hydrolysis (weight constant above 600°); (c), magnesium 8-hydroxyquinoline complex; (d), $MgNH_4PO_4 \cdot 6H_2O$; (e), fibrous asbestos; (f), $BaSO_4$. Curve (c) acc. Borel and Paris; other curves acc. Duval.

drop in weight.[9] The aluminum complex of 8-hydroxyquinoline, however, is quite satisfactory, for its pyrolysis curve (not shown) has a flat portion, corresponding to the anhydrous compound, between 102° and 220°C.[10] Likewise, the ferric complex of neocupferron may

[9] There is disagreement between different workers concerning the pyrolysis curve of the magnesium 8-hydroxyquinoline complex. Much depends on the rate of heating, and also, presumably, on the humidity of the air. It *is* possible to weigh the dihydrate, $MgQ_2 \cdot 2H_2O$, and obtain fairly good results; the anhydrous complex with 8-hydroxyquinaldine, however, is a far more reliable weighing form for magnesium (Duval).

[10] For thermogravimetry of metal 8-hydroxyquinoline complexes, see M. Borel and R. Paris, *Anal. Chim. Acta*, **4**, 267 (1950).

be weighed as the anhydrous compound between 25° and 107°C—contrary to earlier statements in the literature.

The curves for hydrous alumina shown in Figure 4 are very interesting. When ammonia solution is used as the precipitant (which is the usual procedure), the product must be heated above 1000°C before it loses all its water, but when the urea-succinate method of homogeneous precipitation is used (see Chapter 3), the precipitate reaches constant weight at 610°C. Another interesting curve is that for fibrous asbestos. This loses weight steadily above 283°C, showing that asbestos filter mats should not be used for ignitions above this temperature. A glass filter mat, sintered glass, or porous porcelain is quite suitable.

In all, Duval and his group have examined about a thousand analytical precipitates. The value of their data in selecting drying and ignition temperatures is obvious. Further, the thermobalance has given an insight into the course of pyrolytic reactions and has led to the discovery of new compounds, such as metaboric acid, HBO_2. Finally, we must re-emphasize the fact that the precipitate is weighed while it is actually in the furnace. This is a great advantage with hygroscopic precipitates, such as beryllium oxide.

PROBLEMS

1. From the data shown in Figure 1, estimate the dissociation pressure of $CaCO_3$ at 300°C.

2. Suggest specific applications of the thermobalance in the analysis of mixtures, analogous to the simultaneous determination of Ca and Mg mentioned in the text.

3. Give several examples to show how the thermobalance could reveal the presence and amount of coprecipitated impurities.

4. How will the state of subdivision of a substance affect its thermal decomposition?

5. How would you expect the weight-temperature curves of calcium sulfate dihydrate and hydrous silica to differ?

6. A certain salt hydrate starts to lose water to the air at 120°C. By how much will this temperature be lowered if the humidity of the air is reduced by one-half? Assume equilibrium conditions exist, and that the heat of dissociation of the hydrate into anhydrous salt and water vapor is 10,000 calories per mole of water lost.

7. Which decomposes at the lower temperature, $CaSO_4$ or $BaSO_4$? $BaSO_4$ or Na_2SO_4? $FeSO_4$ or $Fe_2(SO_4)_3$? (See the author's *Inorganic Preparations*, Prentice-Hall, 1948.) What might be a suitable ignition temperature for $PbSO_4$? Explain your answers.

5

Electrolytic methods of analysis

ELECTROLYSIS can be applied to chemical analysis in several ways. The oldest, and commonest, kind of electrolytic analysis is simply quantitative electroplating; it is applied almost exclusively to metals, and consists in collecting and weighing the metal or other substance which is liberated. The electric current may be regarded as a gravimetric precipitating agent. It is always passed in an amount exceeding that which is theoretically necessary, to ensure complete deposition. In the second type of electrolytic analysis the current is used simply as a means of separation, to deposit certain metals and not others, or to oxidize or reduce certain substances and not others; the final determination of these substances is made in another way. The third, and newest, type of electrolytic analysis is that in which the quantity of electricity needed to oxidize or reduce the substance being determined is measured accurately, and the amount of the substance is calculated from the quantity of electricity used. This technique is known as "coulometric analysis."

Theory

Current requirements. The current used in carrying out an electrolysis is governed by Faraday's laws. These state that the quantity of electricity passed is proportional to the weight of substance liberated at the anode or cathode and also to the chemical equivalent weight of that substance. It takes 96,500 coulombs of electricity to liberate one gram equivalent weight of any substance, one coulomb being the amount of electricity passed when a current

58

of one ampere flows for one second. Thus to deposit 1 gram of copper from a cupric salt solution takes 96,500/31.78 or 3036 coulombs. This would be passed by 1 ampere in 3036 seconds, by 2 amperes in 1518 seconds, and so on. This information may be used to estimate the minimum time needed to deposit a certain weight of material, or it may be used to determine accurately the amount of material liberated if the quantity of electricity used in liberating it is accurately known.

Potential requirements. The potential, or voltage, needed in electrolysis depends on the substance being electrolyzed, which determines the amount of electric energy needed to cause its decomposi-

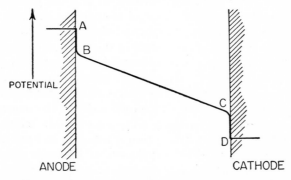

Fig. 5-1. Potential across electrodes and solution in an electrolytic cell (schematic).

tion. The product of the voltage drop across an electrolytic cell and the number of coulombs of electricity passed through the cell gives the energy consumed in joules.

The voltage drop, or potential drop, across a cell may be divided into two parts. One part is due to the resistance of the cell, and is proportional to the current according to Ohm's law. Nearly all of this drop takes place in the solution between the two electrodes, as is indicated by the line *BC* in Figure 1. The other part of the potential drop is that which occurs across boundary regions at the surface of the two electrodes, as indicated by *AB* and *CD* in Figure 1. At each electrode surface the potential drop may be further subdivided into a *reversible* potential, which would be required even if the current passed infinitely slowly, and an *irreversible* potential, or *polarization*, caused by the slowness of one or more of the physical and chemical processes occurring at the electrode.

We shall consider the reversible potential first. This is given by the Nernst equation. For an electrode of the metal M in equilibrium with a solution of its ions, M^{+n}, according to the reaction

$$M^{+n} + ne \rightleftharpoons M,$$

the reversible potential is given by the equation

$$E = E^\circ + \frac{RT}{n\mathfrak{F}} \ln a_{M^{+n}}, \tag{1}$$

where E° is the "standard potential" which the electrode would have if it were placed in a solution of its ions having unit activity, and $A_{M^{+n}}$ is the activity of the ions in the solution in question. Both E and E° are referred to the same standard, usually the standard hydrogen electrode unless otherwise stated. Taking the example $Cu^{++} + 2e \rightleftharpoons Cu$,

$$E = 0.337 + \frac{RT}{2\mathfrak{F}} \ln a_{Cu^{++}}$$

$$= 0.337 + \frac{0.0592}{2} \log_{10} a_{Cu^{++}} \quad \text{at } 25°C.$$

If we electrolyze a solution of copper sulfate in which the cupric ion activity is 0.1, the cathode must have a potential $0.337 - 0.0295 = 0.307$ volt with respect to the hydrogen electrode, or a more negative potential than this, before any copper can deposit. (There is nothing inconsistent in the cathode, or negative electrode, having a positive potential on the hydrogen scale, for the anode would have a still more positive potential—at least 1.33 volts if the solution were of unit activity in hydrogen ions and if oxygen were being evolved at the anode.) As cupric ions are neutralized at the cathode and converted into metallic copper, the activity of cupric ions in the solution falls, and the cathode potential accordingly becomes more negative. When the cupric ion activity has fallen to 10^{-6} (by which time the deposition of copper may be considered quantitatively complete) the cathode potential is $0.337 - 6 \times 0.0295 = 0.160$ volt; this is 0.147 volt more negative than it was originally.

Such calculations tell us the minimum voltage needed for electrolysis and they also give us an idea of the feasibility of electrolytic separations. For example, the standard potential of the reaction

$BiO^+ + 2H^+ + 3e \rightarrow Bi + H_2O$ is $+0.32$ volt. If we had a solution in which the activity of BiO^+ was 1, and which also contained copper, bismuth metal would start to deposit even before the cupric ion activity had fallen to 0.1. The separation is quite impossible unless one or other of the ions is first converted into a complex, such as $Cu(CN)_3^=$. On the other hand, copper is easily separated from tin by electrolysis, for the standard potential of the reaction $Sn^{++} + 2e \rightarrow Sn$ is -0.136 volt. At this cathode potential the concentration of cupric ions in the solution at equilibrium would be antilog $(-0.136 - 0.337)/0.0295 = 10^{-16}$ approximately, so the copper is quantitatively removed from the solution well before the tin starts to deposit. In general we can say that a divalent cation can be quantitatively reduced in the presence of another cation if its standard reduction potential is 0.2 to 0.3 volt less negative than that of the second cation.

A more complete discussion of standard potentials appears in Chapter 11.

Complex ions in separations. In electrolytic analysis, just as in any precipitation process, complex ions are useful in making separations. Bismuth may be quantitatively deposited in the presence of copper by adding cyanide, which changes the deposition potential of copper from $+0.34$ volt to almost -1.0 volt through the formation of extremely stable cuprous cyanide complexes; likewise cadmium can be deposited from a cold cyanide solution in the presence of copper. Copper can be plated out in presence of bismuth by adding tartaric acid.[1] This forms complexes with both copper and bismuth, but the bismuth complex is much the more stable. In the same way tartaric acid keeps antimony in solution while copper is deposited.[2] Oxalic acid is used in hydrogen sulfide precipitation to keep tin in solution while antimony is precipitated, and the same can be done in electrolytic analysis, although the addition of oxalic acid is unnecessary if the cathode potential is carefully controlled.

Any substance which combines with a metal ion to form a complex makes the reversible electrode potential of that metal more negative when in contact with the complex solution, as is required by the Nernst equation. If the instability constant of the complex is

---

[1] H. J. S. Sand, *Electrochemistry and Electrochemical Analysis*, 2 vols., London, Blackie, 1939 and 1940.

[2] J. J. Lingane, *Ind. Eng. Chem., Anal. Ed.*, **17**, 640 (1945).

known, the electrode potential can be calculated, but more commonly it is electrode potential measurements which are used to calculate the instability constant. A few representative standard electrode potentials of metals in complex salt solutions are given in Table I. The standard potential is that for which the activities of the complex ion *and* of the complexing ion or molecule are both unity.

TABLE I

COMPLEX ION FORMATION AND STANDARD ELECTRODE POTENTIALS

Electrode reaction	Potential, volts
$Ag^+ + e \longrightarrow Ag$	0.7991
$Ag(NH_3)_2^+ + e \longrightarrow Ag + 2NH_3$	0.373
$Ag(CN_2)^- + e \longrightarrow Ag + 2CN^-$	−0.31
$Cu^+ + e \longrightarrow Cu$	0.521
$Cu^{++} + 2e \longrightarrow Cu$	0.337
$Cu(NH_3)_2^+ + e \longrightarrow Cu + 2NH_3$	−0.12
$CuCl_2^- + e \longrightarrow Cu + 2Cl^-$	0.19
$CuCl_3^= + e \longrightarrow Cu + 3Cl^-$	0.178
$Cu(NH_3)_4^{++} + e \longrightarrow Cu(NH_3)_2^+ + 2NH_3$	0.00
$BiO^+ + 2H^+ + 3e \longrightarrow Bi + H_2O$	0.32
$BiCl_4^- + 3e \longrightarrow Bi + 4Cl^-$	0.16
$Cd^{++} + 2e \longrightarrow Cd$	−0.403
$Cd(NH_3)_4^{++} + 2e \longrightarrow Cd + 4NH_3$	−0.61
$Cd(CN)_4^= + 2e \longrightarrow Cd + 4CN^-$	−1.03
$Zn^{++} + 2e \longrightarrow Zn$	−0.763
$Zn(NH_3)_4^{++} + 2e \longrightarrow Zn + 4NH_3$	−1.03
$Zn(CN)_4^= + 2e \longrightarrow Zn + 4CN^-$	−1.26

Note: data taken from W. Latimer, *Oxidation Potentials*, New York, Prentice-Hall, 1938, 1952 editions.

These potentials often depend strongly on temperature, since the dissociation of the complexes changes with temperature. Electrolytic separations which are possible at a low temperature may be impossible at a high temperature, and vice versa. For example, at 20°C the standard potentials of nickel and zinc in ammonia solutions are −0.93 volt and −1.15 volts respectively; at 90°C they are −0.60 volt and −1.10 volts. Nickel is easily separated from zinc in an ammoniacal solution at 90°C, but not at 20°C.

The physical form of a metal deposit is sometimes affected by formation from a complex salt solution. Silver, plated from a solution of silver nitrate, tends to form large loose crystals, but from solutions of its complexes with cyanide or ammonia smooth adherent deposits result. The silver deposited from a cyanide solution is seldom pure, however. It contains inclusions of a cyanide compound. A similar difficulty appears with cadmium which can be completely removed from a solution if cyanide is added, yet the deposit is always 1–2% too heavy. Electrolysis is a good method for separating cadmium from other metals, but not a good method for determining cadmium; for best accuracy the deposit must be dissolved in acid and the metal precipitated and weighed as $Cd_2P_2O_7$.[3]

Separations from hydrogen. It is evident that metals such as copper, whose standard potentials are more positive than that of hydrogen, can be deposited from acid solutions without discharging any hydrogen. Metals with potentials more negative than hydrogen cannot be deposited from acid solutions without some hydrogen being formed at the same time, and if reversible potentials were the only criterion, they would not deposit from acid solutions at all. In neutral or alkaline solutions, however, the hydrogen ion concentration is very small and the hydrogen electrode potential correspondingly more negative. Nickel is generally deposited from a strongly ammoniacal solution of pH about 11. At pH 11, the reversible hydrogen electrode potential is $-0.059 \times 11 = -0.65$ volt at 25°C. This is sufficiently negative so that little if any hydrogen deposits along with the nickel. Likewise zinc can be deposited from a sodium zincate solution 1 M or more in sodium hydroxide.

Though it helps to make the solution alkaline in such cases, we must remember that the deposition potential of the metal, as well as that of hydrogen, is made more negative because of complex ion formation. The plating of "active" metals from aqueous solutions would still be difficult or impossible were it not for hydrogen overvoltage. This effect will be discussed in a later section.

Depolarizers. It is a familiar fact that nickel and metals more reactive than nickel do not deposit well from solutions containing nitrate. The reason is that nitrate ions are reduced at the cathode in preference to nickel ions; they act as "cathodic depolarizers," that is, they limit the negative potential which may be applied to the

[3] H. Diehl and R. Brouns, *Iowa State College J. Sci.*, **20**, 155 (1945); H. Diehl, *Electrochemical Analysis with Graded Cathode Potential Control*, Columbus, G. Frederick Smith Chemical Co., 1948, p. 26.

cathode by providing an alternative, competitive electrode reaction. The action of the nitrate ions can be counteracted by adding a reducing agent such as sodium sulfite to the ammoniacal nickel solution. The depolarizing action of nitrate ions is an advantage in the deposition of copper, however, for it delays the liberation of hydrogen and so gives a bright, smooth deposit.

Another depolarizer which can be a great nuisance is the ferric ion. This is easily reduced at the cathode, for the reversible potential of $Fe^{+++} + e \rightharpoonup Fe^{++}$ is $+0.78$ volt, which is more positive than that of $Cu^{++} + 2e \rightharpoonup Cu$. The ferrous ions formed at the cathode are reoxidized at the anode to ferric ions, so that in the usual type of cell, where the anode and cathode are close together, it may be impossible to deposit copper and other metals quantitatively in the presence of iron unless a second depolarizer, such as hydroxylamine, is added. A similar situation arises in depositing copper from a hydrochloric acid solution. Because of the stability of the cuprous chloride complex the reduction of cupric ions proceeds in two distinct stages:

$$Cu^{++} + 3Cl^- + e \rightharpoonup CuCl_3^=; \qquad E° = 0.51 \text{ volt.}$$

$$CuCl_3^= + e \rightharpoonup Cu + 3Cl^-; \quad E° = 0.178 \text{ volt.}$$

These potentials show that cupric ions can oxidize metallic copper in the presence of chloride, and cupric ions are easily formed from $CuCl_3^=$ by oxidation at the anode or even by air. Copper cannot be completely deposited from a hydrochloric acid solution unless the anode and cathode are separated by a diaphragm or unless something is added to reduce the cupric ions to cuprous and keep them there. Such a substance is hydroxylamine hydrochloride. This acts as an anodic depolarizer, for at the anode the hydroxylammonium ion is oxidized (for as long as it lasts) in preference to $CuCl_3^=$. Hydrazine and titanous chloride have the same effect.[3] Several other procedures have been recorded in which hydrazine or hydroxylamine is added in cases where a metal having two positive oxidation states is deposited, for example, tin, mercury, or iron. In every case their function is the same, namely, to act as an anodic depolarizer and prevent reoxidation of metal ions at the anode.

Instead of adding a depolarizer in such cases one can separate the anode and cathode by a porous partition, or one may use an anode whose potential is less positive than the usual platinum anode. The latter has a potential of $+1.7$ volts or more, the sum of the reversible potential of the oxygen electrode, which is $+1.33$ volts in a solution of unit hydrogen ion activity, and the overvoltage of oxygen on platinum. By contrast, a silver gauze anode in a chloride solution has a potential of only $+0.22$ volt, and so cannot oxidize $CuCl_3^=$ to Cu^{++}. Finally, anodic reoxidation can be overcome by applying so large a potential to the cell that the intermediate product cannot diffuse or migrate away from the cathode before it is reduced completely to the metal. The drawback to this practice is that the metal deposit forms very rapidly and is likely not to adhere properly to the cathode.

A novel use for depolarizers in electrolytic analysis has been introduced by Furman.[4] A depolarizer is a substance which limits the potential that can be applied to the anode or cathode. Ferric ion was cited above as a substance which prevents the cathode potential becoming more negative than $+0.78$ volt, the standard potential of the ferric-ferrous system, so long as no more than an equal quantity of ferrous ions is present. The ferric-ferrous system acts as a buffer, in other words, to control the cathode potential. In presence of a ferric-ferrous mixture silver ions can be reduced to silver (E° for $Ag^+ + e \rightharpoonup Ag$ is $+0.799$ volt) but cupric ions cannot be reduced to copper. Thus silver could be separated quantitatively from copper by electrodeposition from such a solution without the need for external potential control. Similar "potential buffers" studied by Furman are Ti(IV) plus Ti(III), V(III) plus V(II), and U(IV) plus U(III). This last mixture inhibited completely the deposition of Cr, Mn, and Mo at a mercury cathode, while allowing the deposition of Cd. As the more highly oxidized component of the buffer is reduced at the cathode, the less highly oxidized component is oxidized at the anode, so that a fairly constant proportion of the two is maintained.

Irreversible electrode effects: overvoltage. During electrolysis the potential across a cell is always more than the reversible electrode potentials would indicate, even after allowance is made for the potential drop due to the internal resistance of the cell. The potential drops along AB and CD, Figure 1, are greater than the Nernst equation predicts. The additional potential existing between an elec-

[4] N. H. Furman and C. E. Bricker, *U. S. Atomic Energy Commission Report MDDC–691* (1947); C. J. Rodden (editor), *Analytical Chemistry of the Manhattan Project*, New York, McGraw-Hill, 1950, p. 520.

trode and the solution, over and above the reversible potential, is called the *polarization*. It is greater, the greater the current passing.

Polarization is of two kinds, concentration polarization and chemical polarization. *Concentration polarization* is caused by the fact that in the layer of solution immediately next the electrode, the concentration of the reacting ions or molecules is not the same as it is in the bulk of the solution. If ions are being discharged at the electrode, the solution near the electrode is impoverished in these ions, because it takes time for them to diffuse up to the electrode. Concentration polarization is governed by diffusion rates. It is represented by the rounded portions of the potential-distance curve in Figure 1, near points *B* and *C*. It can be reduced considerably by efficient stirring, but it cannot be eliminated altogether. It is usually of the order of 0.1 volt in a stirred solution. *Chemical polarization* or *overvoltage* is caused by the slowness of one or more of the chemical reactions taking place at the electrode, and it is not affected by stirring.

Overvoltage is greatest in the discharge of hydrogen and oxygen. In the discharge or dissolution of most metals it is negligible, although overvoltages of 0.3 volt or more have been reported in the discharge of nickel ions,[5] and iron and cobalt show similar overvoltages. Hydrogen is the element whose overvoltage has been most studied, and the one whose overvoltage is most important in electrolytic analysis. The following are the salient facts regarding hydrogen overvoltage:[6]

1. It depends greatly on the material of the cathode at which the hydrogen is discharging. It is least for catalytically active metals, such as nickel and platinum, and greatest for noncatalytically active metals, such as mercury.

2. It depends on the physical structure of the cathode surface (i.e., whether electrodeposited, cast, or rolled) and is lowered by traces of impurities, especially oxygen.

3. In most cases it increases slowly with time, being constant after about an hour of electrolysis.

---

[5] F. W. Salt, *Faraday Soc. Discussions*, **1,** 169 (1947).

[6] See textbooks such as S. Glasstone, *Introduction to Electrochemistry*, New York, Van Nostrand, 1942. For a recent review, see J. O'M. Bockris, *Chem. Rev.*, **43,** 525 (1948).

4. It increases with the logarithm of the current density.

5. It decreases with rising temperature.

We can understand these facts better if we realize that the current passing in electrolysis measures the speed of a chemical reaction occurring at the electrodes. More correctly, it measures the rate of a whole sequence of chemical reactions. The formation of hydrogen at a cathode is a complex process with a number of different steps, such as, for example,

$$H_3O^+ + \text{metal} + e \rightarrow H_2O + \text{H-metal}$$

and

$$2\text{H-metal} \rightarrow H_2 + 2 \text{ (metal)},$$

and whichever of these steps is the slowest will determine the rate of the entire process. There is much discussion as to the nature of this slowest step, but whatever it is, the Arrhenius rate equation must apply:

$$I = k \cdot e^{-E_{act}/RT}, \tag{2}$$

where I is the current density, k is a constant almost independent of temperature, and E_{act} is the *activation energy*, or the minimum energy which molecules must possess on collision in order to react. The activation energy depends on the electrode material, and also on the electrode potential, as follows:

$$E_{act} = E_0 - \alpha V \mathfrak{F}, \tag{3}$$

where V is the overvoltage, defined as the difference between the actual potential of the electrode and the potential which it would have if it were in equilibrium with the solution and hydrogen gas; $\mathfrak{F}$ is the faraday; and α is an empirical constant, less than 1, usually 0.2 to 0.5. Evidently the excess potential energy which the electrons in the cathode metal have by virtue of the overvoltage can contribute in part to the energy of activation; the greater the overvoltage, the more electric energy is available for activation of the reacting molecules, and the faster is the reaction. The current is found to increase exponentially with the applied overvoltage, which is what one would expect.

In electrolytic analysis the current density at the cathode is of the order 0.01 ampere per square centimeter. The overvoltages needed to give this current density at room temperature are listed for different cathode metals in Table II. These values were obtained with oxygen and other impurities carefully excluded; under ordinary analytical conditions the overvoltages would be somewhat less than these values.

TABLE II

HYDROGEN OVERVOLTAGE ON METALS

Cathode metal	Overvoltage	Cathode metal	Overvoltage
Pb*	1.24	Ag	0.66
Cd	1.20	Cr	0.67†
Hg	1.15	Cu*	0.62
Tl	1.13	Fe	0.53
Sn	0.98	Ni	0.42
Pb	0.97	Pt	0.39
Bi	0.83	Pt*	0.35
Cu	0.75	W	0.35
Ta	0.75	Au*	0.25
Al	0.71	Pt black	0.03

Notes: * Electrodeposited metal.

† Current density 0.1 amp./cm.^{2}

Current density 0.01 amp./cm.^{2} except for Cr. Temperature 16°C. Data of A. Hickling and F. W. Salt, *Trans. Faraday Soc.*, **36**, 1226 (1940); also J. O'M. Bockris, *Trans. Faraday Soc.*, **43**, 417 (1947).

The overvoltage of hydrogen is what makes it possible to deposit metals from aqueous solutions even where their reversible potentials are more negative than that of hydrogen in the same solution. To deposit a metal at an analytically useful rate requires only the reversible potential plus 0.1 volt or less for the concentration polarization; to deposit hydrogen at a comparable speed requires not only its reversible potential, but often a considerable overvoltage in addition. Thus zinc can be deposited quantitatively from an acetic acid-sodium acetate solution even though its reversible potential is nearly 0.5 volt more negative than that of hydrogen in the same solution. Cadmium can even be deposited from dilute sulfuric acid, though an acetate buffer or cyanide solution is preferable. Tin and lead can be deposited quite conveniently from acid solutions. Commercial chromium plating, which is done at high current density from an acid solution, would be impossible if it were not for hydrogen overvoltage.

The overvoltage of hydrogen is greater, the faster it discharges, so that the proportion of hydrogen discharging along with a metal is lessened by raising the current density. Theoretically, *some* hydrogen is always liberated whenever the electrode is more negative than a reversible hydrogen electrode. In favorable cases this hydrogen liberation is extremely small, but in other cases the hydrogen may permeate the metal deposit and cause it to weigh more than it should. This sometimes happens with nickel. Obviously coulometric analysis is out of the question where there is the possibility of hydrogen being discharged with the metal.

The mercury cathode. The overvoltage of hydrogen depends on the metal at which it is liberated. This means that in conventional electrolytic analysis the hydrogen overvoltage cannot be regulated at will, for it depends on the metal which is being deposited. If nickel is being deposited on a platinum gauze cathode, for instance, the cathode becomes to all intents and purposes a nickel cathode once electrolysis has started, and the overvoltage of hydrogen is that which is characteristic of nickel.

There is one way, however, to ensure a high hydrogen overvoltage regardless of what metal is deposited, and that is to use a cathode of mercury. Mercury has one of the highest hydrogen overvoltages of any metal, and since it is a liquid, the metals deposited on it do not have to remain on the surface but will diffuse or dissolve in it, leaving the surface practically pure mercury. Not only is the liberation of hydrogen discouraged by the high overvoltage, but the liberation of metal is facilitated by amalgam formation in many cases. Zinc can be quantitatively deposited from dilute acid solutions at a mercury cathode, and so can all the following:[7] Cr, Fe, Co, Ni, Cu, Ga, Ge, Mo, Tc, Rh, Pd, Ag, Cd, In, Sn, Ir, Pt, Au, Hg, Tl, Bi, Po. The following elements can be deposited incompletely from an acid solution; more completely from a neutral solution: Sb, Mn, Ru. Even sodium and potassium can be deposited quantitatively if the solution is strongly alkaline and enough mercury is provided so that the amalgam remains very dilute.

Because the mercury cathode is a "catchall," its main use is in group separations, for example in the analysis of aluminum alloys to remove all metals less active than aluminum from the solution, or in the analysis of iron ores to remove the iron before determining minor

[7] J. A. Maxwell and R. P. Graham, *Chem. Rev.*, **46**, 471 (1950).

constituents such as Ca, Al, Mg, and Ti.[8] It is used more often for separations than actual determinations, because a mercury cathode is inconvenient to weigh. The determinations which follow may be made either on the amalgam or on the solution. The mercury cathode is especially suited to electrolytic separations made under controlled potential, since the potential required for a given operation can be found directly from polarograms, i.e., current-voltage curves obtained at a dropping mercury cathode.[9] The mercury cathode is also adaptable to coulometric analysis.[10]

Most metals dissolve in mercury, but there are some that are practically insoluble, in particular iron, cobalt, nickel, and platinum. When these are deposited in traces the mercury may still look bright and clean, but its surface characteristics are changed. The hydrogen overvoltage is lowered, possibly enough to prevent the complete deposition of active metals such as chromium and zinc. At the same time, the overvoltage of discharge of the iron group metals themselves is higher on mercury than on the massive metal. It takes about 0.25 volt more to deposit nickel on mercury than it does to deposit it on solid nickel at a current density of 0.01 ampere per square centimeter.[11] This additional overvoltage is reflected in the polarographic half-wave potential of nickel, which is more negative than the standard electrode potential of nickel by about 0.6 volt. This example shows the value of the polarograph in predicting potentials needed for electrodeposition at a mercury cathode.

Arsenic is reduced in acid solution at a mercury cathode to arsine, AsH_3, which is a gas and comes off with hydrogen. The reduction is quantitative and is used to determine arsenic, or rather to separate it for subsequent determination. It is a modification of the classical Marsh method in which the solution is reduced with zinc and dilute acid, and it has the advantage that the arsine is evolved gradually in a reproducible manner instead of most of it coming off in the first few seconds, which is the case when zinc is used. In the Marsh method the amount of arsenic is estimated by passing the gas through a narrow tube heated to redness at one point; here the arsine decomposes to arsenic and hydrogen, and the arsenic deposits as a shiny

[8] T. D. Parks, H. O. Johnson and L. Lykken, *Anal. Chem.*, **20,** 148 (1948).

[9] J. J. Lingane, *Faraday Soc. Discussions*, **1,** 203 (1947).

[10] J. J. Lingane, *J. Am. Chem. Soc.*, **67,** 1916 (1945).

[11] G. E. Gardham, *Faraday Soc. Discussions*, **1,** 182 (1947).

black stain beyond the heated portion. The stain is compared with standard stains obtained from known amounts of arsenic. The electrolytic technique naturally gives a more reproducible stain than do zinc and sulfuric acid. A divided cell is used to avoid reoxidation of arsenic at the anode.[12] Attempts have been made to determine antimony in an analogous way, but reduction is incomplete unless special precautions are taken. The mercury becomes coated with a trace of antimony, which lowers the overvoltage of hydrogen and so lowers the yield of stibine. A lead cathode is better than one of mercury for this reduction.[13]

Anodic deposition. In most electrolytic analyses the desired product is formed at the cathode; in some, however, the anode product is of interest. Two metals, lead and cobalt, can be determined as anodic deposits; lead is deposited as lead dioxide from a solution which is 2 N or more in nitric acid, and cobalt is deposited as cobaltic oxide, Co_2O_3, from an acetate buffer. In the latter case a divided cell is used to prevent reduction of cobaltic ions at the cathode.[14] Neither of these oxides is quite pure, indeed no completely pure specimen of PbO_2 has yet been made in the laboratory; the products always contain somewhat less oxygen than the formulas imply; but the deposits are sufficiently reproducible so that an empirical correction factor can be used.

Chloride, bromide, and iodide ions can be determined electrolytically by deposition on silver gauze as the insoluble halides. To prevent the solution becoming too alkaline during electrolysis, the sodium or other cations are taken out simultaneously by using a divided cell with mercury separating the two compartments.[15]

A novel application is the determination of pectin by deposition on a platinum gauze anode from a solution which has been freed from inorganic salts by ion exchange.[16] The same method could in principle be used for any colloid, such as carboxymethylcellulose or rubber in rubber latex. In such cases the voltage needed is much higher than in ordinary inorganic analysis owing to the small electrical mobility of the colloidal particles.

[12] F. S. Aumonier, *J. Soc. Chem. Ind.*, **46,** 341T (1927); T. Callan and R. T. P. Jones, *Analyst*, **55,** 90 (1930).

[13] J. Grant, *Analyst*, **53,** 626 (1928).

[14] S. Torrance, *Analyst*, **64,** 109 (1939).

[15] J. H. Hildebrand, *J. Am. Chem. Soc.*, **29,** 447 (1907).

[16] K. T. Williams and C. M. Johnson, *Ind. Eng. Chem., Anal. Ed.*, **16,** 23 (1944).

Techniques

Conventional gravimetric electroanalysis. The equipment used in the commonest kind of electrolytic analysis, that in which a metal is deposited on a weighed cathode or anode, is shown diagrammatically in Figure 2.   It consists of a source of direct current giving up to 10 volts, a series rheostat, an ammeter and voltmeter, and a pair of electrodes which are cylinders of platinum gauze.   These are mounted concentrically in a beaker which holds the solution to be electrolyzed, and provision is made for either raising the electrodes or lowering the beaker when the electrolysis is finished.

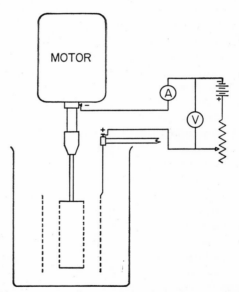

Fig. 5-2.   Conventional circuit for electrolytic analysis.

Good stirring is obviously very important in electrolytic analysis, and it is commonly accomplished by rotating the inner electrode, as shown in Figure 2.   This inner electrode may be either the anode or the cathode.   If it is the cathode, then the anode can be simply a square of platinum gauze mounted beside it.   The use of gauze electrodes permits good circulation of the solution, and it also gives a large surface area, which means a low current density and hence a more coherent deposit.

An ingenious way of stirring the solution is to surround the vessel with a solenoid or cylindrical coil of wire carrying a direct current. This produces a magnetic field along the axis of the electrodes, and since the solution carries a current radially to this axis, it rotates just as a wire carrying a current moves in a magnetic field which is at right angles to the flow of current. A disadvantage to this technique is that the speed of stirring depends on the strength of the current passing through the solution, and towards the end of the electrolysis, just when good stirring is most needed, this current may fall off. It *will* fall off, and drop to zero, in most controlled potential electrolysis.

The current density used in electrolytic analysis is, as was stated earlier, of the order 0.01 ampere per square centimeter. Too high a current density gives a powdery or flaky deposit which does not stick, too low a current density prolongs the analysis unnecessarily. Sometimes it is advantageous to start with a low current, and when the deposit has built up sufficiently, to use a higher current. If hydrogen is formed simultaneously with the metal a loose deposit may result. The lower the current density, the lower the hydrogen overvoltage and the greater the proportion of hydrogen which is formed; in such cases, therefore, the optimum current density must be found by trial.

Certain metals alloy with platinum when they are deposited on it, and when they are dissolved off they leave a roughened, disintegrated surface. Such metals are zinc, cadmium, mercury, and lead (deposited cathodically). The procedure in such cases is to plate the platinum gauze cathode first with copper or silver, then weigh it, then deposit the desired metal. Mercury forms a solid amalgam with copper and silver which can easily be washed and dried, but mercury evaporates from these amalgams at about 0.5 mg. per hour.

To test whether all the desired metal has been deposited, the common practice is to raise the level of the solution, or lower the electrodes farther into the solution, and pass current for another few minutes. If any deposit is formed on the newly immersed portion of the electrode it will be easily visible. Alternatively, chemical or polarographic tests may be made on the solution to see if any metal remains undeposited.

We might mention here that electrodeposition sometimes remains incomplete even though the potential seems adequate for quantitative deposition.   In such cases the metal remaining in solution may be estimated colorimetrically and a correction applied.   Cobalt is a common offender, but even copper may be incompletely deposited under certain conditions, for example, in presence of nitrite.   (A trace of chloride helps to make the copper deposit completely.)   An opposite source of error in electroanalysis, noted on p. 63 above, is the inclusion of salts in the deposit.[17]

When electrolysis is complete, the electrodes are removed from the solution and rinsed.   It is important to keep the current turned on until the electrodes are finally withdrawn from the solution, otherwise some of the deposited metal goes back into solution.   The easiest way to dry the electrodes after they have been rinsed is to pour a little acetone over them, then leave them to dry in the air at room temperature for five to ten minutes.   Drying in an oven is not recommended, as a freshly deposited metal oxidizes very easily.

Electrolysis with controlled cathode potential. The drawback of conventional electroanalysis is that it is very difficult to plate out one metal selectively in the presence of another metal ion unless the discharge of hydrogen intervenes, as it does when copper is plated from an acid solution containing copper and nickel ions.   Zinc and cadmium ions, with standard reduction potentials -0.763 and -0.402 volts, respectively, cannot be separated electrolytically with the equipment shown in Figure 2.   They can, however, be separated if the cathode potential is controlled.

The first step in controlling the cathode potential is to know what it is.   For this purpose the voltmeter shown in Figure 2 is not sufficient, for it records the entire potential drop across the cell, the drop represented by AD in Figure 1.   We need, instead, the drop CD, the potential difference between the cathode surface and the solution 0.1 mm. or so from it.   To find this we introduce a reference half-cell, shown by D in Figure 3.   This carries none of the electrolysis current; its purpose is solely to be a standard of reference to which the potential of the cathode may be compared.   The electromotive force existing between the cathode and the reference half-cell is measured by the potentiometer circuit P.   The sliding contact X is

[17] For a discussion of the sources of error in electrolytic analysis, see S. E. Q. Ashley, *Anal. Chem.*, **22**, 1379 (1950).

adjusted until no current passes through the sensitive galvanometer G; the distance XY along the potentiometer slide wire is then proportional to the electromotive force between C and D. To make this correspond as closely as possible to the desired potential between the cathode and the solution, the capillary tip E of the half-cell is placed as close to the cathode as practicable. It is placed on the side of the cathode which faces *away from* the anode, so that it will be out of the main path of the electrolysis current and include as little as possible of the Ohm's law potential drop through the solution (BC in Figure 1).

The rheostat R, Figure 3, regulates the current flowing through the cell and the potential which is applied across the electrodes A and C.

To carry out an electrolysis at a controlled cathode potential, the slider X is set so as to give the same voltage drop along XY as is desired between the reference half-cell and the cathode, and the rheostat R is kept adjusted so that the deflection of the galvanometer G is zero. The electrolysis is continued until the current registered in the ammeter Q drops to zero.

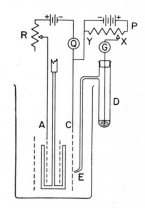

Fig. 5-3. Circuit and cell for controlled potential electrolysis.

A circuit somewhat like that just described was used by Sand,[18] in his pioneer researches on selective electrodeposition. The technique did not find general acceptance, however, for the obvious reason that it was very tedious. The operator had to tend the apparatus constantly during the whole time of electrolysis, which might be half an hour or more. In recent years, however, equipment has been devised which keeps the potential adjusted automatically. The operator needs only to set the controls for the potential desired, then go away and come back when the electrolysis current has dropped to zero. The potential control may be completely electronic, in which case the whole electrolysis current flows across vacuum tubes and is regulated by the grid po-

---

[18] H. J. S. Sand, *J. Chem. Soc.*, **91**, 373 (1907); also footnote 1.

tentials,[19] or it may use relays and a reversing electric motor to move the rheostat *R* (Figure 3) according to the direction of the galvanometer deflection at *G*.[20]   Such equipment has made practicable a whole range of electrolytic separations.   Silver can be deposited in presence of copper, tin in presence of cadmium, and cadmium in presence of zinc.   With the help of complex ion formation still other separations are possible, for example the deposition of copper in presence of antimony using tartrate[21] or fluoride[22] to combine with the antimony.   A number of procedures have been worked out for the analysis of ores and alloys, and are reviewed by Diehl[3] and Sand.[1]

The application of automatic potential control to coulometric analysis is evident and will be discussed below.   The technique has uses outside of analytical chemistry, for example in the preparation of organic compounds by electrolytic oxidation or reduction.[9]

The mercury cathode. Two typical mercury cathode cells are shown in Figures 4 and 5. Both provide for vigorous agitation at the mercury-water interface, one using an air jet for this purpose, the other a mechanical stirrer.   Both provide for drawing off the mercury when the electrolysis is finished.   It is important to see that the cathode is kept polarized until all the mercury has been removed from contact with the solution, for if

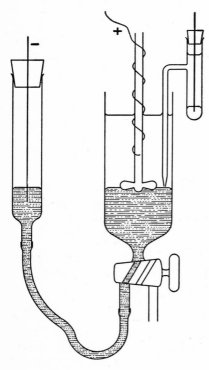

Fig. 5-4.   Cell for electrolysis with mercury cathode.

[19] A. Hickling, *Trans. Faraday Soc.*, **38**, 27 (1942).

[20] J. J. Lingane, *Ind. Eng. Chem., Anal. Ed.*, **17**, 332 (1945); C. W. Caldwell, R. C. Parker, and H. Diehl, *Ind. Eng. Chem., Anal. Ed.*, **16**, 532 (1944).

[21] J. J. Lingane, *Ind. Eng. Chem., Anal. Ed.*, **17**, 640 (1945).

[22] S. Torrance, *Analyst*, **62**, 719 (1937).

this is not done, some of the deposited metal will go back into the solution. The cell in Figure 5 uses a platinum wire anode; that in Figure 4 uses a silver-silver chloride anode, which has a less positive potential than platinum and so will not oxidize cuprous copper to cupric in hydrochloric acid solution, for example. This cell also includes a reference half-cell for cathode potential control.

Some mercury cathode cells are water-jacketed, so that large currents may be passed without undue heating. These cells are used in routine steel analyses to remove the iron preliminary to determining such trace elements as aluminum and titanium. Currents of 8 amperes, which will deposit a gram of iron in ten minutes, can be passed in a water-cooled mercury cathode cell.

Where the mercury cathode is used for the collection of trace elements, as in the work of Furman and Bricker cited above, it is kept as small as possible, and

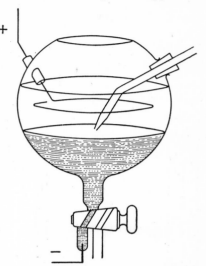

Fig. 5-5. Cell for electrolysis with mercury cathode, stirring by gas stream.

the trace elements are recovered from the mercury after electrolysis by running the amalgam into a silica dish and evaporating off the mercury. They may then be determined polarographically.[4]

Internal electrolysis. "Internal electrolysis" is the technique of electrolysis without an external source of current. The electrons needed for the deposition of one metal come from another, more active metal, which goes into solution as the first metal is deposited. The process is simply a displacement reaction carried out in a two-compartment cell, such as that shown in Figure 6.[23] The anode *A* is a rod of an active metal, such as magnesium, aluminum, or zinc, and it is immersed in a concentrated solution of one of its salts, such

[23] A. Schleicher, *Z. anal. Chem.*, **126**, 412 (1944); A. Schleicher and T. Todoroff, *Z. Elektrochem.*, **50**, 2 (1944). See also H. J. S. Sand, *Analyst*, **55**, 309 (1930); B. L. Clarke and L. A. Wooten, *Trans. Am. Electrochem. Soc.*, **76**, 63 (1939).

as magnesium nitrate or aluminum chloride. It is enclosed in a sack *B* of parchment or collodion; the tubular membranes used for dialysis are very suitable. Outside the sack is the solution to be analyzed, and also a cathode *C* of platinum gauze. In operation, *A* and *C* are joined by a wire; electrons flow along this wire from *A* to *C*, and the metal ions in the outer solution are reduced to metal, which deposits on *C*. In this way Schleicher deposited cobalt, nickel, lead, antimony, and tin, using a magnesium anode in each case.

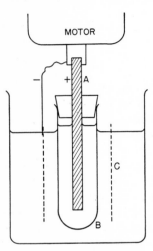

Fig. 5-6.   Cell for internal electrolysis.

If desired, an ammeter may be inserted between the anode and cathode to follow the progress of the electrolysis.

The technique has several advantages. First, no platinum anode is necessary. This not only saves the investment in a costly metal, but permits free use of chloride solutions which in the ordinary type of electrolytic analysis can attack a platinum anode with subsequent deposition of platinum on the cathode. Second, a certain degree of control of cathode potential is automatically ensured, for the cathode can never become more negative than the equilibrium potential of the anode in its solution. If the anode is of lead, then only those metals which are below lead in the activity series, that is, metals whose ions have more positive reduction potentials than that of the lead ion, can be deposited on the cathode. Internal electrolysis with a lead anode has been used to determine copper and bismuth in lead bullion.[24]

Coulometric analysis. Fundamental to the theory of electrolysis are Faraday's laws, which relate the amount of an element or compound formed at the anode or cathode to the quantity of electricity passed. One "faraday," or 96,490 coulombs of electricity, is the charge on 6.023×10^{23} electrons (Avogadro's number), and it

[24] E. M. Collin, *Analyst,* **55,** 312 (1930); A.S.T.M., *Methods of Chemical Analysis of Metals,* 1950.

liberates the equivalent weight in grams of any element by neutralization of the ionic charge.

In the absence of side reactions, therefore, the quantity of electricity used in liberating an element is a measure of the amount of that element present. It is a very accurate measure, moreover. The same current which passes through the experimental cell is made to pass through a second electrolytic cell, called a *coulometer*, which is in series with it; in this cell it either liberates silver from a silver nitrate solution, or it liberates hydrogen and oxygen from a dilute sulfuric acid solution. Both of these processes are virtually free from side reactions, and the weight of silver or the volume of the mixed hydrogen and oxygen can be found very accurately, thus giving the quantity of electricity.

The accuracy possible in coulometric analysis was studied by Szebelledy and Somogyi.[25] They found the amount of hydrochloric acid in a solution by electrolyzing it between a platinum cathode and a silver gauze anode. Hydrogen escaped at the cathode, while chloride ions combined to form solid silver chloride at the anode; thus hydrochloric acid was removed from the solution, one gram-equivalent of it for each faraday of electricity passed. Electrolysis was continued until an acid-base indicator in the solution changed color. The amount of electricity passed up to this point was found with a silver coulometer. They called the process "coulometric titration" from the analogy of titrating the acid with a standard base. A precision of better than 1 part in 1000 was obtained. Later they determined thiocyanate ions, hydrazine, and hydroxylamine by electrolyzing in a bromide solution with a platinum anode, stopping the electrolysis as soon as the color of free bromine appeared.

The scope and utility of coulometric analysis is greatly increased if the electrode potentials are suitably controlled, for then the current automatically stops flowing as soon as a particular substance in the solution is used up. No indicator is needed, and the operator need not be watching to stop the electrolysis as soon as a particular decomposition is complete. Lingane[10] used the cell shown in Figure 4, with a mercury cathode and silver-silver chloride anode, to determine copper, bismuth, lead, and cadmium in this manner. The instrument was set for a cathode potential sufficiently negative to

[25] L. Szebelledy and Z. Somogyi, *Z. anal. Chem.*, **112,** 313, 323, 332, 385, 391, 400 (1938).

deposit lead, for example, but not sufficiently negative to deposit cadmium; current passed until all the lead had been plated out, but none of the cadmium, and then it stopped.   The volume of gas which had accumulated in the meantime in a hydrogen-oxygen gas coulometer placed in series with the cell was then read.

Instead of holding the potential constant, it is often more practical to hold the current constant and measure the time needed to reduce or oxidize the substance being determined.   Circuits have been devised which maintain a constant current, and this technique has become popular in recent years.[26, 27, 28]   The "end point," or the time at which the titration is complete, can be determined by a reference half-cell, a platinum-tungsten electrode pair,[27] or a pair of platinum electrodes with a small and constant potential impressed across them.[28] These methods of locating titration end points are discussed in Chapter 12.   The last method has been the most studied.   The current passing between the two *indicator electrodes* (so called to distinguish them from the *generator electrodes*, which perform the electrolysis) is extremely small, and depends on the concentrations of certain of the oxidizable or reducible substances present.   It is zero, or near zero, on one side of the end point and rises or falls steadily on the other. The process is analogous to amperometric titration, and the graphs of current against time look like Figure 13, Chapter 20.   This "amperometric" method of end point detection has the limitation that the generator current may not be too high, or it causes stray currents in the indicating system.   The highest permissible generating current is usually 0.01 ampere, and this takes 160 minutes to oxidize or reduce one milliequivalent of a substance.   This is a limitation in one sense, but an advantage in another; the coulometric method is ideally adapted for micro and semimicro analysis.   Microgram quantities of metals have been determined coulometrically through the electrolytic bromination of their 8-hydroxyquinoline complexes.[29]

We have noted that in some coulometric titrations the substance is directly oxidized or reduced by the current, while in others it reacts with a second substance which is generated at the electrode.   The

[26] F. I. Trishin, *Zhur. Anal. Khim.*, **3**, 21 (1948); *Chem. Abstracts*, **43**, 959 (1949).

[27] W. D. Cooke and N. H. Furman, *Anal. Chem.*, **22**, 896 (1950).

[28] R. J. Myers and E. H. Swift, *J. Am. Chem. Soc.*, **70**, 1047 (1948); F. S. Farringdon and E. H. Swift, *Anal. Chem.*, **22**, 889 (1950).

[29] W. N. Carson, *Anal. Chem.*, **22**, 1565 (1950).

determination of 8-hydroxyquinoline, just mentioned, is an example; a solution is electrolyzed which contains the 8-hydroxyquinoline together with potassium bromide, which yields bromine at the anode, which then attacks the 8-hydroxyquinoline. Many substances are not oxidized or reduced quantitatively at platinum electrodes, but can be oxidized or reduced through the action of an intermediate; thus Szebelledy and Somogyi[25] oxidized thiocyanate ions by bromine,

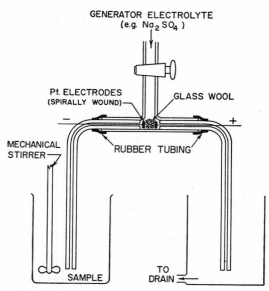

Fig. 5-7. Apparatus for coulometric titration with externally generated reagents. DeFord, Pitts and Johns, *Anal. Chem.*, **23**, 938 (1951).

which was liberated at the anode from bromide ions in accordance with Faraday's law. In the same way, Swift[28] determined arsenite by oxidation with electrolytically generated chlorine or bromine, and chromate and vanadate by reduction with electrolytically generated cuprous ($CuCl_3^=$) ions,[30] while Cooke and Furman[27] determined ceric and dichromate ions by reduction with electrolytically generated ferrous ions.

In all these experiments the active reagent was generated and con-

[30] D. J. Meier, R. J. Myers, and E. H. Swift, *J. Am. Chem. Soc.*, **71**, 2340 (1949).

sumed in the same vessel. A new development is to generate the reagent outside the titration vessel.[31] The way in which this is done is shown in Figure 7. An appropriate solution flows into an inverted T tube, in each arm of which is a platinum electrode. Between these electrodes a constant current flows. The products of electrolysis flow out of the two arms of the T tube, the cathode product from one arm, the anode product from the other. Whichever of these is wanted is led through a capillary connection into the titration vessel. Suppose, for example, an acid is to be titrated. A neutral solution of sodium sulfate is led into the T tube. The solution which flows out of the cathode side of the T contains sodium hydroxide, carbonate-free, in an amount which is determined by the current flowing. This solution is led into the titration vessel, and the time taken to reach the end point is measured. The end point may be determined by a color indicator or electrically.

This technique has several advantages. As in other forms of coulometric analysis, no standard solutions are necessary, even very small amounts of substance can be determined accurately, and automatic recording can easily be arranged. By generating the reagent outside the titration cell, unwanted side reactions at the electrodes are avoided; for example, one could not titrate an acid by the direct electrolytic reduction of its hydrogen ions if a strong oxidizing agent were present, but in the new technique the oxidizing agent would cause no difficulty. Another advantage of the external generation technique is that quite large currents can be passed without their affecting any indicator electrodes that might be placed in the titration vessel. The end point can thus be located amperometrically if desired.

PROBLEMS

1. 0.50 milligram of magnesium is precipitated as its 8-hydroxyquinoline complex, $Mg(C_9H_6ON)_2$. This is dissolved in acid and brominated by bromine which is liberated at an anode with a steady current of 0.0100 amp. Calculate the time, in seconds, needed to complete the reaction.

2. In the coulometric titration described in Problem 1, how could the end point be determined?

[31] D. D. DeFord, J. N. Pitts, and C. J. Johns, *Anal. Chem.*, **23**, 938, 941 (1951).

3. Using the dissociation constants for the cupric ammonia complexes quoted in Chapter 7, calculate the potential of a copper electrode in equilibrium with a solution which is 1 M in total NH_3 and 0.01 M in total Cu(II).

4. From the calculations of Problem 3 and the data of Table I, predict which will happen at the cathode when a solution 1 M in total NH_3 and 0.01 M in total Cu(II) is electrolyzed: reduction to $Cu(NH_3)_2^+$, or reduction to Cu metal.

5. From the data of Table I, calculate the standard potential of the reaction $Cu^{++} + 3Cl^- + e \rightarrow CuCl_3^=$. *Note:* free energies are additive, but standard potentials are not. See Chapter 11 for this type of calculation.

6. Zinc is to be deposited electrolytically from a solution of pH 4. The minimum zinc ion concentration in the solution is to be 10^{-5} M. The overvoltage of hydrogen on zinc at the current density used is 0.75 volt; zinc itself has no overvoltage. Calculate the discharge potentials of zinc and hydrogen at 25°C. $E°$ for $Zn^{++} + 2e \rightarrow Zn$ is -0.76 volt.

7. The nickel content of commercial nickel sulfate crystals is found electrolytically and by the dimethylglyoxime method. The electrolytic determinations show a somewhat higher percentage of nickel than the dimethylglyoxime determinations. What is the most probable reason?

6

Organic precipitants

ORGANIC PRECIPITANTS have a special place in inorganic analysis, not because they are organic, but because the precipitates which they form are for the most part qualitatively different from the purely inorganic precipitates. Barium sulfate is a good example of the latter. It is an ionized salt, and its ionic nature determines its physical and chemical properties and also governs the coprecipitation of impurities. The compound of nickel with dimethylglyoxime, on the other hand, is not ionic. Its crystal lattice is that of a covalent compound, its scarlet-red color is characteristic neither of dimethylglyoxime nor of the nickel ion, and unlike ionic compounds it is very soluble in chloroform and other nonpolar solvents. It is a coordination compound, with the following structure:

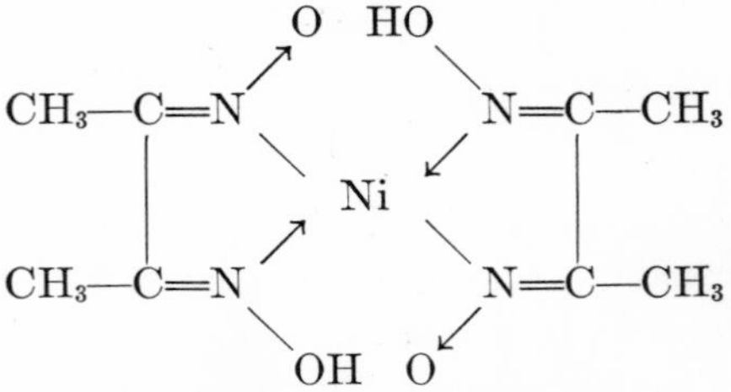

The arrows represent coordinate links, or semipolar bonds, formed by the donation of pairs of electrons from the nitrogen atoms to the nickel atom. The ring structures which result are called *chelate rings*, from the Greek word *chele*, a crab's claw. A chelate ring is one which is closed by one or two coordinate links.

The great majority of organic precipitants form such chelate rings, but there are some that do not. We recognize three classes of organic precipitants, namely: (1) complex formers; (2) salt formers; (3) lake formers. The "complex formers" are those which form chelated compounds, and they are the main concern of this chapter. The "salt formers" include reagents such as oxalic acid, which form salts which happen to be insoluble, such as calcium oxalate; there is no fundamental difference between these precipitates and the purely inorganic precipitates. The third group, the "lake formers," include such reagents as tannin and the sodium salt of aurin tricarboxylic acid ("aluminon"). These adhere to gelatinous precipitates such as hydrous oxides and hydroxides, forming colored adsorption complexes or "lakes" of indefinite composition. Since the adsorption process probably involves coordinate links, this class may possibly be regarded as a subdivision of the first.

Another class of organic precipitants are those which form complex ions with metals which then give precipitates with suitable anions; for example, pyridine, which coordinates with cupric ion and several other metallic ions to give complex ions which have insoluble thiocyanates, e.g., $Cu(C_5H_5N)_2(CNS)_2$. These will be discussed in Chapter 7.

The reagents which form chelated complexes are much the most important group; so we shall consider them first. We shall discuss their general properties and then describe a few of the commoner reagents individually.

Complex Formers: General Considerations

Structural requirements. To be able to form a neutral chelated compound with a metal atom, an organic molecule must have a dual character. On the one hand, it must be an acid; that is, it must have a displaceable hydrogen atom. On the other hand, it must also be a base; that is, it must have a pair of unshared electrons which is available for coordination. Further, the acidic and basic groups must be so spaced that the chelate ring, when formed, is free from strain or nearly so. This means in practice that the chelate ring must have either five or six atoms, including the metal atom.

These conditions are fulfilled by dimethylglyoxime, the example quoted above. In this particular case, the $=N \cdot OH$ groups are both acidic and basic; while one loses a proton, the other coordinates with the nickel through the nitrogen. One further requirement must be met. Dimethylglyoxime exists in three isomeric forms, as follows:

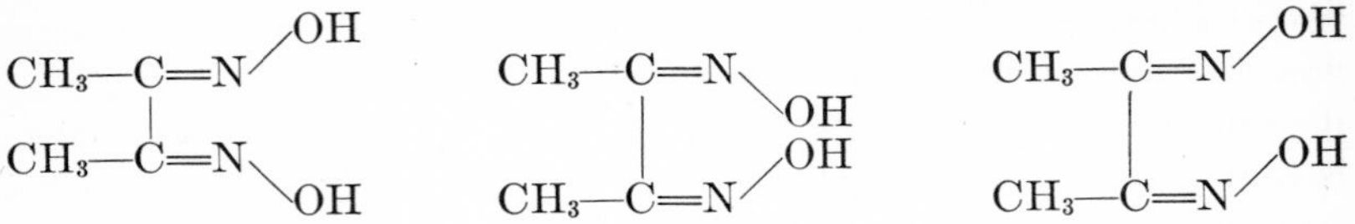

$$
\begin{array}{ccc}
\text{CH}_3\!-\!\text{C}\!=\!\text{N}\diagup^{\text{OH}} & \text{CH}_3\!-\!\text{C}\!=\!\text{N}\diagdown & \text{CH}_3\!-\!\text{C}\!=\!\text{N}\diagup^{\text{OH}} \\
\mid & \mid \quad^{\text{OH}} & \mid \\
\text{CH}_3\!-\!\text{C}\!=\!\text{N}\diagdown_{\text{OH}} & \text{CH}_3\!-\!\text{C}\!=\!\text{N}\diagup^{\text{OH}} & \text{CH}_3\!-\!\text{C}\!=\!\text{N}\diagup^{\text{OH}} \\
\alpha & \beta & \gamma
\end{array}
$$

Of these, only the α form can give the five-membered ring shown above, and only this is specific for nickel. The γ form gives six-membered chelate rings with a number of metal atoms and is not at all specific, while the β form gives no insoluble metal complexes. Fortunately, the usual methods of synthesis of dimethylglyoxime give almost pure α form.

Not only must the organic molecule be of the right size and shape to give a strain-free chelate ring, but so also must the metal atom. It must have the right size, the right oxidation state, and the right coordination number. Referring again to the nickel dimethylglyoxime complex, x-rays show the molecule to be flat. For such a structure to be possible, the nickel atom must have an oxidation number of $+2$, a coordination number of 4, and a planar distribution of valence bonds. Nickel happens to be one of the few atoms which satisfies all these conditions; the others are palladium, platinum, copper, and dipositive silver.[1] Of these only palladium gives a precipitate with dimethylglyoxime. Evidently only nickel and palladium have atoms of the right radius to give strain-free five-membered chelate rings which fit into the crystal lattice of an insoluble solid.

We note in passing that the architecture of the solid crystal lattice is at least as important to the specificity of a precipitant as the stability of the chelate ring. The cupric complex of dimethylglyoxime is actually more stable than that of nickel; its dissociation constant is 3×10^{-23} compared with 2×10^{-21} for the nickel complex, yet the nickel complex is much the less soluble of the two (see page 94).

Most organic precipitants are highly selective in their action, and from this example we see why. Dimethylglyoxime happens to be an extremely favorable case, however. Not only are nickel and

---

[1] A. F. Wells, *Structural Inorganic Chemistry*, New York, Oxford, 1945, p. 87.

palladium the only elements in the whole periodic table which are completely precipitated by this reagent, but they precipitate in entirely different pH ranges. Nickel precipitates from a neutral or weakly basic solution, pH 8 being the optimum, while palladium precipitates best from an acid solution of pH 1. At pH 1 the reagent is quite specific for palladium, at pH 8 it is quite specific for nickel (subject to certain qualifications which will be mentioned later). The pH is always important in precipitations with complex-forming organic reagents, because these are all weak acids, and the higher the pH, the more easily are their hydrogen atoms displaced. The solubility of the complexes decreases with rising pH, just as does the solubility of a metal phosphate. At high pH, the solubility of the complex may increase again. This is due to the formation of complex ions between the metal atom and the hydroxyl ion or the ammonia molecule. Palladium gives no precipitate with dimethylglyoxime in neutral or basic solutions containing ammonium salts, because the complex ion $Pd(NH_3)_4^{++}$ is so stable. It precipitates in dilute acid solutions, however, while nickel does not, because the solubility of palladium dimethylglyoxime is very much smaller than that of nickel dimethylglyoxime. The situation is analogous to the precipitation of zinc and magnesium from ammonium phosphate solutions; $ZnNH_4PO_4 \cdot 6H_2O$ is far less soluble than $MgNH_4PO_4 \cdot 6H_2O$, and so precipitates at pH 6, while the magnesium salt does not precipitate below pH 9; however, zinc ions form a stable complex with ammonia while magnesium ions do not, so the zinc precipitate dissolves above pH 8.5 or 9.

From the structure of nickel dimethylglyoxime and the basic requirement of a strain-free five-membered chelate ring, we might surmise that the essential precipitant for nickel is the grouping

$$\begin{array}{c} -C=N \cdot OH \\ | \\ -C=N \cdot OH, \end{array}$$

the two methyl groups being merely incidental. This is found in practice; not only dimethylglyoxime, but a large number of 1,2-dioximes are selective precipitants for nickel. The only limitation seems to be that the two carbon atoms may not both be part of the same aromatic ring. The compound orthobenzoquinone dioxime will not precipitate nickel. Presumably the 60° angle between the two C═N bonds is unfavorable. On the other hand, so long as we can get a strain-free five-membered ring with one nitrogen on either side of the nickel, many structural variations are possible. All of the following groupings precipitate nickel selectively:[2]

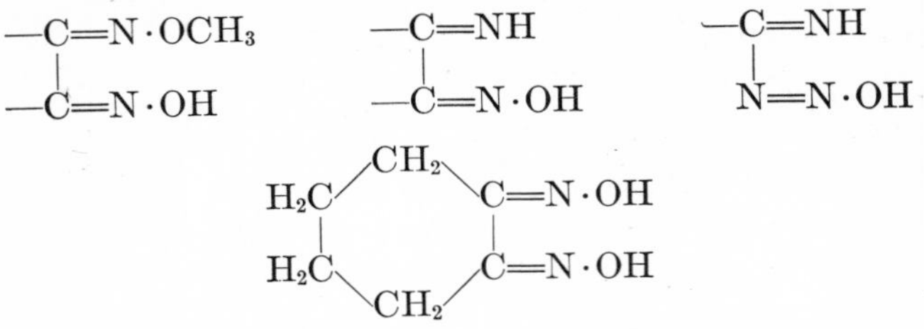
—C═N·OCH₃
—C═N·OH
—C═NH
—C═N·OH
—C═NH
N═N·OH
CH₂
H₂C
C═N·OH
H₂C
C═N·OH
CH₂

Other characteristic groupings are known which have a selective affinity for certain metals. Thus compounds having the groups shown below are selective for the elements named:

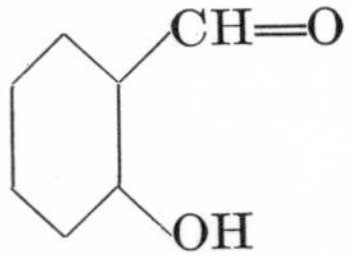
CH═O
OH

Cu (Pd, V)
(in strong acid)

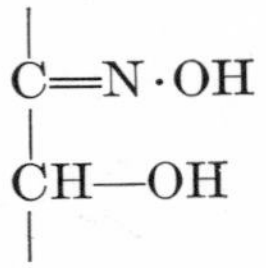
C═N·OH
CH—OH

Cu (Mo, W)

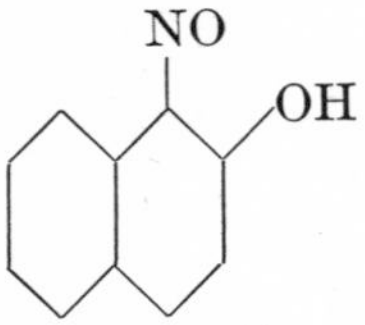
NO
OH

Co (Fe, Cr)

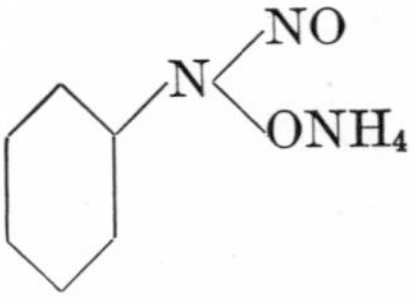
N
NO
ONH₄

Fe(III), Ti(IV), Zr, Sn(IV) (in strongly acid solution)

None of these is quite as selective as dimethylglyoxime, and some reagents are known which are very unselective; 8-hydroxyquinoline, for instance. The relation between structure and selectivity is not at all well understood yet. Substituent groups outside of those forming the chelate ring do influence the precipitation reactions to some extent; thus 8-hydroxyquinoline precipitates aluminum while

[2] J. F. Flagg, *Organic Reagents Used in Gravimetric and Volumetric Analysis*, New York, Interscience, 1948, Chap. 1. See also footnote 8.

2-methyl-8-hydroxyquinoline does not.[3] Here the acid and basic strengths of the chelating compound may be significant. These are affected by substituents, and it is known that there is a correlation between the acid strengths of various substituted o-hydroxybenzalde-hydes and β-diketones and the stability of their copper complexes.[4]

Substituent groups also influence solubility. Adding hydrocarbon substituents generally decreases the solubility of the precipitate in water, thus increasing the sensitivity of the reagent; thus neocupfer-ron will detect a lower concentration of iron than will cupferron:

cupferron   neocupferron

The advantage which this brings is usually (though not always) accompanied by the disadvantage that the substituted reagent is less soluble in water. The solubility of both the reagent and the precipitate in water is increased, on the other hand, by introducing sulfonic acid groups, which are highly ionized. A well-known example is 1-nitroso-2-hydroxy-3,6-naphthalene disulfonic acid, or "nitroso R salt," which gives a red water-soluble complex with tripositive cobalt; the unsulfonated compound gives a red precipitate. Nitroso R salt is used in the colorimetric determination of cobalt.

Practical considerations. Having reviewed the general nature of organic precipitants and their compounds with metals, we are in a position to assess their usefulness in inorganic analysis. They have certain advantages and certain disadvantages compared with the inorganic precipitants. We shall summarize these characteristics in the paragraphs following, taking the advantageous characteristics first.

Selectivity. This is the greatest advantage which organic precipi-tants have. Separations are easily possible through selective pre-

---

[3] L. L. Merritt and J. K. Walker, *Ind. Eng. Chem., Anal. Ed.*, **16**, 387 (1944).
[4] M. Calvin and K. W. Wilson, *J. Am. Chem. Soc.*, **67**, 2003 (1945). See also A. Martell and M. Calvin, *Chemistry of the Metal Chelate Compounds*, New York, Prentice-Hall, 1952.

cipitation with these reagents that with inorganic reagents alone would be very difficult or almost impossible; for example, the following: cobalt from nickel using α-nitroso-β-naphthol or dimethylglyoxime, aluminum from iron or iron from phosphate using cupferron, cadmium from copper using quinaldic acid and thiourea, antimony from arsenic using pyrogallol, zirconium from thorium and titanium using mandelic acid.[5]   In selective precipitations the pH is, of course, very important.   One reagent, such as 8-hydroxyquinoline or anthranilic acid, may be used to precipitate two or three metals successively by suitable adjustment of the pH.   Again, one metal may be held in solution as a soluble complex by one reagent while another is precipitated by a second reagent; thus tartaric or citric acid is used to hold bismuth in solution while nickel is precipitated with dimethylglyoxime, for the bismuth complex with dimethylglyoxime is sparingly soluble and would otherwise precipitate with the nickel if much were present.   Another example is the use of thiourea to hold mercury, silver or copper in solution while precipitating zinc or cadmium with quinaldic acid.   Copper is first reduced to Cu(I) by adding bisulfite.

Freedom from Ionic Coprecipitation.   Because the precipitates are not ionized salts, they do not coprecipitate impurities in the way that barium sulfate and other ionic precipitates do (see Chapter 2).   There is no electrical attraction between the solid and ions in the solution, and moreover, it would be very difficult for an impurity to fit into the complicated crystal lattice of a chelated compound.   Nevertheless, coprecipitation of metals does occur.   It has been little studied, but in some cases it is as bad as in inorganic precipitates.[6]   These precipitates may also be contaminated in other ways; see below.

High Molecular Weight.   A little metal gives a lot of precipitate; the copper complex of quinaldic acid, for instance, contains only 14.94% of copper.   Moreover, the precipitates are generally light and voluminous.   This makes organic reagents a natural choice for micro and semimicro work.

Adaptability to Volumetric Methods.   Many of the precipitates can be dissolved in acid and the liberated organic reagent titrated oxidimetrically.   This is commonly done with 8-hydroxyquinoline, which is titrated with bromine (i.e., standard bromate solution is

[5] C. A. Kumins, *Ind. Eng. Chem., Anal. Ed.*, **19**, 376 (1947).

[6] P. W. West and L. J. Conrad, *Anal. Chim. Acta*, **4**, 561 (1950).

added to a solution containing bromide and excess acid); 1 mole of 8-hydroxyquinoline reacts with 4 equivalents of bromine, and 1 gram-atom of aluminum, for example, combines with 3 moles of 8-hydroxyquinoline. Obviously, the titrimetric factors are very favorable, and the method is well suited to micro work. Titration may be done coulometrically (see Chapter 5), and instead of titrating the reagent, one may often determine it polarographically.

Color. Many of the precipitates have a characteristic color, often a very intense color. Hence the use of organic reagents for "spot tests" in qualitative analysis; these tests are very sensitive and selective. The color also permits quantitative colorimetric analysis, and it is not necessary in this case for the metal complex to be insoluble. It may be water-soluble, or it may be extracted by an organic solvent and determined photometrically in the latter.

Solubility in Organic Solvents. Because of their covalent nature, most metal complexes with organic reagents are soluble in nonpolar solvents, chloroform being usually the best. Such solvents are used to extract the complexes for colorimetric determination, or they may be used simply for separating one element from another; thus the complex of cupferron with tripositive iron is very soluble in ether and chloroform, which allows one to remove large amounts of iron from solutions containing aluminum, or better still to concentrate very small amounts of iron and other metals present in large volumes of solution;[7] the actual determination, after the traces have been concentrated, may be made by another method. In all such extractions the pH must be carefully adjusted to give the separations desired.

Not all chelated metal complexes are soluble in nonpolar solvents.[8] In particular, the complexes which are water-soluble by reason of substituted sulfonic acid groups are insoluble in most nonpolar solvents.

Ease of Drying. Most solid chelated metal complexes are anhydrous and, being substantially nonpolar, are not easily wet by water. This is a disadvantage in that the precipitates tend to float on the surface of water and creep up the sides of glass and porcelain vessels, but on the other hand the precipitates dry quickly. A drop of a wetting agent added to the solution before or after precipitation makes the precipitates easier to transfer and filter, without making

[7] N. H. Furman, W. B. Mason, and J. S. Pekola, *Anal. Chem.*, **21**, 1325 (1949).
[8] F. Feigl, *Anal. Chem.*, **21**, 1298 (1949).

them any harder to dry. To hasten the drying, precipitates may generally be washed with alcohol, but not with acetone as this may dissolve the precipitate.

A few complexes do precipitate with water of hydration, and if so, they may be hard to dry without volatization or decomposition. The most notable of these is the magnesium complex of 8-hydroxyquinoline, which cannot be dried to a definite composition unless the temperature is very carefully controlled (footnotes 5 and 9, Chapter 4).

Volatility. Here we meet the first of the practical disadvantages of organic precipitants. Because chelated compounds are nonpolar, the forces between individual molecules in the crystal are not very great. The simpler chelated compounds, such as the copper complex of acetylacetone, can be distilled unchanged at a low temperature; most of the metallic complexes which are precipitated in analytical chemistry are appreciably volatile above 130°–150°C, and some decompose above this temperature.[9] Fortunately, most of them can be dried satisfactorily at 105°–110°C, thanks to their hydrophobic character.

Low Solubility of the Reagent in Water. This is the greatest disadvantage which organic precipitants have in comparison with inorganic precipitants. Most of them are so little soluble in water that they have to be added as a solution in another solvent, such as alcohol or acetic acid. It is usually possible to add a small excess without the reagent itself separating out, but one has to be careful not to add too much. It takes a certain amount of experience to know how much reagent to add. The usual way of telling when excess of a reagent is added is to let the precipitate settle, then to add a little more reagent carefully to the supernatant liquid and see whether any fresh precipitate is formed. This technique is of no use here, because the added reagent is sure to precipitate where it mixes with the water. One can, however, filter off the precipitate and see whether the clear filtrate gives a permanent precipitate when a little more reagent is added and the solution stirred. Usually the color of the solution or of the freshly formed precipitate is a guide. If some of the excess reagent does precipitate along with the metal com-

---

[9] J. F. Flagg, *Organic Reagents Used in Gravimetric and Volumetric Analysis,* New York, Interscience, 1948, p. 283.

plex, it may often be washed out of the precipitate afterwards with hot water or hot alcohol.

The character of a reagent may sometimes be modified by substitution to make it more soluble in water without increasing the solubility of its metal complexes. Thus 1,2-cyclohexanonedioxime and 1,2-cyclopentanonedioxime are many times more soluble in water than dimethylglyoxime, and they may be used as reagents in saturated aqueous solutions, yet their nickel and palladium complexes are even less soluble than those of dimethylglyoxime.[10] Where the reagent can be added in aqueous solution, addition of an excess does no harm.

Impurities and Side Reactions. The more complicated a substance is, the harder it is to get it pure. It is very difficult to prepare an organic reagent of the same degree of purity as, say, reagent grade potassium chloride. By-products of reactions used in preparation may be present and may enter into the precipitate during the analysis. A particular danger is that of unwanted isomers of the reagent; for example, in dimethylglyoxime the γ form, page 86, may be present and precipitate metals other than nickel. Keto-enol isomerism in such compounds as dithizone will cause errors in colorimetric work unless conditions are carefully standardized. In spite of these and other sources of error, however, organic reagents are highly reliable if prepared and used properly.[11]

Representative Complex-forming Reagents

The 1,2-dioximes.[12] The structure and general characteristics of these reagents were discussed above, and were used as examples of the chelating agents in general; so a brief treatment will suffice here. The dioxime in common use is dimethylglyoxime, and it is obtainable in high purity as the α form. It is used as a 1% solution in ethyl alcohol, and precipitates palladium from dilute hydrochloric acid, nickel from solutions of pH 5 or greater. When it is used to deter-

[10] R. C. Voter and C. V. Banks, *Anal. Chem.*, **21**, 1320 (1949).

[11] P. W. West, *Anal. Chem.*, **21**, 1342 (1949).

[12] H. Diehl, *The Application of the Dioximes to Analytical Chemistry*, Columbus, G. Frederick Smith Chemical Co., 1940.

mine nickel in steel, the steel is dissolved in hydrochloric acid and the solution boiled with nitric acid to oxidize the iron to the ferric state. Tartaric acid is added to form a complex with the iron and the chromium, if any is present, dimethylglyoxime is added, then the pH is raised by adding either sodium acetate or (more often) ammonia. The temperature is kept above 60°C.

Dimethylglyoxime forms soluble complexes with ferrous iron, cobalt, and zinc, a rather sparingly soluble complex with cupric copper, and a more sparingly soluble complex with bismuth. The formation of soluble complexes uses up dimethylglyoxime, so that more has to be added than if nickel alone were being precipitated. Moderate amounts of cobalt cause no trouble unless ferric iron is also present, when they will form a complex precipitate containing both cobalt and iron; to avoid this, iron should be reduced to the ferrous condition with sulfite before adding dimethylglyoxime. Cupric copper should likewise be reduced to cuprous. Bismuth is kept from precipitating by adding tartrate.

A very sensitive test for copper, which may also be used for its colorimetric determination, is to add an oxidizing agent, such as potassium periodate, to an ammoniacal solution of the cupric salt in the presence of excess dimethylglyoxime. An intense purple color is produced, the exact cause of which is unknown.[13]

Other dioximes which have found practical use are α-furildioxime,[14] cyclohexanonedioxime,[15] and cycloheptanonedioxime;[10] these all have the advantage of being much more soluble in water than dimethylglyoxime and having a more favorable gravimetric factor. Cycloheptanonedioxime seems to be the best of these. It precipitates a yellow nickel complex above pH 2.7, and bismuth, copper, cobalt, manganese, and other elements do not interfere.

8-Hydroxyquinoline (*8-Quinolinol, "Oxine"*):

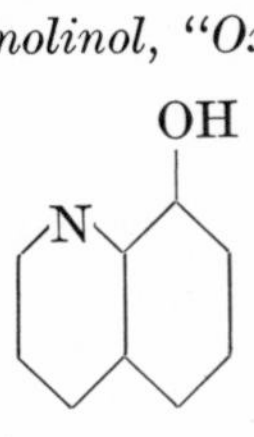

[13] L. C. Hurd and J. S. Chambers, *Ind. Eng. Chem., Anal. Ed.*, **4**, 236 (1932).
[14] B. A. Soule, *J. Am. Chem. Soc.*, **45**, 981 (1925).
[15] R. C. Voter, C. V. Banks, and H. Diehl, *Anal. Chem.*, **20**, 458 (1948).

This compound is at the opposite extreme to dimethylglyoxime in regard to selectivity; for it precipitates almost every metal in the periodic table. Only the alkali metals and, in low concentrations, the alkaline earth metals escape precipitation with this reagent. However, the various metal-hydroxyquinoline complexes differ in solubility quite considerably, so that by suitable adjustment of pH, certain metals can be precipitated and not others. Since the reagent has to lose a proton before it can combine with the metal ion, the more soluble complexes precipitate at higher pH values. Table I gives the pH ranges in which the various metals precipitate, and the formulas of the complexes. (It will be understood, of course, that

TABLE I

METAL COMPLEXES WITH 8-HYDROXYQUINOLINE

Metal	Formula of complex	Drying temperature, C	pH of precipitation
Al	AlQ_3	130°–375°	4.2– 9.8
Bi	BiQ_3	130°–140°	4.8–10.5
Cd	$CdQ_2 \cdot 2H_2O$	<116°	5.4–13
	CdQ_2	195°–345°	
Co	$CoQ_2 \cdot 2H_2O$	<115°	4.2–12
	CoQ_2	206°–306°	
Cu	CuQ_2	100°–300°	3.0–13
Fe	FeQ_3	95°–335°	2.8–12
Pb	PbQ_2		8.4–12.5
Mg	$MgQ_2 \cdot 2H_2O$	(<120°)	9 –12.5
Mn	$MnQ_2 \cdot 2H_2O$	<117°	6 –10
	MnQ_2	188°–320°	
Mo	MoO_2Q_2	140°–330°	
Ni	$NiQ_2 \cdot 2H_2O$	<123°	4.5–10
	NiQ_2	220°–340°	
Th	ThQ_4	275°–345°	4.4–12
U	$UO_2Q_2 \cdot HQ$	<157°	4.1–13.5
Zn	$ZnQ_2 \cdot 2H_2O$	<72°	4.5–13
		170°–330°	

Notes: 1. The symbol Q means the 8-hydroxyquinoline radical. 2. The drying temperatures are quoted where possible from Borel and Paris, *Anal. Chim. Acta,* **4,** 267 (1950). 3. pH ranges are average values taken from the table in I. M. Kolthoff and E. B. Sandell, *Textbook of Quantitative Inorganic Analysis,* New York, Macmillan, 1943, p. 80. 4. Rodden (*Analytical Chemistry of the Manhattan Project,* New York, McGraw-Hill, 1950, p. 184) recommends weighing thorium as $ThQ_4 \cdot HQ$, dried at 130°C.

the solubility changes gradually with pH in accordance with ionization and solubility equilibria.)

Table I indicates that certain selective precipitations should be possible; for example, zinc in presence of magnesium at pH 5–7. However, in the presence of the zinc precipitate, magnesium 8-hydroxyquinolinate starts to precipitate at pH 5.5, instead of pH 7.5 as it does when magnesium alone is present.[16] This is apparently due to surface adsorption—really a species of coprecipitation, but not the kind discussed in Chapter 2, which involves ionic charges.

The 8-hydroxyquinoline is used most often for precipitating aluminum and magnesium. Magnesium can be precipitated in presence of moderate amounts of calcium with little or no coprecipitation, and the method is also useful for determining magnesium in presence of potassium. Here the phosphate method is bad, because potassium ions replace ammonium ions isomorphously in $MgNH_4PO_4 \cdot 6H_2O$. The magnesium complex cannot be dried to constant weight because of volatilization, so for accurate work the magnesium precipitate is best determined volumetrically by titration with bromate. The precipitate is washed with hot water, dissolved in dilute hydrochloric acid, potassium bromide added, and the solution titrated with standard potassium bromate. Bromine is liberated by the reaction

$$BrO_3^- + 5Br^- + 6H^+ \rightarrow 3Br_2 + 3H_2O$$

and then reacts with hydroxyquinoline as follows:

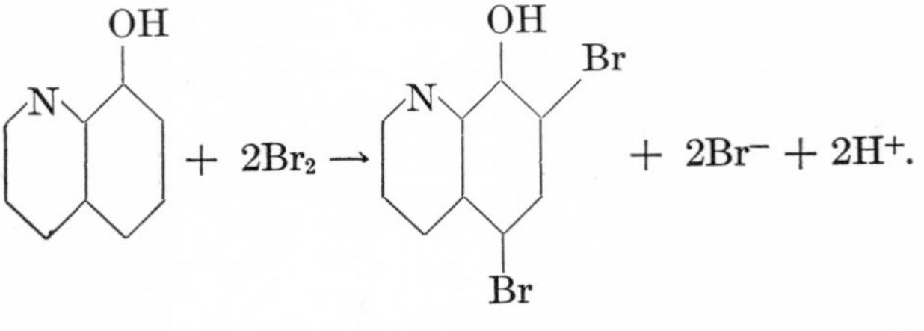

The end point is detected by the yellow color of excess bromine, by the decolorizing of methyl red, or, better, by the reversible indicators α-naphthoflavone or p-ethoxychrysoidin. An interesting alternative to adding bromate is to liberate bromine electrolytically and measure the amount of electricity used (see Chapter 5). The reaction be-

[16] H. V. Moyer and W. J. Remington, *Ind. Eng. Chem., Anal. Ed.,* **10,** 212 (1938).

tween bromine and 8-hydroxyquinoline is rather slow, however, and this titration is most often done by adding excess bromate, then potassium iodide, and titrating the liberated iodine with thiosulfate. Much of the usefulness of 8-hydroxyquinoline lies in the fact that the precipitates can be titrated in this manner.

The aluminum complex can easily be dehydrated and dried to constant weight at 140°C, and here the gravimetric method has the advantage that the precipitate can be filtered, dried, and weighed in much less time than can hydrous aluminum oxide.

Cleaner separations of one metal from another can be made using 8-hydroxyquinoline if the reagent is used in a chloroform solution to extract metals from aqueous solution. The amount of metal extracted depends very much on the pH, as will be seen from Table II. The extraction technique is particularly useful in separating trace quantities and determining them colorimetrically.[17, 18]

TABLE II

EXTRACTION OF METALS BY 8-HYDROXYQUINOLINE
IN CHLOROFORM

Metal	pH range for complete extraction
Mo	1.6– 5.6
Sn	2.5– 5.5
Fe	2.5–12.5
Cu	2.8–14
Ni	4.5– 9.5
Al	4.8– 6.7
Mn	7.2–12.5
Bi	4.0– 5.4

Note: 1% solution of 8-hydroxyquinoline shaken with buffered solutions for one minute. Data of Gentry and Sherrington, *Analyst*, **75**, 17 (1950), except for Bi, taken from Moeller, *Ind. Eng. Chem., Anal. Ed.*, **15**, 346 (1943).

The substance 8-hydroxyquinoline is amphoteric, as are all the complex-forming, chelating reagents we are discussing. As a base, it can form salts with acids, and its salts with the heteropolyacids (phosphomolybdic, phosphotungstic, silicomolybdic, etc.) are of an-

[17] C. H. R. Gentry and L. G. Sherrington, *Analyst*, **75**, 17 (1950); **71**, 432 (1946).

[18] S. E. Wiberly and L. G. Bassett, *Anal. Chem.*, **21**, 609 (1949).

alytical interest. The compounds $(C_9H_7ONH)_4[SiMo_{12}O_{40}]$ and $(C_9H_7OHN)_3[PMo_{12}O_{40}]$ have been used as weighing forms for silicon and phosphorus, respectively.[19,20] The former compound has the following advantages over hydrous silica as a form of precipitating silicon: no long evaporation or white-heat ignition is necessary; the gravimetric factor is extremely favorable; the compound can be precipitated in presence of much fluoride if boric acid is added to complex the latter; the compound can be determined volumetrically or colorimetrically if desired. Of course, in these applications 8-hydroxyquinoline acts simply as a base, not as a complex-former.

2-Methyl-8-Hydroxyquinoline, or 8-hydroxyquinaldine, has been mentioned above.[3] Not only is it more selective than 8-hydroxyquinoline, in that it does not precipitate aluminum, but it is a better reagent for magnesium, since its magnesium complex can easily be dried and weighed as the anhydrous salt (Chapter 4, footnote 9).

Cupferron and Neocupferron:[21]

These reagents form five-membered chelate rings with ferric iron and a great many other metals, of the form

In 3–4 N sulfuric or hydrochloric acid, only the following precipitate: Fe(III), Ti(IV), Ce(IV), Zr, Hf, V, Cb, Ta, Mo, W, Pd, Ga, Sn(IV), Sb, Po.[22] In neutral solutions Cu, Pb, Al, and certain other metals

---

[19] J. A. Brabson, H. C. Mattraw, G. E. Maxwell, A. Darrow, and M. F. Needham, *Anal. Chem.*, **20**, 504 (1948).

[20] R. Berg, *Das o-Oxychinolin*, Stuttgart, Enke, 1936.

[21] G. F. Smith, *Cupferron and Neo-Cupferron*, Columbus, G. Frederick Smith Chemical Co., 1938.

[22] G. E. F. Lundell and J. I. Hoffman, *Outlines of Methods of Chemical Analysis*, New York, Wiley, 1938, pp. 117–119.

precipitate, but these reactions are of little analytical interest; the main use of cupferron is for separating those metals which form precipitates in strongly acid solution.

Cupferron is soluble in water, and is used as a cold 6% aqueous solution, to which ammonia should be added to retard decomposition. The solution will keep for a month if it is cold. On heating, cupferron solutions decompose to give nitrosobenzene; they are also easily oxidized by the air. Cupferron-metal complexes are similarly unstable and easily oxidized.[23] Furthermore, when precipitated from acid solution, they are always contaminated by excess reagent; for nitrosophenylhydroxylamine, the acid corresponding to cupferron, is quite insoluble in water. For these reasons, cupferron precipitates are never weighed as such, but after filtration are ignited to the oxides.

Cupferron is mainly used in separations; for example, to remove iron and titanium before determining aluminum in steel, or before determining phosphorus in an alloy or a slag. Because it precipitates titanium and vanadium as well as iron, it may be used to supplement separations with a mercury cathode (see Chapter 5). Another important use for cupferron (and, still better, neocupferron) is to collect and determine traces of iron in natural waters; it was for this purpose that O. Baudisch developed neocupferron.

The metallic cupferron complexes are soluble in ether and chloroform; the conditions needed for their extraction from aqueous solutions have been studied experimentally and theoretically by Furman and others.[7]

α-Nitroso-β-Naphthol:

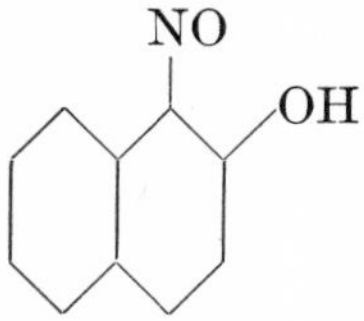

This compound and its isomer, β-nitroso-α-naphthol, are used as precipitants for cobalt. The point to notice here is that cobalt becomes

---

[23] However, the ferric-neocupferron complex is stable in air below 107°C; see page 55. Complex formation stabilizes the chelating molecule as well as stabilizing the oxidation state of the metal atom (page 124).

oxidized to the +3 condition and forms the cobaltic complex $Co(C_{10}H_6ONO)_3$; this oxidation takes place at the expense of excess of the reagent, so the precipitate is contaminated by decomposition products, and cannot be weighed without further treatment. It is ignited to Co_3O_4 and can be weighed in this form, though a better procedure, if accuracy is desired, is to dissolve the oxide in acid and determine the cobalt electrolytically.

If the cobalt is oxidized in alkaline solution with hydrogen peroxide beforehand, a pure cobaltic complex may be precipitated, but the method is unreliable.[24] The same complication is found in the colorimetric determination of cobalt with nitroso R salt, but here hydrogen peroxide clears up the solution and gives clean, reproducible results.[25]

The reagent is used as a 2% solution in 50% acetic acid, and precipitation is done in a hot 0.2 N hydrochloric acid. Not only cobalt, but Fe(III), Cr(III), W(VI), U(VI), V(V), Sn(IV), Ti, Ag, and Bi will precipitate under these conditions, and must be removed before precipitating cobalt. Extraction of ferric chloride by ether is satisfactory for removing iron, even though it is not quite complete.[26] Nickel does *not* interfere.

α-Benzoin Oxime:

$$C_6H_5 \cdot CHOH \cdot C(:N \cdot OH) \cdot C_6H_5.$$

This is a very good reagent for copper, molybdenum, and tungsten. It is added as a 1% alcoholic solution, and a small excess can be added without causing error, as it can be washed out of the precipitate on the filter with hot alcohol. Copper is precipitated from an ammoniacal solution,[27] molybdate and tungstate ions from 4 N sulfuric acid.[28] In the latter cases the reagent is not acting as a complexformer, but as a base.

The copper precipitate is a typical chelated metal complex. It is usually very pure and dries easily. Its only disadvantage is its somewhat slimy hydrophobic character; it filters very slowly.

[24] C. Mayr and F. Feigl, *Z. anal. Chem.*, **90,** 15 (1932); see also I. M. Kolthoff and A. Langer, *J. Am. Chem. Soc.*, **62,** 3172 (1940).

[25] H. C. Whealy, private communication.

[26] American Society for Testing Materials, *Methods of Chemical Analysis of Metals*, 1943. See also Chapter 9.

[27] F. Feigl, *Ber.*, **B 56,** 2083 (1923).

[28] H. Yagoda and H. A. Fales, *J. Am. Chem. Soc.*, **60,** 640 (1938).

Anthranilic Acid:

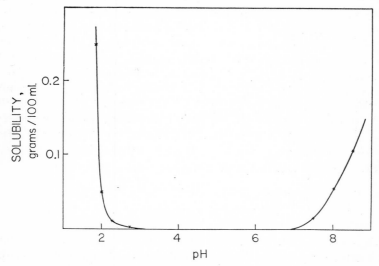

This easily available reagent is somewhat like 8-hydroxyquinoline in its characteristics; that is, it precipitates many metals, but in differ-

Fig. 6-1.   Solubility of copper anthranilate versus pH.   This relationship is characteristic of chelated metal complexes.
Unpublished data of D. B. Sullenger, University of Colorado.

ent pH ranges.   It precipitates primarily those metals which form ammonia complexes, such as copper, zinc, cadmium, cobalt, nickel, and silver, but it also precipitates manganese, mercury, lead, and iron.   Copper is quantitatively precipitated in the range pH 2.8 to 7.0 (see Figure 1), zinc above pH 4.7, cadmium above pH 5.2.[29]

It will be evident that anthranilic acid is not a selective reagent; it can be used to precipitate copper in presence of cadmium and zinc if the pH is carefully regulated, but other reagents are better for the purpose.   Its value lies in the fact that it is water-soluble (an aqueous solution, adjusted to pH 6 by adding alkali, is used as the reagent), and that its precipitates are clean, easily filtered, and easily dried. Moreover, they can be determined by bromine titration. Where no interfering elements are present, anthranilic acid is a better precipitant for copper than α-benzoin oxime.

Very similar in their reactions to anthranilic acid are quinaldic acid (Flagg, *op. cit.*, p. 63) and quinoline 8-carboxylic acid:[30]

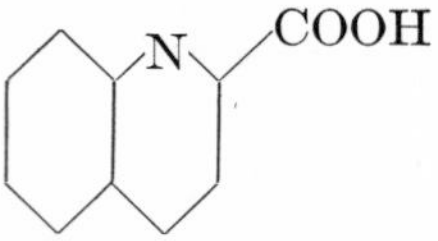

quinaldic acid

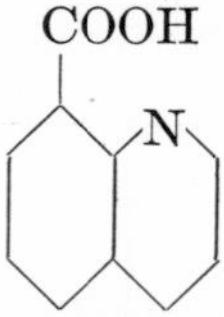

quinoline 8-carboxylic acid

Quinoline 8-carboxylic acid is more selective than the others. At pH 3.5, copper, silver, and gold are precipitated while cadmium, zinc, and lead are not. Thallium can be precipitated, which is not possible with quinaldic or anthranilic acid, and so can cadmium if the pH is raised.

"Thionalide," α-Mercapto-N-2-Naphthylacetamide:

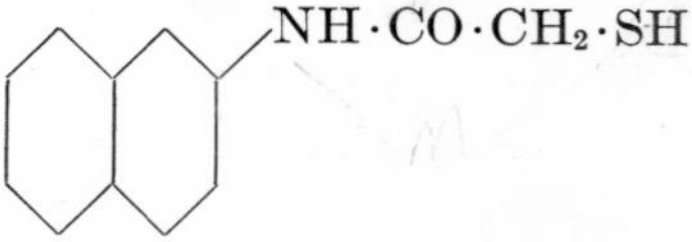

This reagent precipitates the metals of the "hydrogen sulfide group" in qualitative analysis, forming five-membered chelate rings which have no double bonds; the metal is held between the nitrogen and the sulfur. Unlike the metal sulfides, the "thionalates" have definite composition and can be dried easily; furthermore, there is no coprecipitation or postprecipitation. The precipitates are yellow or white instead of black. From a solution 0.1–0.5 N in nitric acid, the following are precipitated: Cu, Hg, Bi, As, Sb, Sn, Au, Ag, Pd, Pt. From a sodium carbonate solution containing tartrate, Cu, Ag, Au, Cd, and Tl are precipitated; from a sodium cyanide solution containing tartrate, Au, Tl, Sn, Sb, Pb, Bi precipitate, but Cd does not; from

[29] H. Goto, *J. Chem. Soc. Japan*, **55**, 1156 (1934); H. Funk and M. Ditt, *Z. anal. Chem.*, **91**, 332 (1933); **93**, 241 (1933).
[30] A. K. Majumdar, *J. Indian Chem. Soc.*, **18**, 419 (1941); J. R. Gilbreath and H. M. Haendler, *Ind. Eng. Chem., Anal. Ed.*, **14**, 866 (1942).

a solution of sodium hydroxide, cyanide, and tartrate, only Tl precipitates.[31]

Thionalide is almost insoluble in water, and is used as a solution in alcohol or acetic acid. Excess thionalide is washed out of the precipitates with aqueous alcohol and, in some cases, acetone. (Some of the precipitates are soluble in nonpolar solvents, others are not.) Thionalide is a reducing agent, which means that oxidizing substances must be removed from the solutions before precipitating; it also means that the precipitates can be titrated oxidimetrically. For this purpose they are dissolved in a 50% acetic acid which is also 1 N in hydrochloric acid, and titrated with iodine. Iodine oxidizes the reagent to a disulfide compound, $(C_{10}H_7NHCOCH_2S)_2$.

"Dithizone," Diphenythiocarbazone:

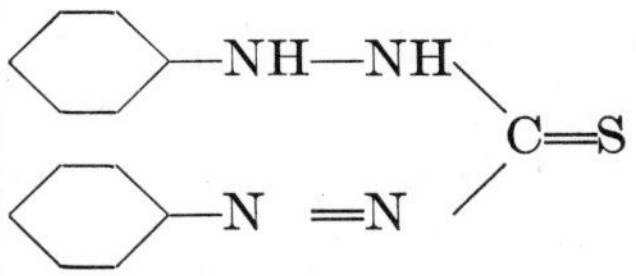

This reagent is not an "organic precipitant" in the ordinary sense; for the precipitates are never collected as such. The metal complexes are all soluble in chloroform or carbon tetrachloride, and they are all intensely colored, usually red, yellow, or brown. They are used, therefore, for colorimetric determinations. The technique is to shake the aqueous solution for a minute or two with an excess of a dilute (0.01%) solution of dithizone in carbon tetrachloride or chloroform, whereupon the metal which forms the complex goes into the organic layer. The color of the dithizone itself is a dark green; one may *either* determine the color intensity of the solution at two wavelengths with a spectrophotometer, and so distinguish the color of the complex from that of the dithizone, *or* extract the unreacted dithizone with a sodium sulfide solution, leaving only the complex in the organic solvent.[32, 33] Both methods are extremely sensitive; the reagent will detect well below one microgram of most metals.

[31] R. Berg and O. Roebling, *Angew. Chem.*, **48**, 597 (1935); R. Berg and E. S. Fahrenkamp, *Z. anal. Chem.*, **109**, 305 (1937); **112**, 161 (1938).
[32] L. G. Bricker, S. Weinberg, and K. L. Proctor, *Ind. Eng. Chem., Anal. Ed.*, **17**, 661 (1945).
[33] E. B. Sandell, *The Colorimetric Determination of Traces of Metals*, 2d ed., New York, Interscience, 1950.

Like other reagents we have discussed, this reagent combines with a great many metals and is at first sight quite unselective. However, by control of the pH and by addition of complex formers to the aqueous solution, very good selectivity can be obtained; thus zinc is determined in presence of moderate amounts of lead and copper by the extraction of its red complex from a solution of pH 6 to which thiosulfate has been added.[32] The conditions for the extraction of certain metals are summarized in Table III.

TABLE III

SELECTIVE DITHIZONE EXTRACTIONS

Solution	Metals extracted
Basic plus CN^-	Pb, Sn(II), Tl(I), Bi
Slightly acid plus CN^-	Pd, Hg, Ag, Cu
Dilute acid plus CNS^-	Hg, Au, Cu
Dilute acid plus CNS^- plus CN^-	Hg, Cu
Dilute acid plus Br^- or I^-	Pd, Au, Cu
pH 5 plus $S_2O_3^=$	Pd, Sn(II), Zn, (Cd)
pH 4–5 plus $S_2O_3^=$ plus CN^-	Sn(II), Zn

Note: Table taken from E. B. Sandell, *The Colorimetric Determination of Traces of Metals*, 2d ed., New York, Interscience, 1950.

The effect of pH on the extraction has been carefully studied by Sandell;[33] (see also Flagg, *op. cit.*). It is connected, of course, with the acid strength of dithizone and the partition coefficients for the various metal complexes between the organic solvent and water. It is important to note that two types of metal-dithizone complex are possible, the keto and the enol:

keto   enol

The keto complexes are formed under the usual analytical conditions.[34]

Salt-forming Reagents

The salt-forming organic precipitants are those which form *salts*, as distinct from chelated complexes, with inorganic ions. By and large, they are less selective than the complex-forming precipitants, but are very useful because they permit the quantitative precipitation of the alkali and alkaline earth metals, of nitrate ions, and also of large complex anions and cations. We shall describe a few typical examples.

Dipicrylamine:

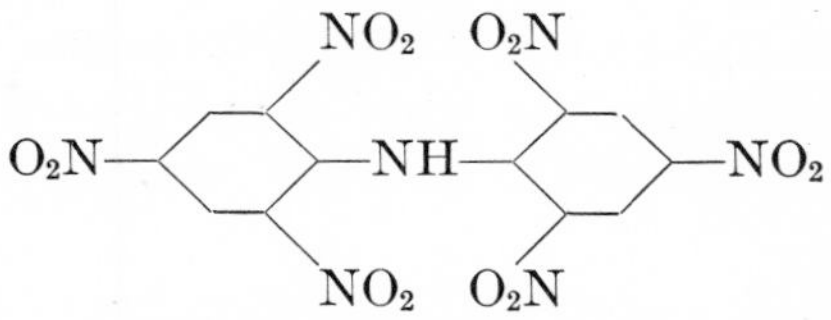

This is a weak acid which is generally used as an aqueous solution of its sodium or magnesium salt. It is a good reagent for potassium, particularly for determining small quantities of the latter. The potassium salt is, however, sufficiently soluble so that the precipitate must be washed with an ice-cold saturated solution of potassium dipicrylaminate.[35]

A study of the freezing point and conductivity of solutions of the sodium salt shows that this is, indeed, a true, ionized salt, but that association between the anions is quite appreciable.[36] The reagent precipitates most metals except lithium, sodium, and the alkaline earths.

Picrolonic Acid:

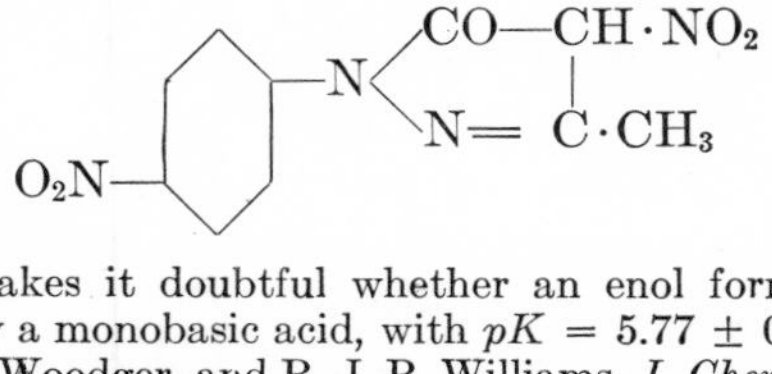

[34] Recent work makes it doubtful whether an enol form exists. Dithizone appears to be strictly a monobasic acid, with $pK = 5.77 \pm 0.25$. See H. Irving, S. J. H. Cooke, S. C. Woodger, and R. J. P. Williams, *J. Chem. Soc.*, 1949, p. 1847.

[35] I. M. Kolthoff and G. H. Bendix, *Ind. Eng. Chem., Anal. Ed.*, **11**, 94 (1939).

[36] J. Kjelland, *J. Am. Chem. Soc.*, **61**, 2285 (1939).

This reagent is water-soluble, and is chiefly used for determining calcium. A tenfold excess of magnesium can be tolerated. Its advantage over oxalate is its very favorable gravimetric factor and the fact that picrolonic acid can be determined polarographically. It is also used in the gravimetric determination of lead and thorium.

Tetraphenylarsonium Chloride:

$$[(C_6H_5)_4As]Cl.$$

This is used for gravimetric determination of Sn, Hg, Au, Pt, Zn, Cd; in concentrated sodium chloride solution these precipitate as the tetraphenylarsonium salts of the appropriate complex anions; e.g., $CdCl_4^=$, $SnCl_6^=$, $PtCl_6^=$.[37] Anions such as ReO_4^-, ClO_4^-, and I_3^- are also precipitated. It seems that the large cation fits well with a large anion in a solid crystal lattice. A convenient technique is to add excess of the reagent and back-titrate the excess potentiometrically with a standard solution of iodine in potassium iodide. $[(C_6H_5)_4As]I_3$ is precipitated.

Benzidine:

$$H_2N\text{—}\langle\bigcirc\rangle\text{—}\langle\bigcirc\rangle\text{—}NH_2$$

Benzidine forms insoluble salts with sulfate, tungstate, and other ions. Its chief use is in determining sulfate. Benzidine sulfate is relatively soluble in water, 49 milligrams per liter at 0°C, so that even in cold solutions, solubility losses are appreciable. Its advantages over barium sulfate are, first, that the technique is faster; second, that the precipitate can be titrated either with permanganate or with standard base. In the latter method, the precipitate is suspended in water at 50°–60°C and phenolphthalein indicator is used; it is the benzidinium ion which is titrated.

Benzidine is used to determine inorganic sulfate in commercial detergents. Organic sulfates, such as $C_{12}H_{25}SO_4Na$, give precipitates with benzidine, but these are soluble in alcohol, whereas benzidine sulfate is not.

In determining tungsten, benzidine tungstate is precipitated together with a little sulfate which makes it easier to filter, and the precipitate is ignited, leaving only WO_3.

[37] H. H. Willard and G. M. Smith, *Ind. Eng. Chem., Anal. Ed.*, **11**, 186, 269 (1939).

Lake Formers

Lake-forming reagents form a coagulum, or "lake," with colloidal precipitates such as hydrous oxides. They facilitate the precipitation of these hydrous oxides, and also confer on them a characteristic color, which is useful in qualitative detection and in colorimetric determination. Lake formers are chelating agents, just like the precipitants discussed above, and the color of the lake is due to chemical combination between the lake former and the hydrous oxide which takes place on the surface of the colloidal particles of the latter.[38] For purposes of colorimetric determination (which can be done only in very dilute solutions) the "lake" is kept colloidally dispersed by adding a protective colloid such as gelatin or dextrin. These dispersions coagulate in course of time, however, and are never quite reproducible. Their virtue lies in the sensitivity of the test rather than its accuracy. Concentrations of a few parts of metallic ion per million can be measured colorimetrically to about 10%.

Typical lake formers of this type are alizarin and "aluminon," the sodium salt of aurin tricarboxylic acid:

alizarin   "aluminon"

These give red lakes with hydrous aluminum oxide. Incidentally, a true stoichiometric compound of 3 molecules of alizarin with 1 aluminum atom has been prepared; it is insoluble in 1 N hydrochloric acid, which the aluminum-alizarin lake is not; this fact emphasizes that lakes must be considered as two-dimensional adsorption compounds rather than ordinary chelated complexes. Other lake formers are quinalizarin, or 1,2,5,8-tetrahydroxyanthraquinone, which forms red

[38] F. Feigl, *Anal. Chem.*, **21**, 1298 (1949).

lakes with beryllium and magnesium hydroxides, *p*-nitrobenzene-azo-resorcinol, which forms a blue lake with magnesium hydroxide, and "titan yellow," which forms an orange-red lake with magnesium hydroxide. For quantitative colorimetric determinations, the concentration of the metal should not exceed 10 parts per million. The technique is to add the reagent and the protective colloid to an acidified solution, then to add ammonia or sodium hydroxide to precipitate the lake.

Tannin is a lake former of a different kind. It is itself colloidal, and the lake particles are formed by adsorption of inorganic ions upon an organic core, rather than vice versa.[38] It was at one time thought[39] that these lakes were a kind of coacervate formed by the attraction of negatively charged colloidal tannin particles to positively charged hydrous oxide particles, but this view fails to explain the most characteristic tannin precipitates, namely, those formed with tungstate, vanadate, niobate, and tantalate ions in weakly acid solutions. These would form *negatively* charged hydrous oxide sols, not positively charged ones.

Tannin is a glucose ester of digallic acid,

The phenolic hydroxyls evidently combine with metallic ions. Tungstic acid and acids like it probably form esters with the phenolic groups.[38]

Many metals form precipitates with tannin, but by the use of complexing agents and pH adjustment selective precipitations are possible. In oxalate solutions at pH 3, only titanium, tungsten, niobium, and tantalum precipitate. In ammoniacal oxalate solutions, iron, vanadium, zirconium, thorium, aluminum, chromium, and uranium precipitate.[39] The most important analytical precipitations are those of vanadium, niobium, tantalum, tungsten, and

[39] W. R. Schoeller and A. R. Powell, *The Analysis of Minerals and Ores of the Rarer Elements*, 2d ed., London, Griffin, 1940.

uranium. The separation of niobium and tantalum from one another is particularly important.[40] This is accomplished by a series of fractional precipitations; tantalum is precipitated first, and niobium afterward, from acid oxalate solutions as the pH and tannin concentration are raised. Like most tannin lakes, these have characteristic colors, the tantalum lake being yellow, the niobium lake orange-red; this makes it easy to follow the separation. For quantitative determination, tannin lakes are ashed and the metals weighed as oxides.

PROBLEMS

1. 10 ml. of chloroform containing 100 micrograms of dithizone were added to 10 ml. of a buffer solution of pH 4.0 containing 10 micrograms of zinc. 2.3 micrograms of zinc were extracted from the aqueous layer [Kolthoff and Sandell, *J. Am. Chem. Soc.*, **63**, 1906–1941]. Assuming constancy of partition coefficients and ionization constant, calculate the weight of zinc remaining in the aqueous layer (a) in a similar extraction at pH 5.5, (b) in a similar extraction at pH 4.0 using 250 micrograms of dithizone.

2. Using organic precipitants, suggest methods for the following determinations: Fe(III) in presence of H_3PO_4; Al in presence of Fe; Bi in presence of Sb; Ti in presence of Fe and Al. Also suggest alternative methods which do not require an organic precipitant or complex former.

3. Why should the copper compound of anthranilic acid dissolve in excess *base* as well as excess acid?

4. How would one tell experimentally whether or not enough 8-hydroxyquinoline had been added in a gravimetric aluminum determination?

5. (a) What are the advantages of 8-hydroxyquinoline over ammonium phosphate as a reagent for magnesium, i.e., in what circumstances would it be preferred?

(b) A solution containing Mg is treated with 8-hydroxyquinoline, and the precipitated complex is dissolved in acid, excess sodium bromide is added, and the solution is titrated with 0.025 M bromate. 16.8 ml. are consumed. Calculate the number of mg. of magnesium in the solution.

(c) An inexperienced analyst gets high and erratic results by this method. What is probably wrong?

6. List ten cases in which the selectivity of organic reagents and complex formers enables separations to be made which would otherwise be difficult, e.g., Ni from Co by dimethylglyoxime, Zn from Cu(I) by quinaldic acid and thiourea.

---

[40] A. R. Powell and W. R. Schoeller, *Analyst*, **50**, 485 (1925).

7

Complex ions in analytical chemistry

COMPLEX IONS AND COMPLEX FORMERS are useful in analytical chemistry in a great variety of ways. Most commonly they are used in separations. By forming a complex ion we can keep one metal in solution while we precipitate another; thus the addition of cyanide prevents copper from being precipitated with hydrogen sulfide, but does not prevent the precipitation of cadmium and zinc. Again, the differing stabilities of the different rare earth citrate complexes make it possible to separate the rare earth elements from one another by ion exchange (see Chapter 8). We have already referred to the use of complex ion formation to permit the separation of certain metals by electrolysis.

The suppression of the reactions of an ion by the formation of a stable complex is called by Feigl "masking." Thus fluoride ion "masks" the ferric ion, so that a ferric salt solution containing an excess of fluoride ion will not react with potassium ferrocyanide, nor will it give the characteristic brown-red color with thiocyanate. By "masking," the interference of one ion in the quantitative determination of another may often be prevented. Where one complex former competes with another for the same ion, "demasking" may occur; for example, the complex ion $FeF_6^=$ may be decomposed by adding an excess of boric acid, which takes away the fluorine to form the very stable fluoboric acid.

Complex formation is frequently used to keep a metal ion in solution at a pH where its hydroxide or oxide would normally precipitate. A well-known example is Fehling's solution, which contains cupric copper and yet has to be strongly alkaline.   Tartrate is added to prevent the copper from precipitating as copper hydroxide.

Complex ions are used for determinations as well as for separations. They may form sparingly soluble salts, in which case the determination is gravimetric, an example being precipitation of copper as $[Cu(C_5H_5N)_2](CNS)_2$ or of silicon as the silicomolybdate salt of 8-hydroxyquinoline (see below).   More commonly the determination is colorimetric, because many complex ions have distinctive colors.   Finally, the reaction between the metal ion and the complex former may be made the basis for the class of titrations described in Chapter 19.

Constitution of complex ions. By "complex ions" we understand, primarily, those ions which are formed by the union of a metal ion with other ions or molecules (other than solvent molecules).   The binding is usually by coordination; that is, by a pair of electrons which is donated to the metal atom by the complexing ion or molecule.   This latter must therefore be an ion or molecule with electrons to donate; it must be a "base" in the Lewis sense.   A well-known example of complex ion formation is that between the cupric ion and four ammonia molecules.   Its structure may be represented as follows:

$$
\left[
\begin{array}{c}
\text{H} \\
\text{H:}\ddot{\text{N}}\text{:H} \\
\text{H} \qquad\qquad \text{H} \\
\text{H:}\ddot{\text{N}}\text{:} \quad \text{Cu} \quad \text{:}\ddot{\text{N}}\text{:H} \\
\ddot{\text{H}} \qquad\qquad \ddot{\text{H}} \\
\text{H:}\ddot{\text{N}}\text{:H} \\
\ddot{\text{H}}
\end{array}
\right]^{++}
$$

Not only ammonia, but amines such as pyridine form such complexes. Other examples of "Lewis bases" which form complexes with metals are ions such as cyanide, oxalate, sulfate, iodide, and chloride.   Fluoride ion is a special case in that it seems to combine with metals by forming "ion pairs" rather than covalent bonds.

Water, of course, is an electron donor molecule, and we know that most ions are hydrated in aqueous solution.   The cupric ion in water is properly represented as $Cu(OH_2)_4^{++}$, just as it is in the crystalline hydrate $CuSO_4 \cdot 5H_2O$, where four water molecules are associated with the cupric ion and one with the sulfate ion.   When ammonia is added to an aqueous copper solution, it does not add on to a bare Cu^{++} ion, but rather displaces water from a hydrated ion. It is not surprising, therefore, to find that this displacement proceeds stepwise. J. Bjerrum[1] has made an extensive study of the stability of complex metal ammines in aqueous solution, and finds that ammonia and the hydrated cupric ion combine in five stages with equilibrium constants as follows:

$$K_1 = \frac{[Cu^{++}][NH_3]}{[CuNH_3^{++}]} = 7.1 \times 10^{-5}.$$

$$K_2 = \frac{[CuNH_3^{++}][NH_3]}{[Cu(NH_3)_2^{++}]} = 3.1 \times 10^{-4}.$$

$$K_3 = \frac{[Cu(NH_3)_2^{++}][NH_3]}{[Cu(NH_3)_3^{++}]} = 1.3 \times 10^{-3}.$$

$$K_4 = \frac{[Cu(NH_3)_3^{++}][NH_3]}{[Cu(NH_3)_4^{++}]} = 7.4 \times 10^{-3}.$$

$$K_5 = \frac{[Cu(NH_3)_4^{++}][NH_3]}{[Cu(NH_3)_5^{++}]} = 3.3.$$

(For simplicity, coordinated water is omitted from these formulas.) The possibility that several complexes may exist together in the same solution must always be borne in mind when complex ions are to be used in analytical determinations. The potentiometric titration of fluoride ions with ferric ions, for example, would be simple and straightforward if only one complex existed, such as $FeF_6^{\equiv}$. Actually, complexes FeF^{++}, FeF_2^{+}, FeF_3, FeF_4^{-}, and $FeF_5^{=}$ all seem to exist,[2] so that this titration is never accurate and is feasible only as a rough, empirical method under carefully standardized conditions.[3] The same complication enters into the colorimetric determination of fluoride by the bleaching of a colored ferric complex.[4]

The number of atoms or groups bound by a central atom is called

[1] J. Bjerrum, *Metal Ammine Formation in Aqueous Solutions*, Copenhagen, Haase, 1941; *Chem. Abstracts*, **35**, 6527–6534 (1941); J. Bjerrum, *Chem. Rev.* **46**, 381 (1950).

[2] A. K. Babko and K. E. Kleiner, *J. Gen. Chem.* (U.S.S.R.), **17**, 1259 (1947); *Chem. Abstracts*, **42**, 1840 (1948).

[3] G. W. Low and E. H. Pryde, *J. Am. Chem. Soc.*, **61**, 2237 (1939); S. T. Talipov and I. L. Teodorovich, *Zavodskaya Lab.*, **15**, 529 (1949); *Chem. Abstracts*, **43**, 6952 (1949).

[4] S. Lacroix and M. Labalade, *Anal. Chim. Acta*, **4**, 68 (1950).

the *coordination number*. The coordination number of an atom depends primarily upon its radius. The elements of the first short period (Li to F) have a maximum coordination number of 4. In the second short period (Na to Cl) and the first long period (K to Br), the maximum coordination number is 6. With the heavier elements, higher coordination numbers are possible. The actual coordination number of an atom may be less than the maximum for its period; thus silver in the oxidation state +1 has a coordination number of only 2. Certain atoms in an oxidation state of +2 have a planar, or square, distribution of valence bonds; for example, Ni, Fe, Pd, Pt, Cu, and Ag(II). In such cases, the coordination number is generally limited to 4, though this number can be exceeded under extreme conditions, as in the copper ammines listed above.

Metals forming complex ions. Every metal ion known, with the possible exceptions of cesium and rubidium, forms complex ions of some kind. Some metals form more numerous and more stable complexes than others, but in the reactions of analytical chemistry the possibility of the formation of complexes must always be considered. Even a weakly bound complex, such as $Mg(NH_3)_6^{++}$ [1] or $Fe(SO_4)_2^-$, may affect solubilities, oxidation-reduction equilibria, color reactions, or coprecipitation.

The binding in complex ions is generally covalent, hence the covalency rules of Fajans and Sidgwick[5] may be used to predict which metals (and nonmetals) will form the most stable complexes. These rules start from the idea that the deformation of the negative electron shell of an anion by the positive charge of a cation promotes the transition from an ionic to a covalent link. Covalence is accordingly favored by: (a) high charge on anion or cation; (b) small radius of cation; (c) large radius of anion; (d) noninert gas structure of ion. The cations most likely to form covalent complexes will be those of high charge and small radius. Al^{+++} will form better complexes than Mg^{++}, and Mg^{++} better complexes than Ca^{++}. Ions having a "noninert gas structure" are those of the transition elements, such as Fe^{++} and Cr^{+++}, and those of the "B" subgroups, such as Ag^+ and Cu^{++}. The electronic structure of the potassium ion K^+ is the same as that of the inert gas argon, and accordingly K^+ is very stable, forming few complexes; the electronic structure of Ag^+ contains 18 electrons in

[5] N. V. Sidgwick, *The Covalent Link in Chemistry*, Ithaca, Cornell University Press, 1932.

the outer "shell," instead of 8 as in an inert gas, and Ag^+ accordingly forms many covalent complexes.   An even greater contrast is found between Ca^{++} and Cd^{++}, ions of equal radius and charge, but different electronic structures.   Calcium forms very few complexes, but cadmium is notorious for its many complex ions, which are far more numerous than those of zinc, even though Zn^{++} has a smaller radius than Cd^{++}.   A cadmium chloride solution, for instance, contains primarily Cd^{++} and $CdCl_4^=$.   Many of these cadmium complexes form insoluble salts which are good gravimetric weighing forms, for example $[Cd(C_5H_5N)_2]Cl_2$, $[Cu(H_2N \cdot CH_2 \cdot CH_2 \cdot NH_2)_2][CdI_4]$, $[Cr(CNS)_4(NH_3)_2]_2$ $[Cd(SCN_2H_4)_2]$.[6]   Precipitation of this last salt is a good way to determine cadmium in presence of much zinc.

Complex ion formation is so common that we cannot do more than point to a few representative examples.

Anions forming complexes.   Any anion can theoretically form a complex with a metallic ion, for every anion is a potential electron donor.   The most deformable anions, such as I^- and CN^-, form the best complexes; other notable complex formers are the various kinds of phosphate ions.   The fewest complexes are formed by the perchlorate ion, which is symmetrical and not easily deformed.   The oxidation-reduction potentials of the ceric-cerous system are affected by complex formation, and are a good measure of the complexing powers of different ions; these increase in the order $ClO_4^- < NO_3^- < SO_4^= < Cl^-$ (see Chapter 11).

In the section which follows we shall discuss some of the most important ions and molecules, inorganic and organic, which form complexes with metal ions.

Complex-forming Agents

Chloride, bromide, iodide.   Of these, the iodide ion is the largest and most deformable, and should form the most covalent molecules and complex ions.   This is in fact the case.   The ion $HgI_4^=$ is far more stable than its chlorine and bromine analogues, a fact which can be used in titrating mixtures of iodide and chloride or bromide

---

[6] C. Duval, *Anal. Chim. Acta*, **4**, 190 (1950); C. Mahr and H. Ohle, *Z. anal. Chem.*, **109**, 1 (1937).

(see Chapter 19), while the existence and stability of I_3^-, which accounts for the great solubility of iodine in potassium iodide solutions, is well known.   Silver iodide readily dissolves in concentrated potassium iodide solutions because of the formation of AgI_2^-, which is considerably more stable than $AgCl_2^-$.

Fluoride. The fluoride ion is the smallest and therefore the least deformable of the halide ions.   According to the covalency rules, it should form the fewest complexes, yet actually it forms far more complexes than the other halide ions.   It is one of the strongest complex-formers that we know.   The inference is that the metal-fluoride complexes are not bound covalently, but rather by electrostatic forces similar to those which hold "ion pairs" together.[7]   The small size of the fluoride ion would permit the close approach which is necessary for ion pairs to be formed.   Support for this view comes from the paramagnetism of such salts as K_3FeF_6.   If the bonding were covalent, the electrons would be paired and the molecule diamagnetic.

The small size of the fluoride ion accounts for another fact; fluorine brings out the highest coordination number of the atoms with which it combines.   Examples of this are $AlF_6^{\equiv}$, $SiF_6^{=}$, SF_6, $TaF_8^{\equiv}$.

The analytical chemistry of fluorine is in large measure the chemistry of complex ions.   Consider first the methods used for the colorimetric determination of fluoride ion.   There are many, and all depend on the ability of the fluoride ion to tear apart colored metallic complexes by forming more stable, colorless fluoride complexes of the metal.   One of the oldest[8] uses the yellow solution formed by adding hydrogen peroxide to an acid solution of a titanium salt.   The yellow color is probably due to the ion TiO_2^{++}.   On adding fluoride, the solution is bleached, and the difference between the initial and final color intensity gives the amount of fluoride present.   The reactions are:

$$TiO_2^{++} \text{ (yellow)} + H_2O \rightleftharpoons TiO^{++} + H_2O_2.$$

$$TiO^{++} + 2H^+ + 6F^- \rightleftharpoons TiF_6^{=} \text{ (colorless)} + H_2O.$$

This method has the advantage that only one colored complex and only one colorless fluoride complex are present, so the reduction in

[7] N. Bjerrum, *Kgl. Danske Videnskb. Selskabs,* **7,** No. 9 (1926); R. M. Fuoss, *Chem. Rev.,* **17,** 27 (1935).
[8] G. Steiger, *J. Am. Chem. Soc.,* **30,** 219 (1908).

color (optical density) obeys Beer's law over a considerable range of fluoride concentrations.[9] Other colored complexes which are bleached by fluoride ions and used for the colorimetric determination of fluoride are ferric thiocyanate,[10] ferric salicylate,[11] ferric sulfosalicylate,[4] ferric bromide,[12] zirconium alizarin.[13] The latter is actually a colloidal lake formed between zirconium hydroxide and sodium alizarin sulfonate. The methods are very sensitive except for that using ferric bromide. In all of these methods, careful attention to details is necessary to get reliable results. Four classes of substance interfere:

(a) Those forming complex ions or insoluble salts with fluoride.
(b) Those forming complex ions or insoluble salts with the metal.
(c) Those forming complex ions with the radicals complexing the metal.
(d) Those having a color of their own.

The hydrogen ion falls in categories (a) and (c), so the acidity of the solution is relevant. Tripositive and tetrapositive metals form complexes with nearly all anions, so the number of substances in class (b) is extremely large. Moderate concentrations of chloride or sulfate, for instance, affect the results considerably, and so do small concentrations of phosphates. Aluminum ion is an example of class (a), forming AlF^{++} at low concentrations,[8] $AlF_6^=$ at high concentrations. Fortunately, the complex ion $SiF_6^=$ is relatively unstable; one may separate fluoride ion from nearly all interferences, if necessary, by steam distillation as SiF_4 from hot concentrated sulfuric acid containing suspended silica or broken glass,[11,14] the SiF_4 being absorbed in water. Borosilicate glass should not be used here, since this may form the very stable BF_4^-, which does not bleach the colored complexes mentioned above.

Certain volumetric methods depend on the formation of $AlF_6^=$. Fluoride is titrated with aluminum chloride solution, and the end

[9] D. Monnier, R. Vaucher, and P. Wenger, *Helv. Chim. Acta*, **33**, 1 (1950).
[10] M. D. Foster, *Ind. Eng. Chem., Anal. Ed.*, **5**, 235 (1933).
[11] M. Kortüm-Seiler, *Angew. Chemie*, **59**, 159 (1947).
[12] K. Erler, *Z. anal. Chem.*, **131**, 103 (1950).
[13] J. M. Sanchis, *Ind. Eng. Chem., Anal. Ed.*, **6**, 134 (1934).
[14] H. H. Willard and O. B. Winter, *Ind. Eng. Chem., Anal. Ed.*, **5**, 7 (1933).

point found by hydrolysis of the excess Al^{+++} [15,16] by formation of a red lake with a dye,[17] or conductometrically.[18] A good review of volumetric and gravimetric methods for fluoride is that by Geyer.[16]

The complex-forming ability of the fluoride ion means that this often interferes in the determination of other substances. In presence of much fluoride, gravimetric determinations of iron and aluminum will be low, and the precipitation of ammonium phosphomolybdate will be incomplete, owing to the formation of $MoO_2F_4^=$. Colorimetric methods depending on phosphomolybdic or silicomolybdic acid are inaccurate in the presence of mere traces of fluoride. Fortunately, fluoride is easily eliminated. One simply evaporates the sample with sulfuric or perchloric acid. Alternatively, one may repress the action of small amounts of fluoride in aqueous solution by adding a large excess of boric acid which forms stable BF_4^-; this is sufficient to prevent interference in the colorimetric determination of silica or phosphorus with ammonium molybdate (see below). Beryllium salts are even more effective than boric acid; by forming the very stable $BeF_4^=$, they even "demask" aluminum so that it can be quantitatively precipitated with 8-hydroxyquinoline.[19]

By forming a complex with ferric iron, fluoride depresses its oxidizing power, and thus prevents it from reacting with iodide in acid solutions. This fact is used in standard procedures for titrating copper from copper ores by the iodide-thiosulfate method (see Chapter 15).

Phosphates. These include the orthophosphates (derived from H_3PO_4), the metaphosphates (from HPO_3), the pyrophosphates (from $H_4P_2O_7$), and many condensed phosphates and polyphosphates, such as $Na_6P_6O_{18}$, and metaphosphate polymers of high molecular weight.[20] All except the simple metaphosphates form soluble complexes with metal ions. The pyrophosphates and polyphosphates even form complexes with sodium; for example, $(Na_2P_2O_7)^=$. Their complexes with calcium and magnesium are important in water conditioning.

In dilute aqueous solution, only the orthophosphate ions are thermodynamically stable. All other phosphates hydrate slowly,

[15] A. Kurtenacker and W. Jurenka, *Z. anal. Chem.*, **82**, 210 (1930).

[16] R. Geyer, *Z. anorg. Chem.*, **252**, 50 (1943).

[17] J. H. Saylor and M. E. Larkin, *Anal. Chem.*, **20**, 194 (1948).

[18] J. Harms and G. Jander, *Z. Elektrochem.*, **42**, 315 (1936).

[19] F. Feigl and A. Schaeffer, *Anal. Chem.*, **23**, 351 (1951).

[20] For an excellent review of complex phosphates, see D. M. Yost and Russell, *Systematic Inorganic Chemistry*, New York, Prentice-Hall, 1944.

forming orthophosphates. This process is accelerated by heating and adding acid. The complete analysis of a mixture containing several different phosphates is difficult, but the total phosphorus can always be found by refluxing with dilute acid for several hours, then determining the orthophosphate present.

Orthophosphoric acid is used in analysis to combine with ferric iron in acid solution. The complex formed is probably $H_2Fe(PO_4)_2^-$. This is colorless, so the interference of iron in colorimetric determinations (e.g., of manganese as permanganate) is suppressed by phosphoric acid. The oxidizing power of ferric iron is also lessened, so that in titrating ferrous iron by dichromate, ferrous iron is completely oxidized to ferric before any of the diphenylamine indicator changes color (see Chapter 17). The oxidation-reduction potential of the ferric-ferrous system is depressed by about 0.4 volt.

Similar complexes are formed with aluminum and chromium (III), and less stable complexes are formed with dipositive metals, such as cupric copper. These are not used in analytical procedures in the sense that the ferric phosphate complex is used, but one has to remember that they are there. For example, the oxidation-reduction potential of the cupric-cuprous system is lowered by phosphoric acid, and in the potentiometric titration of cupric ions by chromous chloride, for instance, this effect may be quite significant (see page 195, Chapter 11).

A very important group of orthophosphate complexes are the heteropoly acids of phosphorus. These will be considered separately below.

Sodium pyrophosphate is used as a reagent to prevent the interference of ferric iron in certain titrations, such as that of copper with potassium iodide and sodium thiosulfate. It has the advantage over orthophosphate that the pH can be higher without precipitation taking place. Its complex with tripositive manganese, $MnP_2O_7^-$, is unusually stable; in presence of pyrophosphate, Mn^{++} can be titrated oxidimetrically to this unfamiliar oxidation state (see p. 285).

Cyanides. The metallic cyanide complexes are too well known to need much discussion here. The most stable, among the commoner metals, are those of Fe(II), Fe(III), Co(III), Cu(I), Ag(I). In the presence of cyanide, the detection and determination of many metals is difficult. Certain cyanide complexes may, however, be broken down by shaking the solution with mercuric oxide. This forms the very stable, soluble, nonionized $Hg(CN)_2$, and the metal in the original complex is "demasked." Nickel, palladium, iron, and copper are released from their cyanide complexes in this way.[21]

Ammonia and amines. These are well known as complexing agents. We shall mention here the complexes of pyridine. All metal ions which form ammonia complexes form pyridine complexes also. The complex with dipositive silver, $Ag(C_5H_5N)_4^{++}$, is very stable, so that in presence of pyridine, silver (I) can be oxidized easily to silver (II). This provides another example of an unfamiliar oxidation state which is stabilized by complex ion formation.

The pyridine complexes of Zn^{++}, Co^{++}, Ni^{++}, Mn^{++}, Cu^{++}, and Cd^{++} are of interest because of their stability and because they form insoluble thiocyanates: $M(C_5H_5N)_4(CNS)_2$ with Co, Ni, and Mn; $M(C_5H_5N)_2(CNS)_2$ with Cu, Zn, and Cd.[22] These are easily filtered and dried at 140°C. Pyridine is useful in the gravimetric analysis of mixtures of these ions with Fe^{+++}, Al^{+++}, or Cr^{+++}. It is used, first, to precipitate the hydrous oxides of the latter ions while holding the dipositive ions in solution. The hydrous oxides are filtered off, and thiocyanate is added to the filtrate. This precipitates the divalent ions as their complex pyridinium thiocyanates. Quinoline, isoquinoline, and o-phenylenediamine may be used in place of pyridine.

The chelated complexes formed between ferrous ions and α,α'-bipyridyl or orthophenanthroline are very important. They are deep red in color and are used for the colorimetric determination of iron, the phenanthroline complex also being a valuable oxidation-reduction indicator (Chapter 17).

Chelating complex-formers: general. The remaining complexing agents to be discussed in this section all form *chelate rings* with metal ions, that is, rings of five or six atoms in which the metal atom is bound by one or more coordinate links. We have previously noted (Chapter 6) that most organic precipitants are reagents of this type. Chelation makes complexes more stable than they would otherwise be, for when one bond has been formed with the metal ion, it is sterically very easy to form the second bond and close the ring. It is easier for a cupric ion to add one molecule of ethylene diamine

[21] F. Burriel-Marti and F. Pino-Perez, *Anal. Chim. Acta*, **4**, 333 (1950).

[22] G. Spacu, *Z. anal. Chem.*, **64**, 330 (1924); **67**, 27 (1925); **71**, 97, 185, 442 (1927); **74**, 188 (1928); E. A. Ostroumov, *Z. anal. Chem.*, **106**, 170 (1936).

than two molecules of ammonia or methylamine. The effect is shown very clearly by the data of Table I, which lists the pK values (the negative logarithms of the dissociation constants) for the zinc and cupric complexes of ammonia, which cannot chelate, and various polyamines, all of which can form chelate rings. The more chelate rings the molecules can form, the more stable are the resulting complexes.

TABLE I

STABILITY OF METAL-AMINE COMPLEXES; EFFECT OF CHELATION

Amine	Cupric complexes:				Zinc complexes:			
	pK_1	pK_2	pK_3	pK_4	pK_1	pK_2	pK_3	pK_4
NH_3	4.3	3.7	3.0	4.3	2.2	2.3	2.3	2.0
$H_2N \cdot CH_2 \cdot CH_2 \cdot NH_2$	10.7	9.3			5.9	5.0		
$HN(CH_2 \cdot CH_2 \cdot NH_2)_2$	16.0	5.0			8.9	5.5		
$N(CH_2 \cdot CH_2 \cdot NH_2)_3$	18.8				14.6			
$(H_2N \cdot CH_2 \cdot CH_2 \cdot NH_2CH_2)_2$	20.5				11.8			
$[(H_2N \cdot CH_2 \cdot CH_2)_2N \cdot CH_2]_2$	22.4				16.2			

Notes: 1. Data according to Schwarzenbach, *Angew. Chem.*, **62**, 218 (1950); *Helv. Chim. Acta*, **33**, 947, 963, 974, 985, 995 (1950) and subsequent papers. See also A. R. Burkin, *Quart. Rev. Chem. Soc.*, **5**, 1 (1951).

2. K_1, K_2, etc. have been corrected for statistical effects but otherwise have the same meaning as on page 112. Polyamine data are for 20°C and ionic strength 0.1.

Polyhydroxy compounds. Hydroxyl groups carry unshared electron pairs, and are thus able to coordinate with metal ions. Polyhydric alcohols, such as mannitol, glycerol, and glucose, are capable of chelation and form complexes with ferric, chromic, and aluminum ions, and, to a lesser extent, with divalent ions also. They are used to hold tripositive ions in solution at pH 7. The α-hydroxyacids, such as citric and tartaric, are even better for this purpose. Thus in determining nickel in steel with dimethylglyoxime, the iron is kept from precipitating in ammoniacal solution by adding tartaric acid. Tartaric acid also keeps aluminum in solution at pH 7.5, while beryllium is precipitated as its hydrous oxide (however, a better way of accomplishing this separation is with 8-hydroxyquinoline; see Appendix II). The complexes with tripositive metals are particularly stable, but certain dipositive metals form important complexes too. "Fehling's solution" is a cupric salt solution which must be strongly alkaline to be able to oxidize sugars; addition of tartrate prevents cupric hydroxide from precipitating.

The stability of complexes of strontium with citrate and tartrate has been studied by ion exchange.[23]   Calcium and other divalent ions form similar complexes.   Whereas the triply charged citrate ion $C_6H_5O_7^=$ is a fairly strong base and therefore extensively hydrolyzed in water, the complex $CaC_6H_5O_7^-$ is an extremely weak base; hence citric acid can be titrated as a tribasic acid in presence of calcium.

A complexing action of a different kind is that between boric acid and mannitol, glycerol, and other polyhydroxy compounds.   Here an addition takes place to form an acid which is as strong as acetic, and can be titrated to a sharp end point:

$$\left[\begin{matrix} HC-O \\ HC-O \end{matrix} \!\!>\!\! B \!\!<\!\! \begin{matrix} OH \\ OH \end{matrix} \right]^- H^+$$

Sulfosalicylic acid. This compound warrants special mention as an aid to separating iron, aluminum, and titanium.   It forms soluble chelated complexes such as

The least stable of these is the ferric complex; on passing hydrogen sulfide into a neutral solution, FeS precipitates.   If the solution is now boiled, the titanium complex hydrolyzes and hydrous TiO_2 is deposited.   The aluminum complex, which is the most stable, is unaffected.[24]

The ferric sulfosalicylate complex is an intense violet color and is used as a colorimetric reagent for fluoride.[4]

The "complexones." The name "complexones" was proposed

[23] J. Schubert and J. W. Richter, *J. Phys. Colloid Chem.*, **52**, 350 (1948).
[24] L. Moser, *Monatshefte*, **53/54**, 44 (1929).

by Schwarzenbach[25] for a group of compounds containing carboxylic groups and tertiary amino nitrogen atoms, which are distinguished by forming interlocking chelate rings with metal ions.[26] The simplest of these is nitrilotriacetic acid, $N(CH_2COOH)_3$, which forms complexes such as:

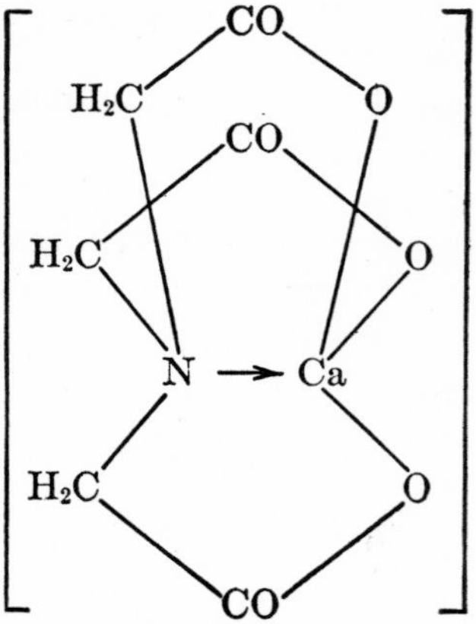

Other "complexones" are shown at the top of page 123, of which the first, ethylenediamine tetraacetic acid, is by far the most important. It is understood that the molecules are probably dipolar ions, with a proton transferred from an acid group to the nitrogen.

The complexes with divalent ions are, in general, the most stable. The "normal" complexes derived from an acid H_3X are MX^-; those derived from an acid H_4Y are $MY^=$. Trivalent ions with H_4Y give complexes such as $AlY(OH)^=$, while univalent ions give complexes such as $LiY^≡$. The latter are much less stable than the divalent metal complexes. Lithium forms the most stable complex of the alkali metal ions, which is what one would expect from the covalency rules.

The stability of the complexes is different for different metals, but with a given metal ion, such as Ca^{++}, and different "complexones," there is a linear relation between pK for the acid $≡NH^+$ cation of

[25] G. Schwarzenbach and H. Ackermann, *Helv. Chim. Acta*, **30**, 1798 (1947); **31**, 1029 (1948); **32**, 1682 (1949); G. Schwarzenbach and W. Biedermann, *Helv. Chim. Acta*, **31**, 331, 459 (1948).

[26] These complexing agents are made in this country by the Bersworth Chemical Company and sold under the trade name "Versene."

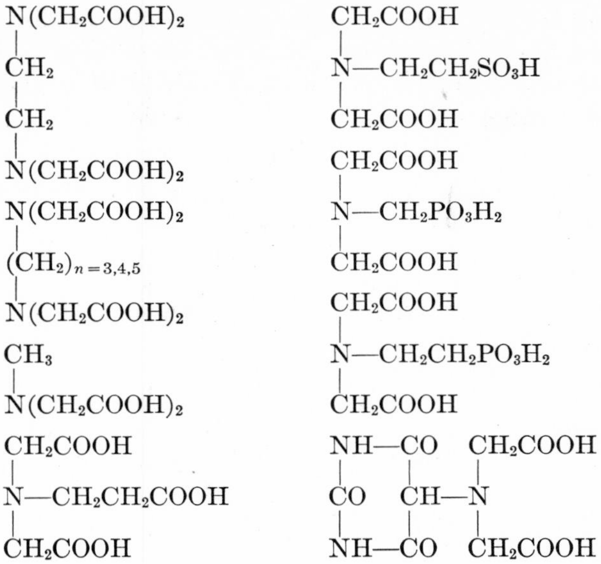

$$N(CH_2COOH)_2$$
$$|$$
$$CH_2$$
$$|$$
$$CH_2$$
$$|$$
$$N(CH_2COOH)_2$$

$$N(CH_2COOH)_2$$
$$|$$
$$(CH_2)_{n=3,4,5}$$
$$|$$
$$N(CH_2COOH)_2$$

$$CH_3$$
$$|$$
$$N(CH_2COOH)_2$$

$$CH_2COOH$$
$$|$$
$$N—CH_2CH_2COOH$$
$$|$$
$$CH_2COOH$$

$$CH_2COOH$$
$$|$$
$$N—CH_2CH_2SO_3H$$
$$|$$
$$CH_2COOH$$

$$CH_2COOH$$
$$|$$
$$N—CH_2PO_3H_2$$
$$|$$
$$CH_2COOH$$

$$CH_2COOH$$
$$|$$
$$N—CH_2CH_2PO_3H_2$$
$$|$$
$$CH_2COOH$$

$$NH—CO \quad CH_2COOH$$
$$| \qquad | \qquad |$$
$$CO \quad CH—N$$
$$| \qquad | \qquad |$$
$$NH—CO \quad CH_2COOH$$

the "complexone" acid and the logarithm of the association constant,[27] $[CaX^-]/[Ca^{++}][X^=]$. In other words, the ability of the tertiary nitrogen to bind a proton parallels its ability to coordinate with a metal ion. Calvin found the same kind of relationship between the association constants of various cupric β-diketones and the ionization constants of the diketones as acids.[28]

Complexes MHY^- exist, but are considerably more dissociated, i.e., are stronger acids, than H_3Y^-. This makes it possible to titrate metal ions with "complexones," using acid-base indicators. This is the most important practical application of these compounds in analysis and is discussed in detail in Chapter 19.

The differences in stability of the different complexes are useful in analytical separations. In the rare earth series, the complexes with nitrilotriacetic acid, $[M^{III}(N(CH_2COO)_3)_2]^=$, increase in stability with increasing atomic weight of M. As a basic solution of the complex is acidified, undissociated nitrilotriacetic acid is formed and free

[27] G. Schwarzenbach, H. Ackermann, and P. Ruckstuhl, *Helv. Chim. Acta,* **32,** 1175 (1949).
[28] M. Calvin and K. W. Wilson, *J. Am. Chem. Soc.,* **67,** 2003 (1945).

metal ions are liberated. In presence of oxalate, these precipitate as the insoluble oxalates, La first, Lu last.[29] To take another example, 8-hydroxyquinoline normally precipitates many metals from acetic acid-ammonium acetate solutions, but if ethylene diamine tetraacetic acid is added, all divalent and trivalent metals are held in solution and only titanium, vanadium, molybdenum, tungsten, and uranium are precipitated.[30] The same reagent prevents iron, cobalt, nickel, manganese, and zinc from interfering in the colorimetric determination of copper with diphenyldithiocarbazone,[31] and by combining more firmly with tripositive cobalt than with dipositive cobalt, it lowers the oxidation-reduction potential to a point where dipositive cobalt can be titrated with potassium dichromate.[32] Furthermore, the complexes formed with tripositive cobalt and other transition metal ions are strongly colored and can serve for colorimetric determinations.[31]

The Heteropoly Acids

This class of complex compounds is of great interest in gravimetric, colorimetric, and volumetric analysis. The number of known heteropoly acids is extremely great, and recent reviews show how much of their chemistry, both descriptive and structural, is still unknown.[33]

Heteropoly acids are oxy acids containing several atoms of one element (other than oxygen) coordinated around a central atom of another element. The central atom may be B, Si, Ge, P, As, Te, or I; the coordinating atoms are usually Mo or W, but may include V. One of the best known heteropoly acids is phosphomolybdic acid, $H_3P(Mo_3O_{10})_4 \cdot 29H_2O$, whose ammonium salt is yellow and insoluble and is used to precipitate phosphorus in dilute nitric acid solution

[29] G. Beck and A. Gasser, *Anal. Chim. Acta*, **3**, 41 (1949).

[30] R. Pribil and M. Malat, *Collection Czechoslov. Chem. Commun.*, **15**, 120 (1950).

[31] V. Sedivec and V. Vasak, *Collection Czechoslov. Chem. Commun.*, **15**, 260 (1950).

[32] R. Pribil and L. Svestka, *Collection Czechoslov. Chem. Commun.*, **15**, 31 (1950).

[33] W. Hückel, *Anorganische Strukturchemie*, Stuttgart, F. Enke, 1948. English translation by L. H. Long, *Structural Chemistry of Inorganic Compounds*, Amsterdam and New York, Elsevier, 1950.

and so separate it from calcium, iron, and other metals occurring in phosphate rock. This belongs to the series of 12-heteropoly acids, or *saturated* acids, having 12 coordinating metal atoms around one central atom. The chief members of this series are the following (water of crystallization is omitted in these formulas).

$$H_5[B(Mo_3O_{10})_4] \qquad H_5[B(W_3O_{10})_4]$$
$$H_4[Si(Mo_3O_{10})_4] \qquad H_4[Si(W_3O_{10})_4]$$
$$H_3[P(Mo_3O_{10})_4] \qquad H_3[P(W_3O_{10})_4]$$

Other series of heteropoly acids exist, of which the following are representative examples.

$$H_3[PO(Mo_3O_{10})_3] \qquad H_6[Te(MoO_4)_6]$$
$$H_5[I(MoO_4)_6]$$

Yet other acids exist in which the number of replaceable hydrogen atoms is uncertain, so we can do no more than write empirical formulas such as $P_2O_5 \cdot 20MoO_3 \cdot xH_2O$, $P_2O_5 \cdot 34MoO_3 \cdot yH_2O$, and $P_2O_5 \cdot 42MoO_3 \cdot zH_2O$. The last two examples are probably binuclear; i.e., they contain two phosphorus atoms linked by a chain of molybdic oxide groups. Again, mixed acids are known which contain both Mo and W, or one of these together with V.

The only heteropoly acids whose structure is known with any certainty are the six "12-heteropoly acids" listed first. Crystals of the solid acids and their salts have been investigated by x-ray diffraction.[34] A typical structure is shown in Figure 1. The central phosphorus atom is linked tetrahedrally to four O atoms, as in the orthophosphate ion. Each of these O atoms is also tetrahedrally coordinated; one valence bond goes to the central P atom, the other three to atoms of Mo. The Mo atoms, however, have a coordination number of 6, and are each surrounded by six O atoms in an octahedral arrangement. Four of these O atoms are shared with other Mo atoms, two on one side, two on the other side of the octahedron. The result is that there are three O atoms to every Mo, in addition to the four O atoms around the central P. The crystals of these acids have a large number of molecules of water of hydration, some of which have additional protons; that is, they are hydronium ions.

[34] J. W. Illingworth and J. F. Keggin, *J. Chem. Soc.*, 1935, 575; A. J. Bradley and J. W. Illingworth, *Proc. Roy. Soc.*, **A 157,** 113 (1936).

The heteropoly salt best known in analytical chemistry is the ammonium phosphomolybdate, or molybdiphosphate, whose formula is $(NH_4)_3[P(Mo_3O_{10})_4]\cdot 2HNO_3\cdot H_2O$. Dried at 130°–150°C, this becomes $(NH_4)_3[P(Mo_3O_{10})_4]$. This is *not* recommended as a weighing form for phosphorus in accurate work, because its composition is not reproducible. This is not surprising when we consider how many other ammonium phosphomolybdates, with different ratios of P to

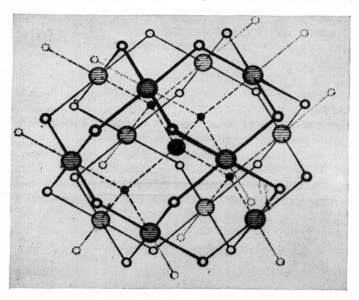

Fig. 7-1.   Structure of the phosphotungstate ion, $(PW_{12}O_{40})^{=}$. The phosphomolybdate ion is probably similar.

From A. F. Wells, *Structural Inorganic Chemistry*, by kind permission of the Clarendon Press, Oxford.

Mo, might be formed by a slight change in conditions, to say nothing of the probability of precipitating molybdic acid if the temperature rises too high during the precipitation. The value of this precipitate in phosphate rock analysis lies in the fact that we can be sure it contains all the phosphorus that was in the sample, and none of the interfering elements such as iron and calcium. However, in rapid work of moderate accuracy, the phosphorus may be weighed in this form, or even estimated from the volume of precipitate after centrifugation.

A more common practice is to dissolve the precipitate in an excess of standard base and back-titrate with standard hydrochloric acid, using phenolphthalein indicator. At the end point we have the ions $HPO_4^=$ and $MoO_4^=$. Or, the precipitate may be reduced with zinc and sulfuric acid to $Mo(III)$ and the solution titrated with permanganate. These methods are open to the same objection as the gravimetric method, namely, that the composition of the precipitate is indefinite.

In general, large anions seem to form sparingly soluble salts with large cations. This is presumably due to favorable packing in a solid crystal lattice. The heteropoly acids form sparingly soluble salts with various organic bases, among which is 8-hydroxyquinoline. The precipitation of phosphorus and silicon as the 8-hydroxyquinoline salts of phosphomolybdic and silicomolybdic acid is a precise, reliable, and sensitive method of determining these elements.[35] The precipitates may be dried at $160°–200°C$, and weighed as $(C_9H_8ON)_4$ $[Si(Mo_3O_{10})_4] \cdot 2H_2O$ or $(C_9H_8ON)_3[P(Mo_3O_{10})_4] \cdot 5 \cdot 5H_2O$ or they may be ignited to $800°C$ and weighed as $SiO_2 \cdot 12MoO_3$ or $P_2O_5 \cdot 24MoO_3$.[36]

The heteropoly acids themselves are very soluble in water, and so are most of their salts. The majority of the analytical methods which are based upon them are therefore not gravimetric, but rather colorimetric. The colorimetric methods are of two kinds: (a) those in which the color intensity of the heteropoly acid itself is measured; (b) those in which the heteropoly acid is reduced to a deep blue colloidal dispersion, and the intensity of this blue color then measured.

Phosphomolybdic and silicomolybdic acid are yellow in color. Though the color intensity may not seem great to the eye, the light absorption in the blue and violet is actually very great. Low concentrations of dissolved silicate may be conveniently determined by adding an excess of ammonium molybdate solution followed by enough sulfuric acid to make the solution 1–2 N in acid. The yellow color develops in a few seconds, and, using a photoelectric colorimeter with a 430 mμ filter, silicate concentrations as low as 3 parts per million (as SiO_2) can be measured. At this high acidity, phosphomolybdic acid dissociates and does not interfere, but at lower acidities, P, As, and Ge can be determined in a similar manner. An-

[35] J. A. Brabson, H. C. Mattraw, G. E. Maxwell, A. Darrow, and M. F. Needham, *Anal. Chem.*, **20**, 504 (1948).
[36] T. Dupuis and C. Duval, *Anal. Chim. Acta*, **4**, 50 (1950).

other element which can be determined by this "direct" method is vanadium; the reagent in this case is phosphotungstic acid, which is colorless; it combines with vanadium in presence of 0.5 N nitric or perchloric acid and 0.5 M phosphoric acid to form an orange-yellow phosphovanadotungstic acid of unknown, but reproducible, composition.[37] The method is good down to 10 parts of vanadium per million.

By a modification of this method, tungsten may be determined,[38] but in general, molybdenum and tungsten have not been determined through their heteropoly acids. The reason is that a large excess of molybdic or tungstic acid is usually needed to form the saturated 12-heteropoly acids, which are the only ones of dependable composition.

On reduction in acid solution, molybdic and tungstic acids form deep blue colloidal solutions. The constitution of the blue compound is not certain, and indeed is not uniform, for the absorption spectrum of the "blue" depends on the conditions of reduction.[39] The molybdenum and tungsten appear to be in the $+5$ oxidation state. Under controlled conditions, the blue colors are reproducible and therefore applicable to analysis. The important point is that the heteropoly acids are more easily reducible than molybdic or tungstic acids themselves, and with suitable reagents the heteropoly acids are reduced under circumstances where molybdic and tungstic acids are not reduced at all. It is suggested that the blue compounds thus formed are heteropoly compounds themselves, such as $H_3PO_4 \cdot 12Mo_2O_5$.

The color of these compounds is intense, so by reduction to a "blue," increased sensitivity is obtained. Phosphorus, arsenic, and silicon can be determined in concentrations well below 1 part per million. The reducing agents used include benzidine, cuprous oxide, ferrous sulfate, stannous chloride. Ferrous sulfate reduces silicomolybdic acid in a weakly acid solution, but not phosphomolybdic.[40]

"Heteropoly blue" formation can be used to determine reducing agents as well as elements forming heteropoly acids. A good exam-

[37] E. R. Wright and M. G. Mellon, *Ind. Eng. Chem., Anal. Ed.*, **9**, 251 (1937).
[38] G. J. Lennard, *Analyst*, **74**, 253 (1949).
[39] J. T. Woods and M. G. Mellon, *Ind. Eng. Chem., Anal. Ed.*, **13**, 760 (1941).
[40] Y. I. Usatenko and Y. Y. Orlova, *Zavodskaya Lab.*, **15**, 1365 (1949).

ple of such a procedure is that of Folin and Wu for blood sugar.   The blood sample is made to reduce Fehling's solution to cuprous oxide, and the precipitated cuprous oxide is then shaken up with a solution of phosphomolybdic acid or, better, a mixed reagent containing $H_3P(Mo_3O_{10})_3(W_3O_{10})$; the intensity of the blue color is a measure of the sugar in the sample.[41]   Other reducing substances have been determined in a similar way.   A simple field test for carbon monoxide is based on the reduction of silicomolybdic acid by CO.[42]

These examples will show the versatility of the heteropoly acids in analytical chemistry.   The great variety of these acids, however, means that interferences are common, that great accuracy is not obtainable, and that conditions must be carefully standardized to get good precision.

Isopoly Acids

The same metals which enter into the coordination sphere of heteropoly acids—molybdenum, tungsten, and vanadium—form complex acids by themselves without the need for a central "hetero-" atom.   Simple acids and salts do exist, but the common ammonium molybdate is not $(NH_4)_2MoO_4$; it is a salt $(NH_4)_6Mo_7O_{24} \cdot 4H_2O$. Other molybdates include $(NH_4)_{10}Mo_{12}O_{41} \cdot 7H_2O$, $Na_2Mo_3O_{10} \cdot 7H_2O$, $Na_2Mo_4O_{13} \cdot 8H_2O$, $Na_2Mo_8O_{25} \cdot 17H_2O$.   These salts give distinctive stepwise pH titration curves when titrated with strong acids.   In view of the complexity of these compounds, special care is needed in interpreting oxidation-reduction data for $+6$ molybdenum and tungsten and $+5$ vanadium.

PROBLEMS

1. Write a comprehensive essay on the analytical chemistry of (a) the fluoride ion, (b) the phosphate ion.

2. In what ways are the dissociation constants of complex ions determined experimentally?

[41] O. Folin and H. Wu, *J. Biol. Chem.*, **38**, 81 (1919)· **41**, 367 (1920); **51**, 209 (1922); O. Folin, *J. Biol. Chem.*, **82**, 83 (1929).
[42] M. Shepherd, *Anal. Chem.*, **19**, 77 (1947).

3. Write a comprehensive account of the uses of 1,10-phenanthroline and its derivatives in analytical chemistry (see also Chapter 17).

4. Difficulties arise in determining chloride in presence of mercuric salts because of the very weak ionization of $HgCl_2$ What "demasking" reactions can be used to free the chloride ions? How would the determination of chloride be carried out?

5. The stereochemistry of 4-covalent copper and zinc has a bearing on the formation of chelate rings with polyamines. One has planar bonds, the other tetrahedral; which is which? Show how the stability of polyamine complexes reflects the stereochemistry of the metallic atom, given that pK_1 for the cupric complex of 1, 2, 3- triaminopropane = 11.1, pK_2 = 9.0. (See Table I and the references quoted there.)

6. Write a general account of stepwise association in metallic complexes, using the references quoted in this chapter.

8

Ion exchange methods in analytical chemistry

Ion exchange, like distillation and solvent extraction, is now one of the recognized "unit processes" of chemical engineering and a tried and valuable tool in chemical separations. Naturally it has been applied to the separation processes of quantitative analysis. Enough applications of this kind have been studied to show that the technique has great possibilities; however, it also has certain inherent drawbacks, and while its place in research is firmly established, it is perhaps too soon to know its rightful place in routine quantitative analysis.

General Principles

By "ion exchange" we mean the exchange of ions of like sign between a solution and a solid insoluble body in contact with it. For such an exchange to be possible, the solid must contain ions of its own, and for the exchange to proceed fast enough and far enough to be of practical use, the solid (called the "ion exchanger") must have an open, permeable molecular structure, so that ions and solvent molecules can move freely in and out. Many substances, both natural and artificial, have ion exchanging properties, some of the most important to our lives being the clays and humic acids of soil. In analytical work, however, we are primarily interested in the synthetic organic ion exchangers. These have a high capacity for holding ions and, which is very important, they are not broken down by acids or alkalies as are the siliceous materials. They have a relatively simple composition. Two typical ion exchanging structures are shown in Figure 1. Figure 1 (a) shows a material derived from polystyrene. It is a synthetic resin made by copolymerizing styrene with divinylbenzene and then sulfonating the product.[1]

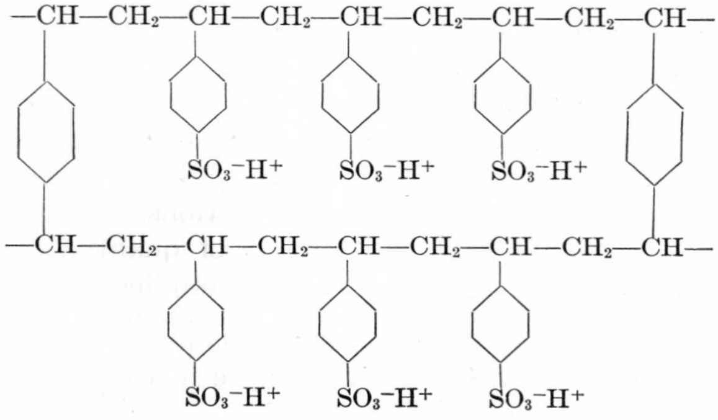

(a)

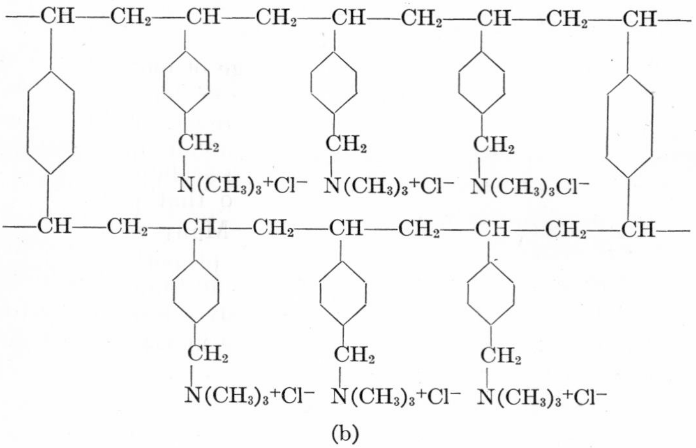

(b)

Fig. 8-1.   Ion exchanger formulas.   (a), a cation exchanger; (b), an anion exchanger.

[1] N. E. Topp and K. W. Pepper, *J. Chem. Soc.*, 1949, p. 3299.

The molecular weight is extremely high and the material is therefore quite insoluble. The solid granules swell when placed in water, but the swelling is limited by the cross linking; the divinylbenzene units "weld" the polystyrene chains together and prevent the resin from swelling indefinitely and dispersing. The resulting structure is somewhat like a sponge or a three-dimensional fishing net, with negatively charged sulfonate ions attached firmly to the framework. Balancing these fixed negative charges are positively charged hydrogen ions. The interior of the resin granule is very like a concentrated solution of benzene sulfonic acid—8 molar or so—except that the sulfonate ions are not free to move. The hydrogen ions are free to move, but they cannot leave the resin particle unless other positive ions come in to take their place and maintain electrical neutrality. When the resin particle is placed in a salt solution an exchange of cations takes place between it and the solution, and an equilibrium is reached in which the different kinds of positive ions present are distributed between the exchanger and the solution. If the exchanger originally contains hydrogen ions, for example, and the solution calcium ions, the reaction is represented thus:

$$2H^+ \cdot R^- + Ca^{++} \rightleftharpoons Ca^{++} \cdot (R^-)_2 + 2H^+,$$

where R^- means one negatively charged unit of the resin structure.

The two kinds of ions are not distributed at random. Certain ions are attracted more strongly to the exchanger than others, and this fact is used in certain analytical separations. In general an ion of a given charge is held more strongly by an exchanger, the smaller its size in the solvated state.[2] Thus K^+ is bound more strongly than Li^+, for Li^+ is more hydrated than K^+ and has a greater hydrated radius, which accounts for its smaller specific conductance in solution; Li^+, however, is more strongly bound than large organic cations such as $N(C_2H_5)_4^+$.[3] This differentiation may be due to the effect of the ions on the swelling of the exchanger granules; larger ions distend the exchanger more, which makes it harder for them to enter. In other words, the free energy of the ion exchange process includes a term for the work done in expanding the resin.[3] The differentiation

[2] H. Jenny, *Kolloid-Beihefte*, **23**, 428 (1927); F. C. Nachod and W. Wood, *J. Am. Chem. Soc.*, **66**, 1380 (1944).

[3] H. P. Gregor, *J. Am. Chem. Soc.*, **73**, 642 (1951); Gregor *et al.*, *J. Colloid Sci.*, **6**, 20 (1951).

between different ions is greater, the greater the degree of cross linking of the resin polymer, i.e., the greater the elastic modulus of the
resin; however, increasing the cross linking slows down the rate at
which ions can pass in and out.

To a first approximation the distribution of two ions between an
exchanger and a solution obeys the law of mass action.[4]   There are
deviations, however; particularly, if the radii of the two hydrated
ions are very different.   The ratio of ion concentrations in the solution changes faster than their ratio in the exchanger.   This effect is
increased by increased cross linking.[3,5]

If the law of mass action is applied to the exchange of two ions of
different charges, such as the calcium ion-hydrogen ion exchange
represented above, one sees immediately that the more dilute the
solution, the more the equilibrium is displaced to the right; that is,
the more calcium ions enter the exchanger.   One cannot, therefore,
generalize and say that divalent ions are more strongly held by an
exchanger than univalent, or vice versa, without specifying the concentration.   In general, with aqueous solutions of 0.1 M concentration and less, divalent ions are more strongly held than univalent,[2]
and trivalent than divalent.   Carboxylic exchangers, such as polymerized acrylic acid, have a specially high affinity for divalent ions.[6]

Column operation. Though ion exchange is reversible, one may
drive the exchange to completion in either direction by passing the
solution through a bed or column of the exchanger (see Figure 2).
Suppose we want to replace the calcium ions in a solution by hydrogen ions.   We pass the solution through a column of an exchanger
containing only hydrogen ions as the replaceable cations.   As the
solution moves down the column, it continually meets fresh hydrogen-
saturated exchanger and the reaction

$$2H^+ \cdot R^- + Ca^{++} \rightleftharpoons Ca^{++} \cdot (R^-)_2 + 2H^+$$

is displaced to the right.   Suppose the first centimeter of the bed
removes half the calcium ions in a certain volume of the solution, the
second centimeter half of those which are left, and so on; it will not
be long before the calcium remaining in the solution is analytically
undetectable.

Eventually, of course, the exchanger column gets so loaded with

[4] G. E. Boyd, J. Schubert, and A. W. Adamson, *J. Am. Chem. Soc.*, **69**, 2818
(1948).
[5] E. Glueckauf, *Endeavour*, **10**, 40 (1951).
[6] R. Kunin and R. E. Barry, *Ind. Eng. Chem.*, **41**, 1269 (1949).

calcium ions that these "break through," and appear in the solution flowing out of the bottom. Then the column may be *regenerated;* that is, restored to its original hydrogen-saturated condition, by passing an excess of hydrochloric or sulfuric acid through it and then rinsing. The cycle of exhaustion and regeneration can be repeated indefinitely, and any cation may be replaced quantitatively by any other cation by appropriate choice of regenerant solution. The same thing may be done with anions, using an anion exchanger such as that represented in Figure 1(b); however, if one wishes to replace the anion of a neutral salt by the hydroxyl ion, one must choose one of the newer quaternary ammonium hydroxide type anion exchangers.

If a mixture of two or more different cations (or anions) is poured into an exchanger bed, and if the amounts of these ions are small compared with the total capacity of the bed for ions, then one may be able to recover the absorbed ions separately and consecutively by using a suitable eluting (or regenerating) solution. If cation A is more strongly held by the exchanger than cation B, all the B present will flow out of the bottom of the bed in the "regeneration" step before any of A comes out, provided the bed is long enough and provided other conditions are right. This separation technique is sometimes called "ion exchange chromatography." Its most spectacular success has been the separation of the rare earth elements; individual rare earths have been obtained in as high as 99.9% purity in 100-gram quantities, and in much higher purity in quantities of 1 gram or less.[7] In this case, the differences in binding by the ion exchanger were reinforced by differences in the stability of soluble complexes; the regenerant was a citrate solution, carefully buffered at a pH between 3 and 4 to give the maximum differences in complex ion formation between the rare earth and the citrate ion. The efficiency of separations in "ion exchange chromatography" is favored by small particle size, high temperature, and slow flow rate (all of which allow the closest approach to equilibrium in the exchange process), and by using a long column. There are, of course, practical limits to the extent to which these factors can be varied. Thus, particle sizes of 325 mesh and finer have been used in research, but they permit only very slow rates of flow. Where true equilibrium is maintained during the passage of an ion down the column, the graph of concentration of the eluted ion against the volume of solution passed is an exact Gauss error curve (Figure 3).

[7] B. H. Ketelle and G. E. Boyd, *J. Am. Chem. Soc.*, **69,** 2800 (1947).

Practical details. In setting up and operating an ion exchange column, there are a number of details which must be borne in mind. First, organic ion exchangers swell considerably in water. They must therefore be stirred up with water in an open beaker and given

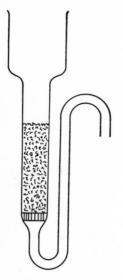

a few minutes to complete their swelling, before they are poured into the column. Second, to remove entrained air bubbles and fine particles and to ensure an even distribution of granules, the exchanger bed must be "backwashed" before use; that is, a stream of water is run up through the bed from the bottom, at a sufficient rate to loosen and suspend the exchanger granules. The enlarged upper portion of the exchanger tube shown in Figure 2 will hold the exchanger during backwashing. Third, the bed should not be allowed to run dry during use for, when flow is resumed, the solution will not pass evenly over all the resin granules, but will flow in irregular channels. The gooseneck outlet to the tube in Figure 2, whose opening is below the top of the exchanger bed, will prevent the bed from running dry. Fourth, exchangers received new from the manufacturer are likely to contain unwanted ionic impurities as well as water-soluble, incompletely polymerized material. These must be washed out before use. This is best done by passing $2 N$ hydrochloric acid and $2 N$ sodium hydroxide alternately, with water rinses in between, and then passing water until the effluent is neutral and salt-free. "Analytical grade" ion exchangers are available which have undergone this preliminary washing.

Fig. 8-2. Ion-exchanging column. The "goose-neck" outlet ensures that the bed will not drain dry; the broadened upper portion facilitates backwashing.

Ion exchangers are not all the same; they differ considerably in properties, and hence in their analytical uses. The characteristics of some representative commercial ion exchangers are listed in Table I.

TABLE I

COMMERCIAL ION EXCHANGERS

Type and name	Capacity, m. eq./g.

CATION EXCHANGERS:

Strong acid;
  phenolic methylene sulfonic:

Amberlite IR-100	1.75
Dowex 30	4.00
Duolite C-3	3.25
Wolfatit K	2.50
Zeo-Rex	2.70

Strong acid;
  nuclear sulfonic:

Amberlite IR-120	4.20
Dowex 50	4.25
Wolfatit KS	2.45
Permutit Q	4.10

Medium acid;
  sulfonated coal:

Zeo-Karb	3 (pH 7)

Weak acid;
  carboxylic:

Amberlite IRC-50	10.0
Permutit 216	5.3
Wolfatit C	7.0

Aluminosilicate gel:

Decalso	3

ANION EXCHANGERS:

Strong base;
  quaternary amine:

Amberlite IRA-400	2.3
Dowex 1	2.4
Permutit S	2.4

Weak base;
  primary, secondary and tertiary amine:

Amberlite IR-4B	10.0
Duolite A-2	7.0
De-Acidite 515	9.3

Note: Taken in part from R. Kunin and R. J. Myers, *Ion Exchange Resins,* New York, Wiley, 1950, p. 58.

Applications in Analytical Chemistry

Production of a distilled water substitute. One of the most important industrial applications of ion exchange today is the removal of electrolytes from water, the so-called "deionizing" or "demineralizing" of water. If the water contained only ionic impurities in the first place, as is the case with most natural and city water supplies, the product is equivalent to distilled water, and may indeed be much better; furthermore, the process is considerably cheaper than distillation.

In "deionizing," the water is first passed through a bed of a cation exchanger saturated with hydrogen ions. All dissolved salts are thus converted to their corresponding acids. The water is next passed through an anion exchanger saturated with hydroxyl ions. The anions of the acids are replaced by hydroxyl ions, which combine with the hydrogen ions to form water. The cation exchanger is regenerated by dilute (2 N) sulfuric acid, the anion exchanger by 2 N sodium hydroxide.

This gives complete removal of salts *provided* the anion exchanger is a strong enough base to combine with very weak acids, such as carbonic, silicic, and hydrogen sulfide. The quaternary base exchangers are strong enough to combine with these, but they are also rather expensive. In many installations, the cheaper weak base anion exchangers are used; the carbonic acid which then remains in the water may be removed by aeration, while the silicic acid (actually colloidal silica) remains. In producing water for analytical purposes, of course, a strong base anion exchanger should be used if possible.

A recent innovation is the mixed bed or "Monobed" technique of deionization. The two ion exchangers, cation and anion, are mixed together in the same column. This technique gives a water of exceptionally high purity—its conductivity is less than that of triply distilled water, its salt content is less than 1 part in 10,000,000—and the capacity of the exchangers is used very efficiently. When the exchangers are exhausted, they are separated by passing water upflow. The anion exchanger is chosen to be less dense than the cation exchanger, so it floats to the top.   The exchange resins are regenerated separately, rinsed, and then mixed by jets of air.[8]   Small laboratory units are also available in which the mixed resins, once exhausted, are discarded and replaced by a refill cartridge.   These are very convenient, but expensive in the long run.

Removal of unwanted electrolytes.   In certain types of analysis for organic constituents, the presence of any kind of electrolyte is undesirable.   Thus pectin may be determined in fruit extracts by electrodeposition from a neutral solution on a platinum anode; the conductivity of the solution is very low, and a high potential must be employed.   Electrolytes which would carry the current in preference to the pectin are clearly unwanted.   They are removed by a two-stage ion exchange process, just as in the deionization of water.[9]   Pectin is a weak acid of high molecular weight, and its electrolysis is like the electrophoresis of a colloid.   Similar methods might be used in analyzing carboxymethylcellulose and rubber latex, or in purifying reagents for microchemical analysis.   Gelatin has been freed from traces of sulfate in this way.

Preparation of carbonate-free base.   Solutions of sodium and potassium hydroxide can be freed from carbonate by passing them through a bed of strong base anion exchange resin.   This is possible because carbonate ions are absorbed preferentially to hydroxyl ions from 0.1 N solutions by these exchangers.   In the recommended procedure, somewhat over a liter of 0.1 N alkali is passed through a column containing 35 ml. of the resin Amberlite IRA-400, originally saturated with chloride.   When the chloride ions are all displaced and no longer appear in the effluent, the solution is collected in the stock bottle; one liter of 0.1 N solution can be prepared in this way.[10]   The method is less tedious than the usual one in which a 50% sodium hydroxide solution is prepared, filtered, or centrifuged free from the insoluble carbonate, then dissolved in boiled distilled water; moreover, it can be applied to potassium hydroxide, which the method just mentioned cannot, since potassium carbonate is soluble in concentrated potassium hydroxide solution.

[8] *Amberlite Monobed De-ionization*, Philadelphia, Rohm and Haas Company.
[9] K. T. Williams and C. M. Johnson, *Ind. Eng. Chem., Anal. Ed.*, **16**, 23 (1944).
[10] C. W. Davies and G. H. Nancollas, *Nature*, **165**, 238 (1950).

Concentration of traces. An example of this use of ion exchange is the determination of copper in milk.[11] Raw milk contains 0.1 to 0.5 part per million of copper, and it is obviously very difficult to determine this directly. Cranston and Thompson treat the milk with perchloric acid to precipitate proteins, then adjust the pH to 5 and pass the solution through a small bed of a cation exchanger saturated with hydrogen ions; 15 ml. of resin was used for 100 ml. of solution. After passing the treated milk solution, the bed was well washed with water. The resin was then eluted with 40 ml. of 2 N HCl; the filtrate was evaporated to dryness, the residue dissolved in 5 ml. of an ammonia-ammonium chloride solution, and the copper determined polarographically. Besides concentrating the trace metal into a smaller solution volume, this technique removes most of the interfering organic matter.

A similar technique has been proposed for collecting minute amounts of Cu^{++}, Cd^{++}, Ni^{++}, Mn^{++}, and Zn^{++} in the residues from ashing plant materials.[12]

In high dilution, ion exchangers hold divalent heavy metal ions relatively strongly; however, a large excess of other ions will obviously interfere with the absorption. It would be hopeless to try to adsorb traces of metal ions quantitatively from 5 M perchloric acid, for example; the hydrogen ions, which are in great excess, would displace some or all of the metallic ions from the resin. Ion exchange is a competitive process and is not highly selective, and this fact must always be borne in mind in analytical applications. Thus in the work just quoted, 10^{-6} mole of metal ion was quantitatively absorbed by 1 ml. of exchanger in the presence of 0.1 M NH_4Cl, but not in a solution 1 M in NH_4Cl. The electrolyte content of a solution must always be kept to a minimum in this type of work, and, if the exchanger does not happen to be a strong acid (e.g., a carboxylic exchanger or a composite exchanger such as Zeo-Karb), it is especially important to limit the hydrogen ion concentration. We shall meet examples of this in the sections to follow.

Ion exchange has been used to extract vitamins such as thiamin, antibiotics such as streptomycin, and alkaloids such as quinine from dilute extracts containing them.[13] In some cases, the efficiency of

[11] H. A. Cranston and J. B. Thompson, *Ind. Eng. Chem., Anal. Ed.*, **18**, 323 (1946).

[12] J. P. R. Riches, *Nature*, **158**, 96 (1946); *Chemistry and Industry*, 1947, p. 656.

[13] D. S. Herr, *Ind. Eng. Chem.*, **37**, 631 (1945); J. C. Winters and R. Kunin, *Ind. Eng. Chem.*, **41**, 460 (1949).

extraction was nearly quantitative, and the process therefore has potentialities as an analytical method.[14]   We must remember (a) that the substance being extracted must be ionized; this may necessitate suitable pH adjustment; (b) that large ions will not enter the particles of ordinary exchangers, so special exchangers with low cross linking or large superficial area must be used; (c) that the penetration of large ions into an exchanger is slow.

Conversion of salts to acids or bases. One of the simplest analytical applications of ion exchange is to determine the concentration of a dissolved salt by passing it through a hydrogen ion-saturated cation exchanger or a strongly basic hydroxyl ion-saturated anion exchanger, and titrating the acid or base which is liberated. Since strongly basic anion exchangers have been available only recently, most published applications of this kind use cation exchangers.[15,16,17]   This is obviously not a selective process, for it will determine only *total* salt concentrations, but some useful applications have been made.   For example, the lime or soda content of bisulfite cooking liquors in the paper industry has been found by titrating the free acid before and after passage through a hydrogen ion exchanger.[15]   Solutions of pure but deliquescent salts, such as calcium nitrate or sodium perchlorate, could be standardized in this way.   The method is used in a field test to determine the total salt content of natural waters.[18]   Acetyl groups in esters and amides can be determined on the micro scale by heating with excess ethanol and a catalyst, distilling out the ethyl acetate formed, saponifying this with an excess of sodium hydroxide, and passing the resulting solution through a hydrogen ion exchanger of the nuclear sulfonic type.   The remaining sodium hydroxide simply forms water, while the sodium acetate liberates acetic acid quantitatively.   This acid is titrated.[19]

A nuclear sulfonic acid exchanger was specified here, because certain cation exchangers of the phenolic type hold weak acids by nonpolar adsorption.[20]   This effect can be used to analyze a mixture of strong and weak acids, but usually it is a mere nuisance.

[14] A. Jindra, *J. Pharm. Pharmacol*, **1**, 87 (1949).

[15] O. Samuelson, *Svensk Papperstidn.*, **3**, 1 (1945).

[16] O. Samuelson, *Iva*, **17**, 1, 5 (1946); *Chem. Abstracts*, **40**, 5657 (1946).

[17] E. Wiesenberger, *Mikrochemie*, **30**, 176 (1942).

[18] M. Blumer, *Experientia*, **4**, 351 (1948).

[19] Wiesenberger, *Mikrochemie*, **30**, 241 (1942).

[20] K. Erler, *Z. anal. Chem.*, **131**, 106 (1950).

Separation of interfering substances. Ion exchange may be used to separate ions which interfere with one another in analytical determinations. This is particularly easy when the interfering ions have opposite charges; an innocuous ion can then be substituted for the interfering ion. Also, ionic substances can be separated from nonionic interfering substances. Elimination of interfering substances is the most important application of ion exchange to analytical chemistry at present.

The earliest application of this sort was to the determination of ammonia and ammonium ion in urine. Nessler's reagent cannot be applied directly to urine, as certain substances present, particularly creatinine, form a precipitate. One therefore extracts the ammonia from the urine by a cation exchanger, then releases it with base before adding Nessler's reagent. The particular exchanger used (which was almost the only one available when the method was developed), called Lloyd's reagent, is a synthetic sodium aluminosilicate which has been treated with dilute acetic acid to replace some of the sodium ions by hydrogen ions. It is in the form of a fine sand which settles easily. Two grams of exchanger are shaken with 2 ml. urine and 5 ml. water in a 50-ml. graduated flask; more water is then added, the solution is decanted, and the exchanger washed once or twice by decantation. Five ml. of 10% sodium hydroxide are then poured over the exchanger, water and 10 ml. of Nessler's reagent are added, and the solution made up to the mark with water. The color of the clear yellow-brown solution is compared with standards.[21]

A somewhat similar application is the separation of streptomycin from fermentation broth by absorption as a cation on a carboxylic acid resin.[22] The latter is used with sodium as its replaceable cation, for hydrogen would be too hard to replace; moreover, in its hydrogen-saturated form this resin is covalent, swells very little in water,[23] and therefore would react very slowly if indeed the streptomycin could penetrate the resin at all. The streptomycin, once adsorbed, is very easily eluted with 0.2 N hydrochloric acid.

Much study has been made of the separation of cations from interfering anions and vice versa. An example of such interference is that between ferric ions and phosphate ions; one interferes with the

[21] O. Folin and R. D. Bell, *J. Biol. Chem.*, **29**, 329 (1917).
[22] H. M. Doery, E. C. Mason, and D. E. Weiss, *Anal. Chem.*, **22**, 1038 (1950).
[23] A. Katchalsky, *Experientia*, **5**, 319 (1949).

determination of the other.   By ion exchange, the problem may be solved as follows.   A solution of the mutually interfering ions is passed through a cation exchanger saturated with hydrogen ions; the effluent contains the phosphate in the form of phosphoric acid, which is easily determined analytically, while the metallic ions remain in the exchanger.   These may then be eluted with hydrochloric acid and determined separately.

The principle is well illustrated by the methods of Rieman for determining phosphate[24] and arsenate[25] in phosphate rock and insecticides, respectively.   In the classical methods, phosphate is separated from calcium and other metals by the lengthy phosphomolybdate precipitation, while arsenic is distilled out as the volatile trichloride to separate it from copper and iron, which would interfere in the iodine titration which follows.   In the new methods, the materials are brought into solution with a minimum of hydrochloric acid (the arsenic being oxidized to arsenate, if necessary) and the solutions are allowed to flow through a hydrogen ion-saturated exchanger.   Phosphoric acid or arsenic acid emerges in the effluent, along with the small excess of hydrochloric acid which was used.   In the case of phosphate, the phosphoric acid is determined in the combined effluent and washings by titration with standard base, taking the volume needed to pass from the methyl red end point (pH 4.63) to the phenolphthalein end point (pH 8.98) as a measure of the phosphoric acid.   It represents the base needed to convert $H_2PO_4^-$ to $HPO_4^=$, *provided* no carbonic acid is present.   The end points are not sharp (see Chapter 13) and would best be found potentiometrically; for the surest results, the phosphoric acid should be determined gravimetrically.   A single precipitation as $MgNH_4PO_4 \cdot 6H_2O$ will suffice, since no foreign cations are present.

Rieman used a sulfonated phenolic cation exchanger in his phosphate procedure and got very good results with phosphate rock.   The author has tested the procedure with a nuclear sulfonic exchanger and has repeatedly got low results with phosphate rock.   This happens only when the samples contain iron and aluminum, these latter evidently forming basic phosphates or complexes of some sort which remain behind in the exchanger.   Samuelson[26] found the same trou-

[24] K. Helrich and W. Rieman, *Ind. Eng. Chem., Anal. Ed.,* **19,** 651 (1947).
[25] J. T. Odencrantz and W. Rieman, *Anal. Chem.,* **22,** 1066 (1950).
[26] O. Samuelson, *Tek. Tid.,* 1946, No. 23; *Thesis,* Stockholm, 1944.

ble, but was able to avoid the error by rinsing the column with very dilute hydrochloric acid instead of water. Further investigation is needed, but meanwhile this case serves to show that ion exchange procedures are not yet "foolproof" and must be carefully tested before use. The chief merit of ion exchange procedures of this kind seems to be their simplicity and speed rather than their accuracy.[27]

Where metals are to be determined in the presence of interfering anions such as phosphate or oxalate, two courses are open. One is to absorb the metal ions on a cation exchanger in the manner just described, and then elute them with hydrochloric acid. The other is to pass the solution through an anion exchanger saturated with, say, the chloride ion, and determine the metal ions in the effluent. This method dispenses with the quantitative elution step. It has been used to determine sodium ions in phosphate solutions.[28]

In Chapter 3, we discussed the difficulty of determining sulfate accurately in the presence of metallic ions, particularly tripositive iron. Coprecipitation introduces serious errors, and the only hope of getting accurate results seemed to be to make the various errors compensate or cancel one another out.[29] By ion exchange, ferric ions and other cations can be quantitatively replaced by hydrogen ions, which cause no coprecipitation difficulties.[30] Very good accuracy is claimed for sulfate determinations by this method; but there is one source of error which must be watched; most cation exchangers contain sulfonic acid groups, and one must make sure that no sulfuric acid is liberated from the exchanger by hydrolysis. With sulfonated coal, this hydrolysis is appreciable, though small.[31] This possibility of error could be eliminated entirely by using a carboxylic exchanger, but these are slow to react in the acid form.

Complex ions formed between positive and negative ions are often "split" by passage through an ion exchanger. Thus calcium ions are absorbed quantitatively by a cation exchanger from solutions containing tartrate, and cadmium ions from solutions containing chloride

[27] R. Kunin, *Anal. Chem.*, **21**, 87 (1949).

[28] R. Klement and R. Dmytruk, *Z. anal. Chem.*, **128**, 106 (1948); see also R. Klement, *Z. anal. Chem.*, **127**, 2 (1944).

[29] E. Hintz and H. Weber, *Z. anal. Chem.*, **45**, 31 (1906); for a comprehensive discussion, see W. Rieman, J. D. Neuss, and B. Naiman, *Quantitative Analysis: A Theoretical Approach*, 3d ed., New York, McGraw-Hill, 1951, p. 278.

[30] O. Samuelson, *Z. anal. Chem.*, **116**, 328 (1939); also *Svensk Kem. Tid.*, **54**, 124 (1942); *Chem. Abstracts*, **38**, 2896 (1944).

[31] L. D. Frizzell, *Ind. Eng. Chem., Anal. Ed.*, **16**, 615 (1944).

or oxalate.   If the complex ions are sufficiently stable, or if they dissociate sufficiently slowly, they may be absorbed as such or pass on, depending on their charge.   Thus one can roughly determine the proportions of the various complex ions, such as $Cr(SO_4)_2^-$ and $CrSO_4^+$, in chromic sulfate solutions by ion exchange.[32]   Sometimes one can use complex ion formation to prevent absorption of one ion by an exchanger while allowing the absorption of another; thus in the analysis of iron ore, calcium and magnesium ions are held by a cation exchanger while iron, complexed by an excess of tartaric acid, passes on into the effluent.[33]

The examples cited in this section are merely illustrative.   Many different analytical separations of this type have been described, particularly by Samuelson.

Ion exchange chromatography.   In ion exchange chromatography, several kinds of ions of similar charge are absorbed at the top of a column of ion exchanger, then displaced downwards by a suitable eluting agent so that the different species emerge separately, one after the other.   The best conditions for such separations were discussed previously (page 135).

Primarily, this technique has been used for preparative purposes and in special research problems.   The separation and purification of the rare earth elements has already been mentioned; a similar application is the quantitative separation of zirconium and hafnium by anion exchange of their fluoride complexes.[34]   In the biochemical field, a very significant achievement has been the separation of the acids obtained in the hydrolysis of nucleic acids.[35]   Nucleic acids are found combined with proteins in cell nuclei; on mild hydrolysis they yield *nucleotides*, whose molecules consist of a molecule of a purine or pyrimidine base, a molecule of the sugar ribose, and a molecule of phosphoric acid, condensed together.   They are very easily hydrolyzed, which complicates any attempt to separate them. They are amphoteric and in solutions of pH below 3 they form cations, while above pH 3 they form anions.   They can therefore be

[32] K. H. Gustavson, *Svensk Kem. Tid.*, **56,** 14 (1944), **58,** 274 (1946); *Chem. Abstracts*, **39,** 4557 (1945), **41,** 7790 (1947).

[33] Y. I. Ustrenko and O. V. Datsenko, *Zavodskaya Lab.*, **14,** 1323 (1948); *Chem. Abstracts*, **43,** 4176 (1949).

[34] K. A. Kraus and G. E. Moore, *J. Am. Chem. Soc.*, **71,** 3263 (1949); E. H. Huffman and R. C. Lilly, *J. Am. Chem. Soc.*, **71,** 4147 (1949).

[35] W. E. Cohn, *J. Am. Chem. Soc.*, **72,** 1471, 2811 (1950).

separated by cation exchange or anion exchange. Both have been tried, but anion exchange is the more suitable; the differences between their degrees of ionization, and hence of their absorption, are greater, and the tendency to hydrolysis is less. The nucleotides contained in a solution of pH 8, are absorbed at the top of a column of a strong base anion exchanger saturated with chloride ions. They are then driven down the column and eluted, one by one, using very dilute hydrochloric acid or a buffered sodium chloride solution as the eluant. If desired, the eluant solution is changed before each new constituent is displaced from the column. The concentration of nucleotide in the effluent is followed by ultraviolet absorption.

Excellent separations of cytidilic, adenylic, uridylic, and guanylic acids were obtained, with almost no hydrolytic breakdown. A more accurate measure was made of their relative amounts than in any previous work. The accurate quantitative analysis of the nucleotides in nucleic acids has given a new insight into the constitution of these acids.

Anion exchange also separates the *nucleosides*, or the acids containing purine or pyrimidine base plus ribose but no phosphoric acid the bases themselves (thymine, uracil, cytosine, guanine, and adenine) are best separated by cation exchange.

Neutral nonionic compounds may be separated by ion exchange chromatography if they can be converted into derivatives which are ionized. Thus aldehydes and certain ketones are absorbed by an anion exchanger which has previously been saturated with bisulfite ions, because the anions $RCH(OH)SO_3^-$ and $RR'C(OH)SO_3^-$ are formed. Ketones are eluted from the exchanger by water, aldehydes by a carbonate-bicarbonate buffer.[36] Another very good example is the separation of sugars by combining them with boric acid, absorbing their boric acid complexes on a bed of strong base anion exchanger previously saturated with borate ions, and then eluting with a borax solution. Sucrose, fructose, and glucose are eluted successively in that order; they may be determined quantitatively by appropriate color reactions.[37]

An example of ion exchange chromatography applied to routine inorganic analysis is the method of Beukenkamp and Rieman[38] for

[36] G. Gabrielson and O. Samuelson, *Svensk. Kem. Tid.*, **62**, 214 (1950).

[37] J. X. Khym and L. P. Zill, *J. Am. Chem. Soc.*, **73**, 2399 (1951), **74**, 2090 (1952).

[38] J. Beukenkamp and W. Rieman, *Anal. Chem.*, **22**, 582 (1950).

letermining sodium and potassium in mixtures. A column of
nuclear sulfonic acid exchanger of "colloidal" particle size (300 mesh
and smaller) is used; it is saturated with hydrogen ions and contains
30 grams of resin, occupying 220 ml. and holding some 240 milliequivalents of H^+. A solution containing 8 milliequivalents of Na^+
and K^+ combined is poured into the column, which is then eluted
with 0.7 M HCl, at a flow rate of 0.6 ml. per min. per sq. cm. Elution takes about five hours at this slow flow rate. The sodium and
potassium emerge from the column quite separately, as the curves
n Figure 3 show. For a given column, one finds by experiment in

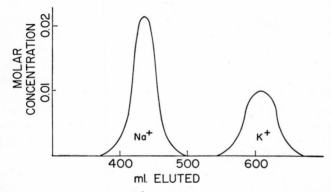

Fig. 8-3. Successive elution of sodium and potassium ions from
an ion exchange column. Beukenkamp and Rieman, *Anal. Chem.*,
22, 582 (1950).

what volume ranges each of these ions emerges. One then collects
he appropriate volume fractions of the effluent. In a sample run
by the authors quoted, the first 370 ml. contained only hydrochloric
acid and was discarded; the next 160 ml. contained all the sodium;
he next 190 ml. all the potassium (the exact volume ranges depend
on the length of the column, particle size of the resin, temperature,
eluant, and flow rate). The solutions are evaporated to dryness and
he alkali chloride weighed. Divalent ions, if present, do not come
out of the exchanger until well after all the potassium has emerged.
Magnesium is the first of the divalent ions to be displaced. The
method has been applied to the determination of the alkali metals
n silicate rocks.

Many other separations of inorganic ions of like charge are possible, though none as yet has been applied to routine analyses.
Examples of anion separations are the separation of halide ions,[39]
of chloride from sulfate,[40] and of ferrocyanide from ferricyanide.[41]

Separation of amino acids.[42] As a final example of the analytical
possibilities of ion exchange, we shall consider the separation of amino
acids from one another.   This is a subject of great practical importance, because alpha amino acids are the building blocks of proteins,
and hydrolysis of proteins yields a mixture of amino acids.   For the
quick semiquantitative analysis of such a mixture, the best method is
probably paper chromatography; for the quantitative determination
of certain individual amino acids, an excellent method is microbio-
logical assay; but for separating a large amount of amino acid mixture
quantitatively into its individual pure components, ion exchange
promises to be the best method.

The α-amino acids all contain the grouping $-CHNH_2 \cdot COOH$, and
are therefore amphoteric in nature.   Some contain additional amino
groups; in these the basic character predominates over the acidic.
In others, additional carboxyl groups are present, which gives them
a predominantly acidic character.   One may therefore classify amino
acids into three groups, as follows:

(a) *Neutral amino acids.   Example:* glycine, CH_2NH_2

$$|$$

$$COOH$$

Other members: alanine, cystine, cysteine, leucine, isoleucine,
valine, proline, hydroxyproline, methionine, serine, threonine,
tyrosine, tryptophane, phenylalanine.

(b) *Basic amino acids.   Example:* lysine.
Other members: arginine, histidine.

(c) *Dicarboxylic amino acids.   Example:* glutamic acid.
Other member: aspartic acid.

Each acid has its characteristic *isoelectric point*, the pH at which
its net charge is zero.   For most neutral amino acids this falls in the

[39] R. W. Atteberry and G. E. Boyd, *J. Am. Chem. Soc.*, **72**, 4805 (1950).
[40] R. J. Myers, J. W. Eastes, and D. Urquhart, *Ind. Eng. Chem.*, **33**, 697 (1941).
[41] J. W. Cobble and A. W. Adamson, *J. Am. Chem. Soc.*, **72**, 2276 (1950).
[42] R. J. Block in *Ion Exchange: Theory and Applications*, New York, Academic
Press, 1949.

range pH 4 to 6.   In this pH range, the dicarboxylic acids have a net negative charge while the basic amino acids are positively charged. By passing over a suitable ion exchanger at this pH, therefore, one group of amino acids is held while the other two groups pass on.   By using an anion and a cation exchanger in succession, it should be possible to absorb first the dicarboxylic amino acids, and second the basic amino acids, while the neutral group remains unabsorbed.

Such a separation scheme has been devised by Winters and Kunin.[43] In an abbreviated form, it is represented in Figure 4.   We note the use of a *weakly* basic and *weakly* acidic exchanger.   If a strong acid

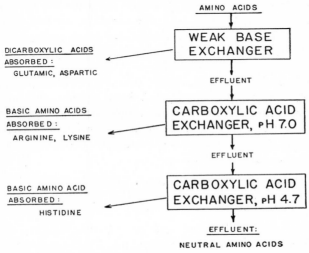

Fig. 8-4.   Scheme for separation of amino acids by ion exchange.

exchanger were used, for example, sulfonated polystyrene in the acid form, or even a sulfonated phenolic exchanger, all the amino acids would be absorbed at once, since all have some basic character. They could, however, be fractionally eluted afterwards.[44]   The weak acid and base exchangers constitute a "solid buffer solution" when partially neutralized, and by using them at the proper pH, one can selectively absorb groups of amino acids according to their isoelectric points.

[43] J. C. Winters and R. Kunin, *Ind. Eng. Chem.*, **41**, 460 (1949).
[44] S. M. Partridge, *Biochem. J.*, **44**, 521 (1949); cf. S. M. Partridge and R. C. Brimley, *Biochem. J.*, **44**, 513 (1949).

To separate the amino acids within an individual group, fractiona absorption and elution are necessary. Here one takes advantage o the differences in strengths of binding between the different amin acids and the exchanger, just as in the separation of the nucleotides or of inorganic ions like the alkali metals. Thus the three basi amino acids, arginine, lysine, and histidine, are separated from on another by successive elution from a sulfonated phenolic exchange or from a carboxylic exchanger.[45]

A modified elution technique, known as *displacement chromatog raphy*, was used for this purpose by Partridge.[44,46] Instead of elutin with a substance which is relatively weakly absorbed by the colum and therefore separates the eluted ions into completely discrete band which are separated by unreacted eluant, he used an eluting agen (ammonia) which was more strongly absorbed by the column tha any of the amino acids. This pushes all the amino acids before it, s that each amino acid is followed out of the column by the acid whic is next most strongly absorbed. This does not give such a clea separation between the acids as conventional ion exchange chroma tography, but it allows much larger amounts of material to be treate at once, and is therefore better for preparative work. The progres of the elution and the degree of overlapping of the bands was fol lowed by paper chromatography.

The separation of amino acids by ion exchange offers an excellen example of different ion exchange techniques, including separation o ions of opposite charge, separation of ions from neutral molecules and separation of similarly charged ions from one another. It als shows how ion exchangers can be used as buffering agents. On could hardly want a better example of present-day problems i analytical chemistry and their solution.

PROBLEMS

1. (a) Draw the structural formula for an ion exchanging resin made by co polymerizing acrylic acid with divinylbenzene. (b) What are the uses of such resin in analytical chemistry? What other uses would you suggest?

[45] B. A. Hems, J. E. Page, and J. G. Waller, *J. Soc. Chem. Ind.*, **67, 77** (1948)
[46] S. M. Partridge, *Faraday Soc. Discussions*, **7, 296** (1949).

2. How may ion exchange be used to determine the dissociation constant of complex ions?

3. Djurfeld and Samuelson (*Acta Chem. Scand.*, 1950) found that concentrated hydrochloric acid was less effective than 5–6 *N* acid in regenerating a cation exchange resin. What was the probable reason?

4. What is the Donnan equilibrium, and what effect does it have on the analytical properties of ion exchange resins?

5. Divalent metal ions are to be removed by ion exchange from a solution containing hydrochloric acid. (a) What type of exchanger should be used? (b) Should the solution be dilute or concentrated? Explain why.

6. Penicillin is to be removed from a solution by anion exchange. What type of exchanger should be used? How would it differ structurally from an exchanger to be used in water purification? How would you synthesize such an exchanger?

7. Account for the fact that phosphonic cation exchangers bind sodium more strongly than potassium ions (*J. Am. Chem. Soc.*, **74**, 1867, 1952).

9

Separations by vaporization and extraction

THOUGH NOT NEARLY AS COMMON in inorganic analysis as separations by precipitation, separations by vaporization and solvent extraction are important for their selectivity and their application where other methods fail. In organic analysis these methods are very common. "Paper chromatography," a technique that has been much used in recent years for the analysis of natural products, is really a special case of solvent extraction in which one solvent is held by the fibers of the paper.

The scope of this book being primarily inorganic, we shall not concern ourselves with the separation of organic substances in this chapter except for one case: the separation of the components of petroleum by fractional distillation and adsorption. This is such an excellent example of quantitative analysis, in the true sense of the term, that it would be a pity to omit it. We shall discuss this briefly after we have reviewed some of the representative applications of vaporization and extraction to quantitative analysis.

Vaporization Methods

The elements forming the most volatile compounds are, of course, the nonmetals. It is primarily the nonmetals, therefore, which are separated in analysis by vaporization. Certain elements of pseudo-metallic character, such as arsenic, antimony, and tin, are also easily separated from mixtures by distillation.   Finally, the metals themselves can be selectively vaporized at low pressures.

We shall consider first the separation of nonmetallic elements in gaseous form from their compounds, and shall include under this heading certain methods for the elementary analysis of organic compounds.   We list the elements in order of their periodic table groups.

Boron is often separated from mixtures containing borates by distillation as methyl borate, CH_3BO_2.   This is the compound which gives the well-known green-edged flame in the qualitative test for borate.   For quantitative analysis the sample is placed in a flask with methanol and a little concentrated hydrochloric acid, and distilled in a current of methanol vapor.   Esterification is very rapid.   The distillate is caught in sodium hydroxide solution, which is subsequently neutralized to methyl red.   Mannitol is then added, which condenses with boric acid to produce a cyclic ester which is a monobasic acid of about the same strength as acetic acid (see page 121).   This is then titrated with standard base to the phenolphthalein end point.[1]   Needless to say, carbon dioxide must be removed before the titration.   An older procedure is to absorb the methyl borate in a weighed flask containing quicklime.   This forms calcium borate as follows:

$$CaO + 2CH_3BO_2 \rightarrow Ca(BO_2)_2 + (CH_3)_2O.$$
$$Ca(OH)_2 + 2CH_3BO_2 \rightarrow Ca(BO_2)_2 + 2CH_3OH.$$

The ether and alcohol vaporize, and the gain in weight of the flask is equal to the weight of boron as B_2O_3.

Carbon is regularly determined by vaporization procedures.   In analyzing steel, alloys containing carbon, and organic compounds, the material is burned in a stream of oxygen and the carbon converted to carbon dioxide; this is absorbed in a weighed bulb containing concentrated potassium hydroxide solution, soda-lime, or, better, Ascarite, a proprietary product made by impregnating asbestos with sodium hydroxide.   Care must be taken to ensure: first, that the sample is fully burned; second, that any water vapor or sulfur dioxide produced in combustion is absorbed before it enters the weighed bulb; third, that the water produced by the reaction between carbon dioxide and the absorbent is not allowed to escape from the weighed bulb; and fourth, that the absorption bulb contains the same gas

[1] L. V. Wilcox, *Ind. Eng. Chem., Anal. Ed.*, **2**, 358 (1930).

(either oxygen or air) in both the initial and the final weighings. A typical combustion train for carbon determinations is shown in Figure 1. Finally, unusual care must be taken to avoid leaky connections.

The carbonate content of a material is determined by treating it with an acid and weighing the carbon dioxide evolved. This may be done in two ways; first, by allowing carbon dioxide, and carbon dioxide only, to escape from the reaction vessel, and determining the loss in weight of the latter; second, by absorbing the carbon dioxide in a weighed bulb containing a suitable absorbent, using a train of the type shown in Figure 1. The first method has the drawback that the apparatus to be weighed is relatively large, but it is simple and well adapted to determinations of gram or decigram quantities of carbon dioxide with moderate accuracy. The second method is

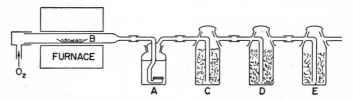

Fig. 9-1.   Combustion train for carbon determination, as used in steel analysis.

the more accurate, especially for small quantities. In both methods provision must be made for drawing air through the apparatus during and after the evolution of carbon dioxide, to make sure all the carbon dioxide is removed from the flask in which it is generated. Provision must also be made for absorbing water vapor and any hydrogen sulfide before these reach the weighed absorption bulb. Hydrochloric acid is generally used to liberate the carbon dioxide, but sometimes phosphoric acid is preferred since it is not volatile.[2]

Silicon can be removed from inorganic materials by evaporation with hydrofluoric and sulfuric acids. This technique is used to determine the coprecipitated silica in hydrous ferric oxide, for example, or the silica in boiler scale.

Nitrogen may be determined either as nitrogen gas, whose volume

[2] A. I. Vogel, *A Text-Book of Quantitative Inorganic Analysis*, London, Longmans, Green, 1939, p. 592.

is measured, or as ammonia, which is determined titrimetrically. The first (Dumas) method is applicable to all organic and most inorganic compounds. The second (Kjeldahl) method is not so generally applicable, but is much used for fertilizers and foodstuffs.

In the Dumas method,[3] the sample is mixed with cupric oxide and heated in a stream of pure carbon dioxide in a long combustion tube. This tube is packed with cupric oxide and copper metal. The organic compound is completely oxidized to carbon dioxide, water, and nitrogen. The gas stream is led into a graduated receiver filled with 50% potassium hydroxide; this absorbs the carbon dioxide, along with any oxides of sulfur, and only the nitrogen remains as a gas. The volume of the nitrogen is measured.

In the Kjeldahl method, organic nitrogen is first converted to ammonium sulfate by digesting with concentrated sulfuric acid, potassium sulfate, and a catalyst such as copper sulfate, mercuric sulfate, or selenium dioxide.[4] The mixture is cooled and diluted somewhat, and excess sodium hydroxide added to decompose the ammonium salt. The ammonia is distilled out, with precautions against bumping and against carrying over sodium hydroxide in spray. The ammonia is absorbed either in a measured volume of standard hydrochloric acid or in a saturated boric acid solution;[5] the boric acid reduces the partial pressure of ammonia considerably by forming ammonium borate:

$$NH_3 + HBO_2 \rightarrow NH_4^+ + BO_2^-.$$

Borate ion is a slightly weaker base than ammonia, and the excess boric acid forces the reaction to the right. After absorption of ammonia the solution is titrated back to the pH of the original boric acid solution, using bromcresol green as indicator. A sample of the original boric acid is set aside and bromcresol green added to it; one then titrates the test solution to the same olive-green shade as this standard. The boric acid method is almost as accurate as the older method in which standard hydrochloric acid is used to absorb the ammonia, and it is much simpler. The exact concentration and volume of the boric acid solution are not important, and only one standard solution is required.

[3] J. B. Niederl and V. Niederl, *Micromethods of Quantitative Organic Analysis*, New York, Wiley, 1942.

[4] R. B. Bradstreet, *Chem. Rev.*, **27**, 331 (1940).

[5] L. W. Winkler, *Z. angew. Chem.*, **27**, 1, 630 (1914).

The Kjeldahl method can be used to determine *nitrates* by reducing these in acid solution to ammonium salts by means of Devarda's alloy, an alloy containing 50% Cu, 45% Al, and 5% Zn.

Oxygen. In the older systems of analysis, oxygen in organic compounds was found by difference, that is, the percentage left over after all the other elements had been determined. This practice is obviously unsatisfactory. A direct method of determining oxygen in organic compounds has been introduced by Unterzaucher[6] and modified by later workers.[7] The compound is vaporized in a stream of dry nitrogen or helium and passed over carbon granules heated to 1120°–1200°C in a silica tube. Oxygen forms carbon monoxide, which is then passed over solid iodine pentoxide, forming carbon dioxide and iodine. The iodine passes on as vapor, and is absorbed in potassium hydroxide and determined titrimetrically.

Sulfur is most often determined as barium sulfate following a Parr bomb fusion, but it can also be separated as hydrogen sulfide or sulfur dioxide. Most metal *sulfides* yield hydrogen sulfide on treatment with hydrochloric acid; if they do not react with hydrochloric acid alone, they may react on heating with the acid and metallic tin. The hydrogen sulfide is absorbed in an ammoniacal solution of zinc or cadmium chloride. A measured excess of potassium iodate is then added and the solution acidified. Hydrogen sulfide reacts as follows:

$$IO_3^- + 3H_2S \rightarrow I^- + 3S + 3H_2O.$$

The excess iodate reacts with the iodide to give iodine, which is titrated with thiosulfate.

This method is often used to determine sulfur in steel; it is called the "evolution method." It does not necessarily give the total sulfur, but only that present as metallic sulfides. A modification which does give the total sulfur in steels and other alloys, as well as in materials such as rubber, is to oxidize the sulfur to sulfuric acid with concentrated nitric acid (plus bromine and perchloric acid if necessary), and then reduce the sulfuric acid to hydrogen sulfide by a mixture of hydriodic and hypophosphorous acids. The hydrogen

[6] J. Unterzaucher, *Ber.*, **73B**, 391 (1940).

[7] V. A. Aluise, R. T. Hall, F. C. Staats, and W. W. Becker, *Anal. Chem.*, **19**, 347 (1947); A. O. Maylott and J. B. Lewis, *Anal. Chem.*, **22**, 1051 (1950); W. W. Walton, F. W. McCulloch, and W. H. Smith, *J. Research Nat. Bur. Standards*, **40**, 443 (1948).

sulfide is carried over in a stream of nitrogen and absorbed and titrated in the manner described, or determined photometrically.[8]

Sulfur compounds are also analyzed by burning them in a stream of oxygen and so converting the sulfur to sulfur dioxide and trioxide. Steel is burned at 1200°–1400°C in a porcelain tube;[9] organic compounds are burned in a tube packed with platinum gauze.[3]   In each case the gas is passed into a hydrogen peroxide solution, which converts sulfur dioxide quantitatively to sulfuric acid.   The sulfuric acid is titrated with standard base.

Selenium and Tellurium.   Both form volatile chlorides and oxychlorides which permit their separation from elements whose chlorides are not volatile at 300–400°C.   Selenides and tellurides yield selenium and tellurium dichlorides and tellurium tetrachloride when heated in chlorine gas; selenates, selenites, tellurates, and tellurites yield these chlorides when heated in hydrogen chloride gas.

The tellurium chlorides are less volatile than selenium chloride, and selenium can therefore be separated from tellurium by distillation. The sample is heated in a distilling flask with concentrated sulfuric acid until the latter is almost at its boiling point, and hydrogen chloride is passed.   Selenium dichloride passes over, along with chlorine, and is absorbed in water, giving a solution of selenious acid.[10]   Selenium may also be distilled as the bromide from a solution containing excess of bromine.[11]

Fluorine.   Many elements interfere in determining fluorine, and fluorine interferes in determining several other elements.   This is due to the great tendency of fluoride ions to form complexes with metals, and to the fact that most metallic fluorides are sparingly soluble.   A method of separating fluorine from other elements, particularly metallic elements, is thus highly desirable.

The commonest separation method where fluorine itself is to be determined is to distill the sample with sulfuric or perchloric acid in presence of glass or silica.   Fluorides are converted to gaseous SiF_4,

[8] C. L. Luke, *Ind. Eng. Chem., Anal. Ed.,* **15**, 602 (1943); *Anal. Chem.,* **21**, 1369 (1949).

[9] C. H. Hale, *Ind. Eng. Chem., Anal. Ed.,* **8**, 317 (1936).

[10] V. Lenher and D. P. Smith, *Ind. Eng. Chem.,* **16**, 837 (1924); W. W. Scott, *Standard Methods of Chemical Analysis,* 5th ed., New York, Van Nostrand, 1939, p. 780.

[11] W. O. Robinson, H. C. Dudley, K. T. Williams, and H. G. Byers, *Ind. Eng. Chem., Anal. Ed.,* **6**, 274 (1934).

which passes over and is absorbed in water. It reacts with water to form fluosilicic acid, H_2SiF_6, and hydrous silica. Fluosilicic acid may be titrated with standard base (it is ,a strong acid) or determined gravimetrically as potassium or lead fluosilicate, or, since it dissociates appreciably to give fluoride ions, it may be titrated with thorium nitrate or aluminum chloride just as if it were fluoride, or determined colorimetrically (Chapter 7).

An apparatus for the distillation is shown in Figure 2. Ground glass, glass wool, or glass beads are placed in the distilling flask to

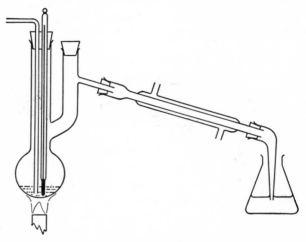

Fig. 9-2. Apparatus for distillation of fluorine as SiF_4. Steam enters through the tube on the left.

supply silica; these should preferably *not* be of borosilicate glass, since borate retards the distillation of silicon fluoride (however, it does not interfere with the thorium nitrate titration). Gelatinous silica also retards the distillation. The silicon tetrafluoride is swept out in a current of steam. The temperature must be at least 125°C, and not over 150°C, since sulfuric and perchloric acids both distill above 150°C and interfere with the thorium nitrate titration and with most of the colorimetric methods. About 100 ml. of distillate are collected for 10 mg. of fluorine, though the minimum amount that must be collected in any given case must be determined by experiment. A very convenient all-Pyrex glass distillation apparatus has been designed in which the temperature is automatically kept constant by refluxing tetrachloroethane (b.p. 146°C at 760 mm.).[12]

Where fluorine must be removed because it interferes in other determinations but need not be determined itself, two or three evaporations to fumes with sulfuric acid will usually suffice. This procedure is not applicable, however, where silicon is to be determined. In this case one may take advantage of the fact that boron trifluoride is more easily formed from boric acid than is silicon tetrafluoride from silica. The sample is evaporated with 20% perchloric acid saturated at 50°C with boric acid.[13] Fluorine vaporizes as BF_3, and meanwhile the silicates are decomposed and yield a well-coagulated precipitate of hydrous silica, which can be filtered, ignited, and weighed.

In some cases this method gives inaccurate results for silica; thus the precipitate may be contaminated with boric acid. The Berzelius method of precipitating silica with ammonium carbonate and ammoniacal zinc hydroxide is more reliable, but much more tedious. Alternatively, one may precipitate silica as 8-hydroxyquinoline silicomolybdate in presence of much boric acid.[14]

Fluorine in organic materials can be determined after a Parr bomb fusion, but an easier method, applicable to plant tissue and biological materials generally, is to mix the sample with magnesium acetate and heat in a muffle furnace until the organic matter is destroyed. In this way the fluoride is "fixed" and loss by vaporization is avoided.[15] The fluorine can be separated from the residue by distillation as silicon tetrafluoride. Fluorinated hydrocarbons and other volatile compounds are best treated by burning them in moist oxygen in a platinum tube, packed with platinum gauze, and heated to 1250°–1275°C. Hydrogen fluoride is formed, which is absorbed in standard alkali and determined acidimetrically.[16]

Chlorine, Bromine, Iodine. These elements are seldom separated from inorganic materials by vaporization, but if necessary they can be liberated and vaporized as the free elements. Traces of iodine in

[12] W. B. Huckaby, E. T. Welch, and A. V. Metler, *Ind. Eng. Chem., Anal. Ed.,* **19,** 154 (1947).

[13] W. T. Schrenk and W. H. Ode, *Ind. Eng. Chem., Anal. Ed.,* **1,** 201 (1929).

[14] J. A. Brabson *et al., Anal. Chem.,* **20,** 504 (1948); see also J. I. Hoffman and G. E. F. Lundell, *J. Research Nat. Bur. Standards,* **3,** 581 (1929).

[15] W. E. Crutchfield, *Ind. Eng. Chem., Anal. Ed.,* **14,** 57 (1942).

[16] O. J. Milner, *Anal. Chem.,* **22,** 315 (1950).

phosphate rock have been determined by heating the rock with concentrated sulfuric acid, which oxidizes bromide and iodide ions but not chloride ions, and sweeping the vapors into a suitable absorber. In organic microanalysis, however, the halogens are nearly always separated by vaporization. The organic compound is either burned in oxygen with the help of a platinum catalyst, or oxidized by warming to 115°–125°C with a mixture of potassium dichromate, silver dichromate, and sulfuric acid.[17] The halogens can be absorbed in potassium iodide solution or in standard sodium hydroxide containing hydrogen peroxide; each mole of halogen uses up two equivalents of base, and so can be determined acidimetrically:

$$Cl_2 + 2NaOH + H_2O_2 \rightarrow 2NaCl + O_2 + 2H_2O.$$

On the micro scale, this method and others like it in which a gas is evolved from a solution can be performed by the diffusion technique of Conway.[18] The apparatus, shown in Figure 3, consists

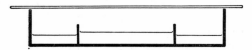

Fig. 9-3.   Conway micro-diffusion cell.

simply of a circular glass dish divided into two concentric sections by a ring. The absorbing solution is placed in the center section, the sample in the outer section. A reagent is added to the latter to liberate the gas concerned (for example, potassium carbonate solution is added to liberate ammonia from an ammonium salt), and immediately the dish is closed by a flat cover plate, lightly greased, slid over the top. The dish is then left to stand until the gas has had time to diffuse into the absorbing solution, after which the latter is titrated.

Pseudometals. The metallic character of an element is estimated chemically by its ability to form ionized salts. The formation of ionic rather than covalent bonds is favored by low ionic charge and high cationic radius, according to the well-known cova-

[17] M. K. Zacherl and H. G. Krainick, *Mikrochemie*, **11**, 61 (1932).

[18] E. J. Conway and A. Byrne, *Biochem. J.*, **27**, 419, 430 (1933); E. J. Conway, *Micro-Diffusion Analysis and Volumetric Error*, London, Crosby, Lockwood, 1939.

lency rules of Fajans and Sidgwick.   This accounts for the distribution of metals and nonmetals in the periodic table.   We shall discuss here four elements which have both metallic and nonmetallic characteristics: germanium, arsenic, tin, and antimony.   Of these the most metallic is tin (in group IV of the periodic system), and the least metallic is arsenic (in group V).   The heavier elements in both groups—lead in group IV, bismuth in group V—are predominantly metallic and form few volatile compounds.

Germanium is distilled as the tetrachloride from a dilute sulfuric acid solution.[19]   Stannic chloride does not volatilize under these conditions (see below).   If arsenic is present with germanium, it can be kept from distilling by passing chlorine gas.

Arsenic, Antimony, and Tin.   These all have volatile chlorides which can be separated by distillation.   Their boiling points are as follows: $AsCl_3$ 130°, $SbCl_3$ 220°, $SnCl_2$ 603°, $SnCl_4$ 114°C.   The chloride $AsCl_5$ apparently does not exist; $SbCl_5$ decomposes before it boils under ordinary pressures.   The contrast between $SnCl_2$ and $SnCl_4$ is to be expected from the covalency rules; $SnCl_2$ should be the more ionic and therefore have the higher boiling point.

Distillation as the chloride is the standard way of separating *arsenic* from mixtures;[20] so long as the arsenic is in the tripositive form, it can be distilled quantitatively from a solution in concentrated hydrochloric acid at 110°C.   It is carried over in a stream of carbon dioxide or other inert gas.   Stannic chloride does not distill under these conditions, presumably because of the formation of $H_2[SnCl_6]$.   The successive distillation of arsenic, antimony, and tin was studied by Scherrer.[21]   His procedure is as follows.   The precipitated sulfides of arsenic, antimony, and tin are heated with a mixture of concentrated sulfuric and nitric acids and evaporated to small volume, fumes of sulfur trioxide being evolved.   The sulfuric acid solution is cooled and diluted with a saturated solution of sulfur dioxide, which reduces arsenic and antimony, but not tin.   (Flowers of sulfur may be used for the same purpose.)   The excess sulfur dioxide is boiled out, and the solution is mixed with concen-

[19] L. M. Dennis and E. G. Johnson, *J. Am. Chem. Soc.*, **45**, 1380 (1923); C. J. Rodden (ed.), *Analytical Chemistry of the Manhattan Project*, New York, McGraw-Hill, 1950, p. 374.

[20] H. Biltz, *Z. anal. Chem.*, **81**, 82 (1930); **99**, 1 (1934).

[21] J. A. Scherrer, *J. Research Nat. Bur. Standards*, **16**, 253 (1936); **21**, 95 (1938); W. D. Mogerman, *J. Research Nat. Bur. Standards*, **33**, 307 (1944).

trated hydrochloric acid and transferred to the distilling flask shown in Figure 4. All-glass construction is important, since these chlorides are absorbed by rubber. Carbon dioxide is bubbled slowly through the inlet shown, and distillation is begun.

Arsenic distills over at 110°–112°C. After this has come over, a few milliliters of 85% phosphoric acid are added to complex the tin, and prevent its distilling in the next stage. *Antimony* is then distilled over at 155°–165°C, concentrated hydrochloric acid being meanwhile dripped in slowly to make up for evaporation loss.

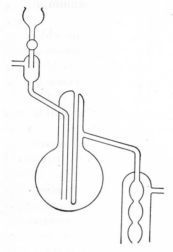

Finally *tin* is distilled over by dripping in, instead of hydrochloric acid, a mixture of one part of concentrated hydrobromic acid and three parts of concentrated hydrochloric acid; the temperature of the distillation is 140°C (bismuth would come over if the temperature rose above 145°C).

In this procedure, the use of mixed hydrochloric and hydrobromic acid to distill the tin is noteworthy. Several explanations suggest themselves to account for the increased volatility obtained with this mixture. It is probable that stannic bromide, being more covalently bound than stannic chloride, is less ionized or hydrolyzed than the

Fig. 9-4. Apparatus for distilling chlorides of As, Sb and Sn.

latter. It is also likely that the chloride and the bromide together form an azeotropic mixture. If the two substances are imperfectly miscible, the vapor pressure of a mixture of the two will be more than the average of the vapor pressures of the individual substances, and may be more than either one of these; in this case the two will distill together at a lower temperature than either of the pure substances. This principle has also been used in distilling arsenic and antimony.[22]

Arsenic may also be separated as *arsine*, AsH₃. This is the basis of the well-known Marsh test. A solution containing arsenic is run

[22] D. M. Hubbard, *Ind. Eng. Chem., Anal. Ed.*, **13**, 915 (1941).

into a flask containing zinc and dilute sulfuric acid; the arsenic is converted quantitatively to arsine along with the hydrogen which is being liberated.   The arsine may then be decomposed to elementary arsenic by passing the gas through a narrow hard glass tube which is heated at one point; the arsenic forms a bright mirror, which is compared with standards produced by known amounts of arsenic.   More conveniently, the gas is passed over a strip of paper impregnated with mercuric chloride or bromide (the Gutzeit method).   This is stained yellow to brown by formation of an arsenide of mercury. From the length and depth of the stain, the quantity of arsenic is estimated.   It is important to remove any traces of hydrogen sulfide from the gas before it meets the test paper.   These methods are rough, but they are very sensitive (detecting one microgram of arsenic or less) and are well adapted to the routine examination of foodstuffs and other materials which may contain traces of arsenic.

The method is more precise if the arsenic is absorbed in an aqueous solution of mercuric chloride.   The mercury is afterwards reduced completely to mercury metal by adding hydroxylamine hydrochloride, and the arsenic in the solution is determined polarographically.[23]

Antimony compounds form *stibine*, SbH_3, with zinc and dilute sulfuric acid.   (Tin does not liberate stibine, nor does aluminum in sodium hydroxide, but both of these will reduce arsenic compounds to arsine.)   The conversion to SbH_3 is not quantitative, however, unless certain conditions of temperature and acid concentration are strictly observed.

Metals. The separation of metals by vaporization is rarely performed, although certain separations are possible.   The easiest metal to vaporize in the elemental state is, of course, *mercury*.   This is released quantitatively from mercury compounds by heating with calcium oxide or sodium carbonate and an oxidizing agent, such as lead chromate, in a stream of air.   At a red heat, mercuric oxide decomposes, and mercury metal is condensed in a suitable receiver. Alternative procedures use a reducing agent in a closed crucible; the mercury vapor is caught on a cooled strip of silver, which amalgamates easily.

By use of a high vacuum, many metals can be quantitatively vaporized.   A technique for the rapid analysis of alloys in this way

[23] D. M. Hubbard and J. Cholak, private communication.

was worked out by Polanyi.[24]   A sample of about 0.2 gram is placed in a small silica test tube, which is weighed with its contents; it is then placed in a larger, vertical silica tube, which is attached by a cooled ground joint to a high vacuum line.   The apparatus is evacuated to 0.001 mm. of mercury, and a preheated cylindrical furnace is raised into position around the tube.   After 5–10 minutes of heating, the furnace is removed and the tube cooled; the sample tube and contents are reweighed.

In the analysis of brass, zinc and lead were evaporated out in six minutes at 1200°C, while copper and tin remained.   Lead-tin alloys were analyzed in a similar manner.   By using a lower temperature and higher pressure, zinc can be distilled out and lead left behind. Again, bismuth can be determined in its alloys with copper, though here the heating time must be half an hour or more.[25]

The method is very rapid, and a precision of better than 0.1% is claimed.   The potentialities, which have not yet been fully exploited, may be judged from the following table of boiling points.

Metal	B.p., °C (760 mm.)
Cd	767
Zn	906
Mg	1100
Bi	1560
Pb	1750
Al	2056
Sn	2260
Cu	2300
Fe	3000

There are practical difficulties, such as spattering or creeping of the liquid metal during distillation, and there are other difficulties due to the fact that two liquid metals are usually miscible, and therefore lower one another's vapor pressure.   They may, moreover, form azeotropic mixtures containing intermetallic compounds from which both metals distill together at a temperature higher than that at which either would distill separately.   This is the case with mixtures of Sb and Bi, and of Sb and Mg.

[24] St. v. Bogdandy and M. Polanyi, *Metal Industries*, **31**, 195 (1927); H. Töpelmann in W. Böttger (ed.), *Physikalische Methoden der analytischen Chemie*, Leipzig, Akademische Verlagsgesellschaft, 1939, Vol. III, p. 74.
[25] E. W. Colbeck, S. W. Craven, and W. Murray, *Analyst*, **59**, 395 (1934).

The technique can be extended to metallic oxides by incorporating with them a reducing agent such as finely powdered iron. Both metals and metallic oxides can also be analyzed by heating to 1150°–1200°C in a stream of hydrogen instead of in a vacuum.[25, 26]

Certain *metallic compounds* can be separated from mixtures by distillation at atmospheric pressure. Thus $BiBr_3$ (b.p. 453°C) can be separated from $PbBr_2$ (b.p. 918°C), although the separation is usually done in other ways. Lithium can be quantitatively vaporized as the chloride in rock analysis; the powdered rock sample is sintered with calcium carbonate and calcium chloride in a platinum tube at 1150°C in a current of air; the other alkali metals and a small proportion of calcium are vaporized along with it.[27] An interesting case is the separation of chromyl chloride, CrO_2Cl_2, in the analysis of corrosion-resistant steels.[28] The steel is dissolved in hydrochloric acid, perchloric acid is added, and the solution evaporated to fumes; dry hydrogen chloride gas is then passed over the mixture, which is heated in a flask on a hot plate. Instead of passing hydrogen chloride, solid sodium chloride may be added a little at a time.

Mercury may be distilled as $HgCl_2$ in a stream of chlorine or hydrogen chloride. Temperatures above 300°C are necessary, and it is best to distill from sulfuric acid containing added potassium sulfate.

Extraction Methods

In this section we shall include the use of immiscible solvents for removing inorganic salts from aqueous solutions, and also the use of nonaqueous solvents for separating the constituents of solid mixtures. We shall not include here the extraction of metal-organic complexes by organic solvents, since this was discussed in Chapter 6.

Extraction of chlorides and nitrates with ether. One of the best known uses of an organic solvent in organic analysis is the use of diethyl ether to extract certain metal chlorides from cold 6 N

[26] L. I. Weinstein and A. A. Benedetti-Pichler, *Mikrochemie*, **11**, 301 (1932).
[27] M. H. Fletcher, *Anal. Chem.*, **21**, 173 (1949).
[28] F. W. Smith, *Ind. Eng. Chem., Anal. Ed.*, **10**, 360 (1938); L. G. Bricker, S. Weinberg, and K. L. Proctor, *Ind. Eng. Chem., Anal. Ed.*, **17**, 661 (1945).

hydrochloric acid. The proportions of different chlorides extracted by a single shaking with an equal volume of ether are the following:[29]

More than 90% extracted: $FeCl_3$, $GaCl_3$, $AuCl_3$, $TlCl_3$, (MoO_3).
50%–90% extracted: $GeCl_4$, $AsCl_3$, $SbCl_3$.
1%–50% extracted: $SnCl_2$, $SnCl_4$, $IrCl_4$.
Not appreciably extracted: Chlorides of Al, Bi, Ca, Cd, Cr, Co,
  Fe(II), Pb, Mn, Ni, Os, Pd, Ag, Ti, W, U, Zr, rare earths.

It will be noted that it is primarily the covalent chlorides which are extracted. The extraction is most efficient with $FeCl_3$ (over 99%), and its usual use is in the analysis of iron alloys, to remove nearly all the iron preparatory to determining the alloying elements. *Isopropyl ether* is even more efficient than ethyl ether for this purpose;[30] it is also less soluble in water and less volatile, causing less fire hazard.

The efficiency of extraction of ferric chloride by ethers depends, first, on the hydrochloric acid concentration. The optimum molarity of hydrochloric acid in the original aqueous solution is 6 M for diethyl ether, 6–8 M for diisopropyl ether; below 3–4 M, and above 9 M, very little extraction occurs.[30] Second, it depends on the iron concentration. Below about 0.002 M $FeCl_3$ the ideal solution laws are obeyed and the coefficient of partition between water and ether is independent of the concentration; above 0.002 M, however, the proportion of iron in the ether layer rises rapidly.[31] This is ascribed to a salting-out effect in the aqueous layer which increases with the iron content of the latter. The species extracted by the ether is apparently $HFeCl_4$.

Ordinarily the last trace of iron, perhaps the last 1% or so, is not extracted by ether, even after several shakings. This difficulty is not due to the lower partition coefficient at lower concentrations, but to a photochemical decomposition of ferric chloride in ether solutions, which gives ferrous chloride and chlorine. Ferrous chloride, being much more ionic than ferric chloride, is not extracted by ether. If the extraction is done in the dark or in subdued light, the iron can be completely removed from the aqueous layer by a continuous ex-

[29] E. H. Swift, *J. Am. Chem. Soc.*, **46**, 2378 (1924); W. F. Hillebrand and G. E. F. Lundell, *Applied Inorganic Analysis*, New York, Wiley, 1929, p. 106.

[30] R. W. Dodson, G. J. Forney, and E. H. Swift, *J. Am. Chem. Soc.*, **58**, 2573 (1936).

[31] N. H. Nachtrieb and R. E. Fryxell, *J. Am. Chem. Soc.*, **70**, 3552 (1948); N. H. Nachtrieb and J. G. Conway, *J. Am. Chem. Soc.*, **70**, 3547 (1948).

tractor (see below) using isopropyl ether.[32]   Where a removal of 99%
of the iron is enough, two or three manual extractions in a separatory
funnel in ordinary diffuse light will suffice.

It is worth noting that *phosphate*, when present along with ferric
iron, is extracted by ether as a ferric phosphate complex.[30]

The extraction of *nitrates* by diethyl ether is applied primarily to
uranium.   Uranyl nitrate is extracted very efficiently in the presence
of nitric acid, and even more efficiently if the aqueous layer is saturated with ammonium nitrate, which salts out the uranium.[33]   This
salting out effect, incidentally, shows that the uranium nitrate is in
a substantially nonionized form.

Bismuth nitrate and a very few others are extracted by ether to a
slight extent, but the presence of uranyl nitrate in the ether layer
represses their solubility in ether.[34]   The separation of uranium from
lead and thorium in this manner is extremely efficient, and the method
is applied to the production of high-purity uranium.

Theory of extraction. The efficiency of an extraction process
depends on the "partition coefficient," defined as

$$X = \frac{\text{concentration of solute in solvent 1}}{\text{concentration of solute in solvent 2}}.$$

If the solute obeys Henry's law in both solvents; that is to say, if its
fugacity is directly proportional to its concentration, then X is a
constant, independent of concentration.   In this case it is easy to
calculate the efficiency of an extraction.   Suppose we start with a
given quantity of a solute, say a moles, contained in a unit volume of
water, say 1 liter; let us shake this with V volumes of an immiscible
solvent until equilibrium is reached.   Let a fraction x of the solute
remain *unextracted*.   Then:

$$X = \frac{(1 - x)a/V}{xa/1} = \frac{1 - x}{Vx}.$$

Rearranging, $XVx = 1 - x; \quad x(XV + 1) = 1,$

and $$x = \frac{1}{XV + 1}.$$

[32] S. E. Q. Ashley and W. M. Murray, *Ind. Eng. Chem., Anal. Ed.*, **10**, 367
(1938).

[33] F. Hecht and A. Grunwald, *Mikrochemie*, **30**, 279 (1943); T. R. Scott,
Analyst, 74, 486 (1949); C. J. Rodden (ed.), *Analytical Chemistry of the Manhattan
Project*, New York, McGraw-Hill, 1950, p. 499.

[34] M. Bachelet, E. Cheylan, and Le Bris, *J. chim. physique*, **47**, 62 (1950).

From this relation we can derive mathematically. what we may see intuitively; namely, that several successive extractions with small portions of solvent are more efficient than one single extraction in which all the solvent is used at once. Suppose two successive extractions are made with equal volumes V of solvent; the fraction of solute remaining in the water is

$$x_2 = \frac{1}{(XV + 1)^2}.$$

Now imagine one extraction with a volume of solvent equal to $2V$. The fraction of solute unextracted is

$$x_1 = \frac{1}{(2XV + 1)}.$$

Then $\qquad \dfrac{x_1}{x_2} = \dfrac{2XV + 1}{X^2V^2 + 2XV + 1}$, which is less than 1;

that is, the one extraction with $2V$ volumes of solvent leaves more solute in the water than two extractions with V volumes. The efficiency of n extractions can be derived by using the binomial expansion.

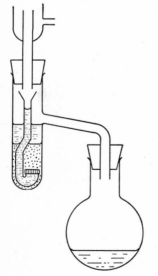

Successive batch extractions with small volumes of solvent are time-consuming and unnecessary, for the same result can be obtained with a continuous extractor. Most continuous extraction processes depend on refluxing the solvent, after the manner of the Soxhlet extractor. A typical apparatus (designed for an extracting solvent which is lighter than water) is shown in Figure 5.

Salting-out and Salting-in Effects. As we have seen, these effects are often very considerable and may lead to considerable deviations from Henry's law. They are difficult to

Fig. 9-5. Continuous extractor, for a volatile solvent which is lighter than water.

predict, but, in general, an electrolyte will salt out a nonelectrolyte by raising its activity coefficient, as expressed by the extended Debye-Hückel equation:

$$\log f = -\frac{A z_+ z_- \sqrt{\mu}}{1 + B\sqrt{\mu}} + C\mu$$

[Equation (8), Chapter 2.]. For a nonelectrolyte, z_+ and z_- are zero, and $\log f = C\mu$; the activity coefficient f is always greater than 1, and increases with the ionic strength μ of the solution.

Extraction of solid mixtures by nonaqueous solvents. The analysis of mixtures of alkali and alkaline earth metal salts by conventional chemical means is notoriously difficult, because nearly all the compounds of these elements are soluble in water. Even where they are insoluble or nearly so, as for example, the sulfates of the alkaline earth metals, there is not enough difference in solubility to permit quantitative separation. The use of solvents other than water facilitates these separations greatly. The usual procedure is to produce the desired salts in aqueous solution, evaporate the solution to dryness, and then treat the residue with the appropriate nonaqueous solvent.

In the *alkali metal series*, the *perchlorates* are efficiently separated by boiling n-butanol, or better, a mixture of equal volumes of n-butanol and ethyl acetate. In n-butanol alone, the perchlorates have the following solubilities (grams per 100 ml.): Li, 49.2; Na, 1.5; K, 0.004; Mg, 44.6. The salts (chlorides or nitrates) are converted to perchlorates by evaporating to dryness with perchloric acid; the dry perchlorates are extracted with the boiling solvent. Sodium and lithium perchlorates dissolve; potassium, rubidium, and cesium perchlorates remain.[35] The solution of sodium and lithium perchlorates is boiled to remove ethyl acetate, and the sodium is precipitated as the chloride by adding a 20% solution of hydrogen chloride in n-butanol. Lithium remains in solution.

Potassium can be determined in presence of sodium by extracting their *chloroplatinates* with 80% ethanol; this is the oldest and still the most accurate way of determining potassium. K_2PtCl_6 (cubic) is insoluble, while $Na_2PtCl_6 \cdot 6H_2O$ (triclinic) dissolves.

---

[35] G. F. Smith, *J. Am. Chem. Soc.*, **45**, 2072 (1923); **47**, 762 (1925); G. F. Smith and J. F. Ross, *J. Am. Chem. Soc.*, **47**, 774 (1925).

Lithium chloride can be extracted from sodium chloride and the other alkali metal chlorides by dioxane or by dry pyridine.

In the *alkaline earth series*, the following separations are possible: calcium nitrate dissolves easily in boiling butyl cellosolve ($C_4H_9OCH_2CH_2OH$, b.p. 170°C) while strontium and barium nitrates do not—an excellent method.[36] By adding pure nitric acid to an aqueous solution, barium nitrate is precipitated when the nitric acid concentration reaches 76%, and strontium nitrate when it reaches 80% (sp. gr. 1.45), while calcium nitrate stays in solution.[37] Calcium chloride is soluble, strontium and barium chlorides insoluble, in a 1:1 mixture of ethyl alcohol and ethyl ether.

Since the development of flame photometry as a precise and sensitive method for determining alkali and alkaline earth metals, these separation processes are less often needed, but relatively few laboratories can afford a flame photometer, and in any case, such instruments must always be checked by the slower, but more accurate and authoritative, methods of orthodox chemical analysis.

The Analysis of Petroleum

Distillation and extraction methods are used much more in the analysis of mixtures of organic compounds than in inorganic analysis. A full discussion of these applications is out of place here; yet one example must be mentioned in any survey of the methods of analytical chemistry—the complete separation of petroleum and petroleum products into their individual pure components, performed by Rossini and co-workers at the National Bureau of Standards under Project 6 of the American Petroleum Institute.[38] Though strictly a research project, this work was quantitative analysis in the purest sense of the term. Unlike such methods as infrared spectroscopy, which are relative and require careful calibration, this method is

[36] H. H. Barber, *Ind. Eng. Chem., Anal. Ed.*, **13,** 572 (1941).

[37] H. H. Willard and E. W. Goodspeed, *Ind. Eng. Chem., Anal. Ed.*, **8,** 414 (1936).

[38] F. D. Rossini, *Anal. Chem.*, **20,** 110 (1948); chapter in R. E. Burk (ed.), *Recent Advances in Analytical Chemistry*, New York, Interscience, 1949. Many papers by Rossini and others in *J. Research Nat. Bur. Standards.*

absolute; every part of the original mixture is isolated and accounted for.

Petroleum consists of three classes of hydrocarbons: paraffins, naphthenes or cycloparaffins, and aromatics (olefins and acetylenic compounds do not occur to any extent). Each of these classes includes many individual substances. The paraffin octane, for instance, has fifteen isomers, any of which may be present. The most obvious way of separating such a mixture is fractional distillation, but aside from the closeness of some of the boiling points, one important difficulty arises here. Paraffins and aromatics, also naphthenes and aromatics, do not mix ideally. Paraffin molecules

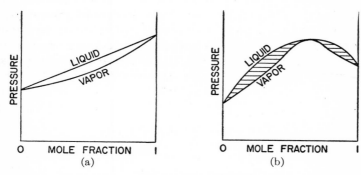

Fig. 9-6. Liquid and vapor composition isotherms for (a) ideal, (b) azeotropic mixtures.

have more attraction for molecules of their own kind than they have for aromatic molecules, and vice versa. This leads to the formation of *azeotropic mixtures* having a maximum vapor pressure and minimum boiling point. In azeotropic mixtures, the vapor and the liquid have exactly the same composition; distillation produces no separation. Different paraffins and naphthenes, on the other hand, give mixtures which are almost ideal. Such mixtures can be separated by fractional distillation provided that their boiling points are at least two or three degrees apart. Figure 6 shows the vapor pressure-composition relations of ideal and azeotropic mixtures.

Though paraffin-aromatic mixtures can generally not be separated by distillation, they can be separated neatly by fractional adsorption. The aromatic ring is more polarizable than a saturated hydrocarbon molecule, and aromatic compounds are more strongly adsorbed on surfaces than are aliphatic compounds. Rossini's group used a column packed with fine mesh silica gel, 8 to 10 feet long. Preliminary tests showed that silica gel did not isomerize or otherwise alter the hydrocarbons to be separated. Enough liquid was poured into the top to saturate one-third of the column. Ethyl alcohol was poured on to the top of column and forced down slowly by gas pressure. The alcohol is more strongly adsorbed than any of the hydrocarbons and so forces the latter out, plunger fashion. At the same time, a separation takes place, and the first liquid to emerge from the bottom contains only paraffins and naphthenes. These are followed by the aromatics, with a sharp boundary between. The composition of the liquid is followed by its refractive index (see Figure 7). The method is that of "displacement chromatography" (see Chapter 8).

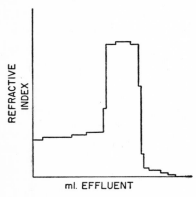

Fig. 9-7. Desorption of paraffins, naphthenes and aromatic hydrocarbons from silica gel. Aromatic hydrocarbons have the highest refractive index.

The aromatic hydrocarbons and the paraffin-naphthene fraction were then fractionally distilled separately, using very long columns with the equivalent of 100–200 theoretical plates. A high reflux ratio, up to 200:1, was used. This means that 200 parts of liquid condense and run down the column for 1 part that actually distills; in this way, a close approach to thermodynamic equilibrium is reached, and the most efficient separation is obtained. It took a week or ten days to distill three liters of liquid in this way. The progress of the operation was followed by measuring the refractive index of the distillate, as well as by the temperature (see Figure 8).

Even with these refinements, ordinary fractional distillation separates certain isomers only partially. In such cases, the distillation process may be modified in two ways. First, distillation can be done at reduced pressure. Thermodynamics predicts that the ratio of vapor pressures of two liquids should become greater, the lower the temperature (Dühring's rule); therefore fractional distillation should be more effective, the lower the pressure (and consequently, temperature) at which it is carried out. A certain paraffin and a naphthene having the same number of carbon atoms per molecule boiled at the same temperature at 760 mm., but at 100 mm., the naphthene boiled 3° lower than the paraffin, and separation by distillation was possible.

Second, an alcohol can be added which forms azeotropes with the different hydrocarbon constituents, and these azeotropes then are

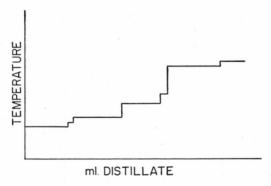

Fig. 9-8.   Fractional distillation of a paraffin-naphthene mixture.

fractionally distilled to give a mixture of hydrocarbon *A* with alcohol, another mixture of hydrocarbon *B* with alcohol, and so on. The alcohol is readily extracted from these mixtures with water.

Finally, a criterion is needed of the purity of the fractions obtained in these ways. This criterion is the freezing point or, rather, the time-temperature curve during freezing, which is determined within an accuracy of 0.001°C. A dissolved impurity always lowers the freezing point of a liquid, provided that it does not form solid solutions with the solvent. Mixtures of isomeric paraffins behave nearly ideally in the liquid state, obeying Raoult's law, but they do not enter into one another's solid crystals, since their molecules have different shapes. For a pure liquid, the time-temperature curve during freezing looks like Figure 9(a); the temperature remains constant until all the liquid has frozen. If the liquid is impure, the curve is like Figure 9(b); the temperature falls constantly during freezing as the impurity becomes more and more concentrated in the liquid which remains. With the hydrocarbon mixtures we are discussing, a curve of type (b) is not only a qualitative indication of impurity, but also permits one to calculate the actual proportion of impurity in the original liquid, and the freezing point of the pure liquid. This is possible because the thermodynamic laws of the ideal solution can be applied.[39]

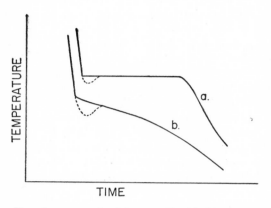

Fig. 9-9. Freezing curves for (a) a pure liquid, (b) an impure liquid.

Fractional freezing can be used as a means of purification of a hydrocarbon, but is used only as a last resort, since the technique is very difficult.

Using these methods, over 100 hydrocarbons of 99.8% purity and better have been prepared from petroleum and petroleum alkylates. In each case, the actual proportion of impurity was determined to 0.01%. These standard preparations and the standard analyzed mixtures from whence they came have been distributed to many laboratories for calibrating mass spectrographs, infrared spectrographs, and other analytical instruments.

[39] A. R. Glasgow, A. J. Streiff, and F. D. Rossini, *J. Research Nat. Bur. Standards*, **35**, 355 (1945); A. R. Glasgow *et al., Anal. Chem.*, **20**, 410 (1948).

PROBLEMS

1. Carbonate is determined by the loss in weight of an apparatus consisting of a 200 ml. flask and a drying tube when the carbonate is decomposed by acid. The operator forgets to displace the carbon dioxide from the flask after the reaction. What error, in milligrams, is introduced? The temperature is 30°C., the barometric pressure 720 mm. Neglect the volume of the drying tube.

2. Why does $SnCl_4$ not distill from a dilute sulfuric acid solution containing chloride? (Suggest likely reasons.)

3. Two types of azeotropes, minimum boiling and maximum boiling, are mentioned in this chapter. What are the conditions favoring the formation of each of these? Illustrate by common examples.

4. A solution containing arsenic and antimony must be evaporated to dryness. How may we ensure that these elements will not be lost by vaporization?

5. Certain copper-zinc alloys show good *precision*, but consistently high results for zinc (0.5% high) in the volatilization method (page 164). Why?

6. How would you analyze gravimetrically a mixture of strontium and barium chlorides? How would you separate strontium and barium ions quantitatively, and how could you analyze the mixture gravimetrically without separating the two?

7. How may organic matter be destroyed in preparing a biological sample for arsenic determination? (See reference 22.)

10

Volumetric analysis: introduction

IT IS EASIER and faster to measure the volume of a liquid than it is to collect and weigh a solid precipitate, and therein lies the chief advantage of volumetric over gravimetric analysis. Volumetric methods are always faster than gravimetric methods, once the necessary standard solutions and indicators are prepared, and they are generally more sensitive, that is, they are applicable to smaller samples or lower concentrations. Under favorable conditions, they can be quite as accurate as gravimetric methods.

In volumetric analysis the substance whose quantity is to be determined is made to react with another substance added from a buret in the form of a solution of known concentration. From the volume of this solution which is just sufficient to react with the substance under investigation, the quantity of the latter is calculated. For this method to be successful, certain requirements must be met. The reagent added from the buret must combine rapidly with the substance being titrated; the reaction must be complete, within the limits of experimental error, when a very small excess of reagent is added; there must be no side reactions, and finally, there must be a way of telling when an excess of reagent has been added. Usually this is done by adding a small amount of an "indicator," a substance which changes color or produces turbidity or fluorescence when enough reagent has been added. Electrical methods are also widely used.

Equivalence point and end point; end point error. The point at which just enough reagent has been added to react completely with the substance determined is called the *equivalence point*. For example, in titrating a soluble chloride with silver nitrate solution the equivalence point is reached when exactly one mole of silver nitrate is added for every mole of chloride ions, in accordance with the reaction $Ag^+ + Cl^- \rightarrow AgCl$. The concentrations of silver ions and chloride ions which remain unprecipitated must be equal at the equivalence point, and from the solubility product of silver chloride they are each 1.2×10^{-5} molar at 25°C.

The point at which the color change of the indicator becomes apparent to the eye is called the *end point*. Ideally, the end point and the equivalence point should coincide. If sodium chromate is added as the indicator in titrating chloride ions with silver nitrate, the red silver chromate color which indicates the end point should appear as soon as the silver ion concentration in the solution reaches 1.2×10^{-5} molar. In practice this is seldom the case, for two reasons. First, silver chromate may precipitate before or after this particular silver ion concentration is reached; second, a certain amount of silver chromate has to be formed before its red color can be seen, and an appreciable amount of reagent is used in its formation. These two sources of error are implicit in all indicator methods: first, the indicator may not change color exactly at the equivalence point, and second, the indicator in changing color uses up some of the reagent.

The difference between the end point and the equivalence point in a titration we shall call the *end point error*. It is inherent in the method used, and is thus distinguished from random errors caused by faulty manipulation, impure chemicals, or incorrectly calibrated glassware. The end-point error can often be calculated theoretically, and it can always be determined experimentally. It is generally additive, that is, it amounts to the same volume of the titrant whether the quantity of substance titrated is large or small. The most reliable way to evaluate it is to titrate two or more known solutions in which the amounts and concentrations of reacting substance are known, but widely different. Suppose, for example, that 25.00 ml. of a standard 0.0876 *N* calcium solution takes 22.00 ml. of a palmitate solution to reach the end point, while 50.00 ml. of the same standard solution takes 43.80 ml. of palmitate. 43.80 is not twice 22.00, but (43.80 − 0.20) is exactly twice (22.00 − 0.20); therefore the end point correction is 0.20 ml., to be subtracted, and the normality of the palmitate is 0.0876 (50.00/43.60) = 0.1005.

By using potentiometric or conductometric methods to locate the equivalence point, the end point error can be eliminated entirely.

When this is done, the maximum accuracy of volumetric analysis is realized.

Standard solutions: primary standards. All volumetric methods depend on standard solutions which contain exactly known amounts of the reagents in unit volume of the solution. The concentration of such solutions is generally expressed in *normality*, that is, the number of gram equivalents of reagent per liter of solution. Normality, like equivalent weight, depends on the particular type of reaction for which the solution is employed. A potassium permanganate solution which is 0.1 normal in the reaction

$$MnO_4^- + 8H^+ + 5e \rightarrow Mn^{++} + H_2O$$

is only 0.02 normal in the reaction

$$MnO_4^- + e \rightarrow MnO_4^=,$$

which is the way permanganate reacts in strongly alkaline solution.

Wherever possible, a standard volumetric solution is prepared by weighing out a known amount of the pure solid reagent, dissolving it in water, and making the solution up to a known volume in a graduated flask. It is not always possible, however, to obtain the desired reagent in pure form. Potassium permanganate crystals, for example, always contain a certain amount of manganese dioxide which must be filtered off before the solution can be used, and the difficulty of obtaining and weighing out sulfuric acid or sodium hydroxide of 100% purity is obvious. In such cases a solution is prepared which will have approximately the concentration desired, and this solution is then standardized by using it to titrate another substance which *can* be obtained in highly purified form. Thus potassium permanganate solution can be standardized against sodium oxalate, which can be obtained by recrystallization in a very high degree of purity, is easily dried, and is not hygroscopic. There are a limited number of substances, of which sodium oxalate is one, which can be obtained in very high purity and are suitable for preparing or standardizing volumetric solutions. These are called *primary standards*. A primary standard must have the following characteristics:

1. It must be readily obtainable in the pure state, or in a state of known purity.

2. It must react in one way only under the conditions of titration; there must be no side reactions.

3. If possible, it must not change weight on exposure to air, by volatilization, deliquescence, loss of water of crystallization, or otherwise. Salt hydrates are generally not suitable as primary standards.

4. The equivalent weight should be fairly high, to reduce weighing errors.

5. An acid or base should preferably be strong, that is, have a high ionization constant; an oxidizing or reducing agent should have a high, or low, oxidation potential.

The most common primary standards are listed in Table I. Wherever possible, a solution should be standardized by the same reaction which is used to determine the unknown. For example, a permanganate solution which is to be used to titrate iron should be stand-

TABLE I

SELECTED PRIMARY STANDARDS

Acids:
  Potassium hydrogen phthalate, $C_6H_4(COOK)(COOH)$
  Benzoic acid, C_6H_5COOH
  Constant-boiling hydrochloric acid, HCl
  Sulfamic acid, $SO_2(NH_2)OH$
  Potassium acid iodate, $KH(IO_3)_2$

Bases:
  Sodium carbonate, Na_2CO_3
  Mercuric oxide, HgO
  Borax, $Na_2B_4O_7$

Oxidizing Agents:
  Potassium dichromate, $K_2Cr_2O_7$
  Hexanitrato ammonium cerate, $(NH_4)_2Ce(NO_3)_6$
  Potassium bromate, $KBrO_3$
  Potassium iodate, KIO_3
  Potassium acid iodate, $KH(IO_3)_2$
  Iodine, I_2

Reducing Agents:
  Sodium oxalate, $Na_2C_2O_4$
  Arsenious oxide, As_2O_3
  Iron metal, Fe
  Ferrous ethylenediammonium sulfate, $Fe(C_2H_4N_2H_6)(SO_4)_2 \cdot 4H_2O$
  Potassium ferrocyanide, $K_4Fe(CN)_6$

Others:
  Sodium chloride, $NaCl$
  Potassium chloride, KCl

ardized against pure iron wire. If the volume of permanganate used in the standardization titration is not very different from that used in titrating the unknown, the end-point errors in the two titration will cancel within the limits of the random experimental errors.

In the absence of suitable primary standards, volumetric solution may sometimes be standardized by analyzing them gravimetrically. Thus a solution of silver nitrate could be standardized by treating a measured portion with excess sodium chloride in acid solution and weighing the silver chloride formed. This assumes, of course, that no other insoluble silver salts are formed, but this would be a reasonable assumption in this case.

Types of titration. In the chapters to follow we shall divide titrations for convenience into four classes according to the type of reaction. These are: (1) acid-base; (2) oxidation-reduction; (3) precipitation; (4) complex formation. The first two classes include the great majority of titrations. Good indicators are available, and potentiometric methods can always be used. The third class includes such reactions as the titration of chloride with silver nitrate or of zinc with potassium ferrocyanide. Such titrations are limited in number and accuracy by the indicators which can be used, and we therefore find it convenient to classify precipitation titrations according to the type of indicator used to detect the end point. Potentiometric or conductometric titration is sometimes possible, but not always. In the fourth class are titrations using mercuric nitrate, in which weakly ionized neutral molecules, such as $HgCl_2$, or complex ions such as $HgI_4^=$ are formed; these are soluble, and do not precipitate out. An important newcomer to this class of titrations is the determination of calcium and magnesium by ethylene diamine tetraacetic acid. Again the number of useful indicators is severely limited. Potentiometric and conductometric methods are sometimes possible, but more often not.

Electrical methods of titration. We have mentioned as electrical methods of titration, potentiometric and conductometric techniques. In potentiometric titration the solution under test is made part of a voltaic cell, and the electromotive force of this cell is measured and recorded as the titration proceeds; in conductometric titration the electric conductivity of the solution is followed. In each case characteristic changes occur which enable one to locate the end point. To these two techniques we must add those of amperometric titration and of high-frequency conductivity titration (in which the dielectric constant of the solution is a factor as well as its ionic conductance). All these methods will be discussed in the chapters to follow. By far the most important method is that of potentiometric titration. This is so important, not only in its practical application but in the insight which it gives into the titration process itself, that we shall begin our discussion of volumetric analysis with two chapters on the theory and practice of potentiometric methods.

11

Oxidation-reduction potentials

Electric potential. The electric potential of a point measures the work needed to bring an electric charge to that point. *Absolute* potential is the work done in moving a unit positive charge from an infinite distance in space to the point in question. This concept is of limited use in chemical systems. We are more often concerned with potential *differences*, or the work required to transport an electric charge from one point to another, and with *standard potentials*, which measure the work required to transport the charge to the point in question from a standard environment. The electric charge of most interest to chemists is the charge on the electron. Potentiometric methods are used to study reactions in which electrons are transferred, that is, oxidation-reduction reactions; however, they are also used to study acid-base reactions, which involve proton transfer, and reactions involving the precipitation of insoluble salts and the formation of soluble complexes from ions in solution.

The "oxidation-reduction potential" of a system, which measures the work needed to withdraw negatively charged electrons from that system, is best defined in terms of the way it is measured. This is shown in Figure 1,[1] for a "system" which is a solution containing ferrous and ferric ions, in which the potential energy of the electrons is governed by the equilibrium $Fe^{+++} + e \rightleftharpoons Fe^{++}$. This solution is placed in one compartment of a cell which consists of two compartments separated by a "salt bridge," a concentrated solution of potassium chloride. In the second compartment is the standard system hydrogen gas at one atmosphere pressure (more correctly, at unit fugacity) in contact with hydrochloric acid solution of unit activity

[1] This is the same as Figure 1 of the next chapter.

Here the potential energy of the electrons is governed by the equilibrium $2H^+ + 2e \rightleftharpoons H_2$. The platinized platinum plate serves the double purpose of catalyzing the exchange of electrons in this equilibrium and of conducting electrons in and out of the cell. The platinum wire dipping into the ferrous-ferric salt solution serves the same dual purpose.

The potentiometer circuit (which is shown in its simplest form) measures the potential difference across the whole cell. The sliding contact is moved until there is no motion of the galvanometer needle

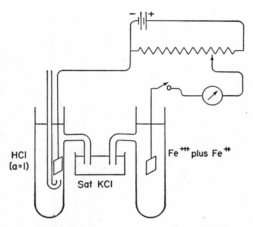

HCl
(a=1)   Fe^{+++} plus Fe^{++}

Sat KCl

Fig. 11-1. Measurement of oxidation-reduction potentials.

when the tapping key is closed. From the position of the contact on the wire one can find the electromotive force of the cell, if the wire is calibrated with a standard cell of known electromotive force.

The *electromotive force* of the cell is the potential across it when no current is drawn from the cell. It is also called the "reversible potential," and is the potential in which we are interested here. It is expressed in volts. A coulomb of electricity, falling through a potential difference of one volt, does one joule of work; 96,500 coulombs, which is the charge on a mole of electrons, falling through one volt, perform 96,500 joules, or 23,050 calories of work.

The electromotive force of the cell described is what is defined as the oxidation-reduction potential of the ferrous-ferric system on the standard hydrogen scale. To measure the oxidation-reduction potential of a

system such as $Zn^{++} + 2e \rightarrow Zn$, the same type of cell is used except
that the metallic zinc is not only a reactant but an electronic conductor.   The platinum wire in the right-hand compartment is replaced by a wire or rod of zinc, and the solution surrounding it is of
a salt of zinc.

It will be well to consider for a moment just what factors contribute to these potentials.   Strictly speaking, the potential which
is measured is that between two pieces of copper wire, the wire attached to the left-hand end of the slide wire, and the wire attached
to the slider.   Wherever two different metals join, there is a difference in potential (the so-called Volta potential), and likewise between
a metal and a solution there is a difference in potential; none of these
differences can be directly measured, but this is not necessary, since
in any closed circuit they must cancel out.   Where two solutions
join there is a liquid junction potential; this too cannot be measured,
although theory and circumstantial evidence both indicate that
where two dilute solutions are joined by a salt bridge of concentrated
potassium chloride or ammonium nitrate, the net liquid junction
potential is very small.

Standard potentials; conventions of sign.   The potential across
the cell shown in Figure 1 depends, naturally, upon the concentrations
of the ferrous and ferric ions in the solution.   The more concentrated
the ferric ions, the harder it is to withdraw electrons from the solution, and the more positive is the right-hand terminal of the cell; the
more concentrated the ferrous ions, the easier it is to withdraw electrons.   It is therefore desirable, in comparing one oxidation-reduction
system with another, to define *standard* oxidation-reduction potentials, which are measured with the reacting substances in standard
states.   For dissolved salts, the standard state is one of unit activity
(or very approximately, 1 molar concentration).[2]   For sparingly
soluble salts, metals, and solid reactants in general, the standard state
is the pure solid.   For gases, the standard state is the gas at unit
fugacity (1 atmosphere pressure, approximately).   Thus for the system $Zn^{++} + 2e \rightarrow Zn$, the standard state is pure metallic zinc dipping into a solution of a zinc salt of unit acitivity.   (For precise
work, the particular zinc salt must be specified.)   The *standard
oxidation-reduction potential* of the system $Zn^{++} + 2e \rightarrow Zn$ is the

[2] One-molal silver nitrate has an activity of 0.428 at 25°C; 7.25 molal silver
nitrate has an activity of 1.00.

electromotive force of a cell with this combination on one side and the standard hydrogen electrode on the other. It is 0.7620 volt at 25°C for a zinc sulfate solution, the wire attached to the zinc electrode being negative with respect to that attached to the hydrogen.[3] Conventionally, this information is summarized as follows:

$$Zn^{++} + 2e \rightarrow Zn; \quad E°_H = -0.7620 \text{ volt.}$$

The zero superscript of E indicates that E is expressed for the standard state; the H subscript (which is often omitted) indicates that the cell is completed with a standard hydrogen electrode.

Note that the equation of the half-cell reaction is written with the electrons on the left-hand side. The negative sign of E means not only that the zinc metal is negative with respect to the platinum coated with hydrogen, but also that this particular reaction is *not* spontaneous if the standard hydrogen ion-hydrogen gas couple is chosen as the source of electrons. That is, the spontaneous chemical reaction which supplies the electromotive force for the cell is one in which the zinc metal releases electrons, i.e., $Zn + 2H^+ \rightarrow Zn^{++} + H_2$, and not one in which zinc ions accept electrons. *A positive sign for $E°$ is associated conventionally with a spontaneous reaction, and vice versa.* Thus the statement regarding the standard potential of the zinc electrode may also be written

$$Zn \rightarrow Zn^{++} + 2e; \quad E°_H = +0.7620 \text{ volt.}$$

Some writers use the first formulation, others use the second.[4] We shall use the former, writing the electrons always on the *left* of the equation, because the sign of $E°_H$ is then the actual sign of the potential of the electrode under discussion, referred to the hydrogen electrode as zero. Thus for the cell illustrated in Figure 1, the electromotive force under standard conditions is 0.782 volt, the electrode dipping into the solution of ferrous and ferric salts being positive; that is,

$$Fe^{+++} + e \rightarrow Fe^{++}; \quad E°_H = +0.782 \text{ volt.}$$

[3] J. Shrawder, I. A. Cowperthwaite, and V. K. La Mer, *J. Am. Chem. Soc.*, **56**, 2348 (1934).

[4] W. M. Latimer, *Oxidation Potentials*, New York, Prentice-Hall, 1938. All the potentials quoted in this chapter are taken from the 1938 edition of this book. The second edition of Latimer, published in 1952, changes some of these potentials slightly to agree with newer data.

The positive sign also indicates that under standard conditions, hydrogen gas will spontaneously reduce ferric ions to ferrous ions.

The Nernst equation. We now ask how the potential is affected if the reactants are *not* in their standard states. The answer is to be found in the thermodynamic definition of activity, which is

$$dF = RT \, d \ln a,$$

F being the molar free energy of a substance whose activity is a. Combining this with the definition of electromotive force, which is essentially

$$\Delta F = -nE\mathfrak{F}$$

where ΔF is the increase in free energy per mole of a substance reacting, n the number of faradays of electricity transferred per mole of that same substance reacting, E the electromotive force, and $\mathfrak{F}$ the faraday, we find that for a reaction

$$M^{+n} + ne \rightharpoonup M,$$

$$E = E° + \frac{RT}{n\mathfrak{F}} \ln \frac{a_{M^{+n}}}{a_M} \tag{1}$$

Let us apply this to the hydrogen electrode itself; the reaction is

$$2H^+ + 2e \rightharpoonup H_2,$$

$E°$ is zero by definition, and the corresponding equation is:

$$E = \frac{RT}{2\mathfrak{F}} \ln \frac{(a_{H^+})^2}{a_{H_2}} = \frac{RT}{\mathfrak{F}} \ln a_{H^+} - \frac{RT}{2\mathfrak{F}} \ln a_{H_2} \tag{1a}$$

If the hydrogen gas has unit activity (pressure very nearly one atmosphere), this equation reduces to

$$E = \frac{RT}{\mathfrak{F}} \ln a_{H^+} = -2.303 \frac{RT}{\mathfrak{F}} \times pH \tag{1b}$$

In other words, in a cell consisting of a standard hydrogen electrode, a salt bridge, and an electrode consisting of platinum black and hydrogen gas at one atmosphere pressure dipping into a solution of variable hydrogen ion concentration, the electromotive force is directly proportional to the pH of the latter solution. Such a cell can be used to measure pH; indeed, *equation* (1b) *is used to define* pH. It is strictly valid only if the liquid junction potential is zero, but there is no way of measuring single ion activities without assuming the liquid junction potential to be known.

We shall illustrate equation (1) by two more examples. For the reaction $Fe^{+++} + e \rightarrow Fe^{++}$,

$$E = E^\circ + \frac{RT}{\mathfrak{F}} \ln \frac{a_{Fe^{+++}}}{a_{Fe^{++}}}. \tag{1c}$$

For the reaction $MnO_4^- + 8H^+ + 5e \rightarrow Mn^{++} + 4H_2O$,

$$E = E^\circ + \frac{RT}{5\mathfrak{F}} \ln \frac{a_{MnO_4^-}(a_{H^+})^8}{a_{Mn^{++}}}. \tag{1d}$$

The E° values are, of course, different in each case, and depend on temperature. Note that the logarithm term is preceded by a plus sign, the activity of the oxidized substance, or substances, is placed in the numerator, and the activity of the reduced substance is placed in the denominator. It is equally correct to write a minus sign before the logarithm term and then invert the activity fraction.

Reactions involving precipitates. The standard potential for the reaction $Ag^+ + e \rightarrow Ag$ is $+0.7995$ volt at 25°C. That is, the potential of silver metal dipping into a silver nitrate solution of activity equal to unity is $+0.7995$ volt with respect to the standard hydrogen electrode. Now suppose the silver ion concentration to be reduced by adding a chloride, so that AgCl is precipitated. As the chloride concentration rises, the silver ion concentration falls, in accordance with the solubility product, and when the chloride ion activity equals 1,

$$a_{Ag^+} = K_{sp}/1 = 1.6 \times 10^{-10}$$
$$E = +0.7995 + 0.0592 \log 1.6 \times 10^{-10}$$
$$= +0.7995 - 0.5773 = +0.2222 \text{ volt.}$$

This is a new standard potential, the potential for the reaction

$$AgCl + e \rightarrow Ag + Cl^-,$$

in which all reactants are in their standard states; silver chloride and silver as the pure solids, and chloride ion as a chloride solution of unit activity.

In actual practice, the potential for such a reaction is generally not calculated from the solubility product, but vice versa; the solubility product is calculated from the experimentally measured potential.

Where applicable, this is the most accurate way of finding solubility products.

The electrode silver-silver chloride-dissolved chloride ion is an example of an "electrode of the second kind," in which the concentration of the dissolved chloride ion determines the potential, not by a direct exchange of electrons with the metal of the electrode, but by regulating the concentration of the ions which do exchange electrons directly with the metal—in this case Ag^+. The Nernst equation for the silver-silver chloride-chloride ion reads as follows:

$$E = E° - \frac{RT}{\mathfrak{F}} \ln a_{Cl^-}$$

$$= +0.2222 - 0.0592 \log a_{Cl^-} \text{ at } 25°C.$$

Another example of an electrode of the second kind is mercury-mercurous sulfate-dissolved sulfate ion; here the reaction is

$$Hg_2SO_4 + 2e \rightarrow 2Hg + SO_4^=,$$

and the corresponding Nernst equation is

$$E = E° - \frac{RT}{2\mathfrak{F}} \ln a_{SO_4^-}$$

$$= +0.6151 - 0.0296 \log a_{SO_4^-} \text{ at } 25°C.$$

Potentiometric titrations: theory. Suppose a cell is set up consisting of a standard hydrogen electrode, a salt bridge, and a beaker of pure ferrous sulfate solution into which a platinum wire is dipped. The hydrogen electrode is called the *reference electrode*, and the platinum wire is called the *indicator electrode*, because in the titration to follow, the hydrogen electrode will remain undisturbed while the conditions around the platinum wire will be changed. According to the Nernst equation, this platinum wire should be infinitely negative with respect to the wire attached to the hydrogen electrode, because the ferric ion activity is zero. Of course, it will not be infinitely negative, because another mechanism, such as ionic adsorption at the surface of the platinum, will determine the potential, but it will be very low. Let us now run a solution of an oxidizing agent into the ferrous sulfate solution. The first drops of the oxidizing agent will increase the fraction $a_{Fe^{+++}}/a_{Fe^{++}}$ very rapidly, and the potential of the indicator electrode will increase rapidly too. Further additions of oxidizing agent will increase the potential still further, but relatively slowly so long as the fraction $a_{Fe^{+++}}/a_{Fe^{++}}$ is in the neighborhood of 1, that is, in the middle portion of the titration. As the equivalence point of the titration is approached, the remaining ferrous ions are rapidly used up as oxidant is added; the fraction $a_{Fe^{+++}}/a_{Fe^{++}}$ again increases very rapidly, and the potential increases rapidly too. It increases most rapidly at the equivalence point itself. After this point is passed, further additions of oxidant do not increase this fraction very much. This can be understood if we consider the equilibrium constant of the reaction. Suppose the oxidant is a ceric salt; then the quotient

$$\frac{a_{Ce^{+++}} \cdot a_{Fe^{+++}}}{a_{Ce^{++++}} \cdot a_{Fe^{++}}}$$

must at all times be the same, and equal to the equilibrium constant. Once the equivalence point is well passed, the ratio $a_{Ce^{+++}}/a_{Ce^{++++}}$ does not change much with further additions of ceric salt; nor does the ratio $a_{Fe^{+++}}/a_{Fe^{++}}$, therefore, and neither does the oxidation-reduction potential of the solution. The graph of the electromotive

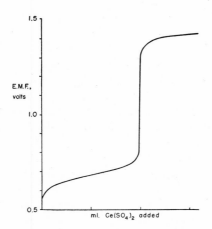

Fig. 11-2.   Potentiometric titration of ferrous sulfate with ceric sulfate.

force of the cell against the volume of added ceric salt is shown in
Figure 2.   The equivalence point in the titration is the point of
maximum slope of this curve, and it is very easy to locate.

It is possible to calculate the oxidation-reduction potential at any
point in the titration without difficulty if the simplifying approximation is made that activities are proportional to concentrations.
This approximation leads to rather serious error in most oxidation-
reduction reactions, because the interionic attractions are great due
to the high charges of the ions participating, and because complex
ion formation is common with highly charged metallic ions; however,
by such calculations the oxidation-reduction potential at equivalence
can be roughly estimated, and so can the ratio of oxidized to reduced
forms, that is, an estimate can be made of the completeness of the
reaction.   We shall illustrate such calculations by two simple cases;
the first is:

$$Fe^{++} + Ce^{++++} \rightarrow Fe^{+++} + Ce^{+++}.$$

(One ion of oxidant reacts with one ion of reductant.)   At equivalence, one mole of ceric ions is added to one mole of ferrous ions.
They react in the ratio 1:1, so that the amounts left unreacted must
also be in the ratio 1:1.   Therefore

$$\frac{[Fe^{+++}]}{[Fe^{++}]} = \frac{[Ce^{+++}]}{[Ce^{++++}]} \tag{2}$$

at equivalence, where the symbols refer to molar concentration.
Replacing activities by concentrations in the Nernst equations, inserting the appropriate standard potentials, and introducing the
numerical value of $2.303RT/\mathfrak{F}$, which is 0.059 at 25°C,

$$E = +0.78 + 0.059 \log_{10} \frac{[Fe^{+++}]}{[Fe^{++}]}. \tag{3}$$

$$E = +1.44 + 0.059 \log_{10} \frac{[Ce^{++++}]}{[Ce^{+++}]}. \tag{4}$$

Note that the solution can have only one oxidation-reduction potential at a time, just as it can only have one temperature or one pH at
a time.   Therefore these two E's are the same.   Subtracting (3)
from (4),

$$0.66 + 0.059 \log \frac{[Ce^{++++}]}{[Ce^{+++}]} - 0.059 \log \frac{[Fe^{+++}]}{[Fe^{++}]}$$

$$= 0.66 - 0.059 \log \frac{[Fe^{+++}]}{[Fe^{++}]} \cdot \frac{[Ce^{+++}]}{[Ce^{++++}]} = 0. \quad (5)$$

Introducing equation (2),

$$0.66 = 0.059 \log \frac{[Fe^{+++}]^2}{[Fe^{++}]^2},$$

$$\log \frac{[Fe^{+++}]}{[Fe^{++}]} = \frac{0.66}{2 \times 0.059} = 5.6, \quad (6)$$

and $[Fe^{+++}]/[Fe^{++}] = 4 \times 10^5$ at equivalence. That is, the oxida-tion of ferrous ions to ferric is virtually complete.

We now calculate the oxidation-reduction potential, E, by substituting (6) into (3):

$$E = +0.78 + 0.059 \times 5.6 = +1.11 \; volts.$$

This falls exactly midway between the two standard potentials. This is the case for all "symmetrical" oxidation-reduction reactions, in which one mole of oxidant reacts with one mole of reductant.

The second case is:

$$Sn^{++} + 2Fe^{+++} \rightharpoonup Sn^{++++} + 2Fe^{++}.$$

(Two ions of oxidant react with one ion of reductant.) At equivalence,

$$\frac{[Sn^{++++}]}{[Sn^{++}]} = \frac{[Fe^{++}]}{[Fe^{+++}]}, \quad (7)$$

by the same reasoning as before. The two Nernst equations read:

$$E = +0.15 + \frac{0.059}{2} \log \frac{[Sn^{++++}]}{[Sn^{++}]}. \quad (8)$$

$$E = +0.78 + 0.059 \log \frac{[Fe^{+++}]}{[Fe^{++}]} \quad (9)$$

$$= +0.78 + \frac{0.059}{2} \log \frac{[Fe^{+++}]^2}{[Fe^{++}]^2}. \quad (9a)$$

Subtracting (8) from (9a),

$$0.63 - \frac{0.059}{2} \log \frac{[Sn^{++++}]}{[Sn^{++}]} \cdot \frac{[Fe^{++}]^2}{[Fe^{+++}]^2} = 0. \quad (10)$$

Introducing (7),

$$0.63 = \frac{0.059}{2} \log \left(\frac{[Sn^{++++}]}{[Sn^{++}]} \right)^3 ;$$

$$\log \frac{[Sn^{++++}]}{[Sn^{++}]} = \frac{0.63 \times 2}{0.059 \times 3} = 7.12, \tag{11}$$

and $[Sn^{++++}]/[Sn^{++}] = 1.3 \times 10^7$ at equivalence. Substituting this value into equation (8),

$$E = +0.15 + 0.21 = +0.36 \text{ volt.}$$

This is not midway between the two standard potentials, but is one-third of the way up from 0.15 volt to 0.78 volt.

Equilibrium constant. In the foregoing section we calculated the proportions of the reactants present at equivalence in the titration, assuming equilibrium to be reached. From this, we could easily have found the equilibrium constant. In this section we shall calculate the equilibrium constant of an oxidation-reduction reaction in a more systematic manner, using the potentials as a measure of the free energy of the reaction. We shall illustrate this method by four practically useful examples.

(a) *The reaction* $Fe^{++} + Ce^{++++} \rightleftharpoons Fe^{+++} + Ce^{+++}$. We have for the two half-reactions at 25°C,

$$Fe^{+++} + e \rightarrow Fe^{++}; \quad (E^\circ_H)_1 = +0.78 \text{ volt.}$$
$$Ce^{++++} + e \rightarrow Ce^{+++}; \quad (E^\circ_H)_2 = +1.44 \text{ volt.}$$

When a mole of ferric ions oxidizes hydrogen gas under standard conditions,

$$\Delta F^\circ_1 = -0.78 \mathfrak{F},$$

and when a mole of ceric ions oxidizes hydrogen gas,

$$\Delta F^\circ_2 = -1.44 \mathfrak{F}.$$

The free energy increase when a mole of ceric ions oxidizes a mole of ferrous ions under standard conditions is therefore

$$\Delta F^\circ = \Delta F^\circ_2 - \Delta F^\circ_1 = -(1.44 - 0.78) \mathfrak{F} = -0.66 \mathfrak{F},$$

and the equilibrium constant, $K = a_{Fe^{+++}} a_{Ce^{+++}} / a_{Fe^{++}} a_{Ce^{++++}}$ is given by

$$F^\circ = -RT \ln K = -0.66 \mathfrak{F},$$

or

$$\ln K = +0.66 \frac{\mathfrak{F}}{RT}$$

$$\log_{10} K = \frac{+0.66}{0.059} = 11.2; \quad K = 1.6 \times 10^{11}.$$

A reaction is generally considered complete enough to be used for titration with an indicator when the ratio of unreacted to reacted substance at the end point is 1:1000 or less. For a reaction of the type $A + B \rightleftharpoons C + D$, the equilibrium constant must therefore be 10^6 or more. The ferrous-ceric reaction is obviously complete enough for titration.

(b) *The reaction*

$$Fe^{++} + V(OH)_4^+ + 2H^+ \rightleftharpoons Fe^{+++} + VO^{++} + 3H_2O.$$

Many oxidation-reduction reactions involve hydrogen ions, and the ratio of oxidized to nonoxidized forms in such cases can be altered considerably by changing the hydrogen ion concentration. An example which is of analytical interest is that between ferrous ions and +5 vanadium; in acid solution, the latter is present largely as $V(OH)_4^+$.

For the reaction $V(OH)_4^+ + 2H^+ + e \rightarrow VO^{++} + 3H_2O$, $E° = +1.00$ volt. Therefore,

$$\log K = \frac{1.00 - 0.77}{0.059} = 3.9,$$

$$K = \frac{a_{Fe^{+++}} a_{VO^{++}}}{a_{Fe^{++}} a_{V(OH)_4^+} a_{H^+}^2} = 8 \times 10^3.$$

For $a_{H^+} = 1$, the ratio of ferric ion concentration to ferrous ion concentration at equivalence is $\sqrt{8 \times 10^3} = 90$, assuming the activity coefficients cancel. This seems barely sufficient for an accurate titration of +5 vanadium by ferrous iron, or of ferrous iron by permanganate in the presence of +4 vanadium, yet this titration is feasible in practice, using orthophenanthroline indicator.[5]

As stated above, calculations of this kind which ignore activity coefficients can give orders of magnitude only. We may certainly use them, however, to estimate the effect of changing the hydrogen ion concentration. Let $a_{H^+} = 10^{-2}$; then at equivalence, $[Fe^{+++}]/[Fe^{++}] = [VO^{++}]/[V(OH)_4^+] = 1$, approximately; that is, when a mixture of +2 iron and +4 vanadium is titrated with permanganate at pH 2, both are oxidized together and the permanganate consumption will be the sum of the iron and the vanadium. By titrating two portions, one in 1 M acid and the other in a buffer of pH 2 or more, a mixture of +2 iron and +4 vanadium can be analyzed.[5]

[5] H. H. Willard and P. Young, *Ind. Eng. Chem., Anal. Ed.,* **6,** 48 (1934).

(c) *The reaction* $2\ Cu^{++} + 5I^- \rightleftharpoons 2CuI(solid) + I_3^-$.

This reaction is used in the volumetric determination of copper, the liberated iodine (which is in the form of the tri-iodide ion) being titrated with thiosulfate. Obviously the completeness of reduction of cupric ions will be greater, the greater the iodide ion concentration. We shall estimate the minimum iodide concentration needed for a satisfactory titration.

The standard potentials concerned are:

$$Cu^{++} + I^- + e \rightarrow CuI; \quad E^\circ_1 = +0.877 \text{ volt.}$$

$$I_3^- + 2e \rightarrow 3I^-; \quad E^\circ_2 = +0.536 \text{ volt.}$$

The corresponding standard free energies, for the oxidation of *one mole* of hydrogen (two equivalents), are:

$$\Delta F^\circ_1 = -0.877 \times 2\mathfrak{F}.$$

$$\Delta F^\circ_2 = -0.536 \times 2\mathfrak{F}.$$

Therefore for the reaction

$$2Cu^{++} + 5I^- \rightleftharpoons 2CuI + I_3^-,$$

$$\Delta F^\circ = \Delta F^\circ_1 - \Delta F^\circ_2 = -0.341 \times 2\mathfrak{F},$$

and $\qquad \log_{10} K = -\dfrac{\Delta F^\circ}{2.303RT} = +\dfrac{0.341 \times 2}{0.0592} = 11.5,$

i.e., $\qquad\qquad K = \dfrac{a_{I_3^-}}{a_{Cu^{++}}{}^2 a_{I^-}{}^5} = 3 \times 10^{11}.$

Now during titration, the iodine liberated reacts with the thiosulfate added, and the end point is that at which the blue starch-iodine color disappears. The lowest concentration of iodine needed to give a visible blue color with starch is between $10^{-5}\ M$ and $10^{-4}\ M$; let us take the latter figure. Let us also suppose that the cupric ion concentration must be not more than $10^{-5}\ M$ at the end point; there will then be no significant end-point error if 0.01 M copper is titrated with 0.01 M thiosulfate. Inserting concentrations in place of activities in the equilibrium constant,

$$K = \frac{10^{-4}}{(10^{-5})^2[I^-]^5} = 3 \times 10^{11}; \quad [I^-] = 0.08.$$

The directions usually given for this determination call for enough potassium iodide to give about twice this concentration of free iodide ion at the end point. Again we must remember that activities may differ greatly from concentrations. Cupric ions associate readily with most anions, especially the acetate ion which is sometimes added to buffer the solution in this titration, to form complex ions or undissociated molecules; such association may make the activity of the cupric ion far less than its stoichiometric concentration, so that $a_{Cu^{++}}$ would have to be well under 10^{-5} at the end point for a satisfactory titration. It is, in fact, quite impossible to titrate cupric copper iodometrically in the presence of much acetate. Adding more potassium iodide helps very little, for if the iodide concentration is high, appreciable cuprous iodide dissolves as $CuI_4^{=}$, which means that even more potassium iodide than the above calculation shows must be added to maintain the desired concentration of free iodide.

(d) *The reduction of a cupric salt with titanous or chromous chloride.*
Cupric ions can be reduced in two stages, first to cuprous ions, then to metallic copper. In aqueous solution the reaction can be halted at the cuprous stage only if something is present to combine with cuprous ions to form a stable complex or sparingly soluble solid; otherwise the cuprous ions disproportionate into cupric ions and copper. Chloride ions combine with cuprous ions to form sparingly soluble CuCl. We shall ask what concentration of chloride ions is necessary to stabilize CuCl sufficiently so that we can titrate Cu^{++} to CuCl.

The standard potentials are:

$$Cu^{++} + Cl^- + e \rightarrow CuCl; \qquad E°_1 = +0.566 \text{ volt.}$$

$$CuCl + e \rightarrow Cu + Cl^-; \quad E°_2 = +0.124 \text{ volt.}$$

The equilibrium constant of the reaction

$$Cu^{++} + Cu + 2Cl^- \rightleftharpoons 2CuCl$$

is given by $$\log K = \frac{0.566 - 0.124}{0.059} = 7.48;$$

$$K = \frac{1}{a_{Cu^{++}} \cdot a_{Cl^-}^2} = 3 \times 10^7.$$

Suppose the reduction of cupric ion to be sufficiently complete for titration purposes when $a_{Cu^{++}} = 10^{-5}$; suppose, too, that reduction of cuprous chloride to copper just begins at this point, so that we have equilibrium between cupric ions, copper, chloride ions, and cuprous chloride. Then

$$a_{Cl^-} = \sqrt{\frac{1}{10^{-5} \times 3 \times 10^7}} = 0.06.$$

This is the minimum chloride concentration which must be present to give a sharp end point. In practice, a higher chloride ion concentration is used. For example, cupric copper is titrated with chromous chloride solution (a titration which is used to standardize chromous chloride) in presence of 1 M HCl. In this case most, or all, of the cuprous chloride goes into solution as a complex ($CuCl_2^-$ or $CuCl_3^=$). Experimental curves obtained in this potentiometric titration may be found in a paper by Lingane and Pecsok.[6]

Formal potentials. The examples just given show that equilibrium calculations made from standard potentials and the Nernst equation, with concentrations substituted for activities, are a useful guide to the practical conditions needed for oxidation-reduction titrations, but they cannot predict these conditions exactly. This is due partly to the high electrostatic interaction between ions of multiple charge, and partly to the large number of complex ions formed by most of the metals which take part in oxidation-reduction titrations (see Chapter 7).

In an attempt to describe oxidation-reduction potentials of solutions in terms of quantities that can easily be measured, the concept of *formal potential* has been introduced by Swift.[7] He defines the formal potential of an oxidation-reduction system as the potential of a solution in which all the dissolved reactants are in one-formal concentration, that is, in a concentration of one mole per liter, without regard to complex ion formation or dissociation. Thus a one-formal ferric salt solution contains 56 grams of tripositive iron per liter, which may be in the form of Fe^{+++}, $FeCl^{++}$, $FeCl_6^=$, or any other combination. The formal potential of the ferrous-ferric system in 4 M HCl is the potential of a solution containing one mole of ferrous chloride, one mole of ferric chloride, and four moles of hydrochloric acid per liter; it is 0.66 volt, whereas the standard potential of the ferrous-ferric system is 0.78 volt. The formal potential can be

[6] J. J. Lingane and R. Pecsok, *Anal. Chem.*, **20**, 425 (1948).
[7] E. H. Swift, *A System of Chemical Analysis*, New York, Prentice-Hall, 1939, p. 50.

measured in a single determination with a reference half-cell, while the standard potential must be found by extrapolation from several measurements. The difference between these two potentials is due mainly to the formation of ferric chloride complexes, but partly also to the liquid junction potential between the experimental solution and the reference half-cell.

Formal potentials are often given the symbol $E^{\circ\prime}$, to distinguish them from standard potentials E°. They may be inserted in the Nernst equation with concentrations taking the place of activities, but calculations made in this way are nevertheless approximate.

Table I lists a few representative formal potentials, with standard potentials given for comparison. The effect of complex ion formation is clearly seen in some cases. Additional data which show the effect of complex formation on electrode potentials are given in Chapter 5, Table I.

TABLE I

FORMAL AND STANDARD POTENTIALS

		Formal potential, $E^{\circ\prime}$, in:		
Reaction	E°	1 M HCl	1 M H$_2$SO$_4$	1 M H$_2$SO$_4$ plus 0.5 M H$_3$PO$_4$
$Ce^{++++} + e \rightarrow Ce^{+++}$	. . .	1.23	1.44	. . .
$VO_2^+ + 2H^+ + e \rightarrow VO^{++} + H_2O$	1.00	1.02	1.0	. . .
$Cr_2O_7^= + 14H^+ + 6e \rightarrow Cr^{+++} + 7HO$	1.36	1.09	1.15	. . .
$Fe^{+++} + e \rightarrow Fe^{++}$	0.782	0.70	0.68	0.61
$Fe(CN)_6^= + e \rightarrow Fe(CN)_6^=$	0.356	0.71	0.72	. . .
$2H^+ + 2e \rightarrow H_2$	0.000	0.005	. . .	. . .

Note: Most of these data are taken from E. H. Swift, *A System of Chemical Analysis,* New York, Prentice-Hall, 1939.

PROBLEMS

1. One hundred ml. of 0.01 M FeCl$_3$ is titrated with 0.10 M CrCl$_2$. Draw a graph of potential against volume of titrant, and calculate the oxidation-reduction

potential (a) when the $FeCl_3$ is half reduced, (b) at the equivalence point, given the following standard potentials:

$$Fe^{+++} + e \rightarrow Fe^{++}; \quad E° = +0.78 \text{ volt.}$$

$$Cr^{+++} + e \rightarrow Cr^{++}; \quad E° = -0.40 \text{ volt.}$$

2. One hundred ml of a solution 0.02 M in Cu^{++} and 0.10 M in Cl^- is titrated with 0.10 M $CrCl_2$. Calculate the potentials at half-change and equivalence, given that:

$$Cu^{++} + Cl^- + e \rightarrow CuCl \text{ (solid)}; \quad E° = +0.57 \text{ volt.}$$

3. Calculate the equilibrium constant of the reaction

$$2Fe^{+++} + 3I^- \rightleftharpoons 2Fe^{++} + I_3^-,$$

using standard potentials, and given that

$$I_3^- + 2e \rightarrow 3I^-; \quad E° = +0.536 \text{ volt.}$$

Calculate also the percentage of Fe^{+++} that remains unreduced when 25 ml. of 0.05 M Fe^{+++} and 25 ml. of 0.25 M I^- are mixed. Under what conditions can this reaction be used in the quantitative determination of ferric ion?

4. Given the standard potentials (both values for nitrate solutions):

$$Ce^{++++} + e \rightarrow Ce^{+++}; \quad E° = 1.61 \text{ volt.}$$

$$Tl^{+++} + 2e \rightarrow Tl^+; \quad E° = 1.21 \text{ volt.}$$

Calculate the percent of Tl^+ which remains unoxidized when equivalent quantities of 0.1 M thallous nitrate and ceric nitrate are mixed, and also calculate the potential at the equivalence point.

5. Given the standard potentials:

$$Cu^+ + e \rightarrow Cu, \quad E° = +0.522 \text{ volt.}$$

$$Cu^{++} + 2e \rightarrow Cu, \quad E° = +0.345 \text{ volt.}$$

Calculate the standard potential for the reaction

$$Cu^{++} + e \rightarrow Cu^+.$$

(*Note:* Calculate the *free energies* for the first two reactions and take the difference.)

6. From your answer to Problem 5 and from the standard potential

$$Cu^{++} + I^- + e \rightarrow CuI \text{ (solid)}, \quad E° = +0.877 \text{ volt}$$

calculate the solubility product of CuI.

7. How may $E°$ for $Cu^+ + e \rightarrow Cu$ be found experimentally?

8. From the potential in Problem 6 and from the standard potential

$$I_3^- + 2e \rightarrow 3I^-, \quad E° = +0.536 \text{ volt}$$

plot graphs to show the potential of both reactions as a function of pI^- ($-\log_{10} [I^-]$) for $[Cu^{++}] = [I_3^-] = 0.1$, and draw conclusions as to the experimental conditions necessary in titrating cupric salts iodometrically.

9. Explain why (a) moderate concentrations of acetate, (b) high concentrations of neutral salts such as sodium sulfate, cause a poor, indistinct end point in the iodometric titration of copper.

10. Will ferric ions interfere in the iodometric titration of Cu^{++}, and if so, how may their interference be prevented?

11. In the iodometric titration of Cu^{++}, some of the potassium iodide may be replaced by potassium thiocyanate, which is cheaper than potassium iodide and often gives a sharper end point. Discuss the theory of this, and estimate how much of the iodide can be replaced by thiocyanate.

12. Which ion will be expected to form the more stable complex CuX_4^- with the cupric ion, Cl^- or Br^-? How will such complex formation affect the iodometric determination of copper?

13. Given the standard potentials

$$Ti^{++++} + e \rightarrow Ti^{+++}; \quad E° = +0.04 \text{ volt}$$

$$Sn^{++++} + 2e \rightarrow Sn^{++}; \quad E° = +0.13 \text{ volt}$$

$$Cu^{++} + 2e \rightarrow Cu; \quad E° = +0.34 \text{ volt and the solubility product of}$$
$$CuCl = 1.0 \times 10^{-6}.$$

Calculate
    (a) The equilibrium constant for the reaction between Ti^{+++} and Sn^{++++}.
    (b) The percentage of Sn^{++++} remaining unreduced when equal volumes of 0.2 M $TiCl_3$ and 0.1 M $SnCl_4$ are mixed.
    (c) The oxidation-reduction potential of the solution in (b).
    (d) Whether $TiCl_3$ will reduce a solution of $CuCl_2$ to metallic Cu or to solid CuCl, if equal volumes of 0.1 M $TiCl_3$ and 0.1 M $CuCl_2$ are mixed.
    (e) The proportion of Ti^{+++} remaining unoxidized in (d).

14. Cupric sulfate is titrated with chromous sulfate, giving metallic copper. What is the maximum chloride ion concentration which may be present without any cuprous chloride precipitating at any stage in the titration, if the cupric sulfate solution is initially 0.1 M and the chromous sulfate the same?

15. The standard potential of the silver-silver bromide electrode at 25°C is −0.073 volt. Calculate K_{sp} for AgBr.

16. List as many factors as you can which cause formal potentials to differ from standard potentials.

17. An indicator electrode in a certain solution is 0.50 volt more positive than a normal calomel electrode used as the reference electrode. What would be the electromotive force of the cell if (a) the standard hydrogen electrode, (b) the saturated calomel electrode (containing 4 N KCl), were used as reference electrodes?

18. Why is it misleading to speak of the activity of a single ion, e.g., Fe^{+++}?

19. Draw as accurate a graph as possible of oxidation-reduction potential against volume of oxidant for 100 ml. of a solution 0.01 M in Sn^{++}, 0.01 M in Fe^{++}, and 0.1 M in $HClO_4$, titrated with 0.1 N $KMnO_4$.

$$(MnO_4^- + 8H^+ + 5e \rightarrow Mn^{++}; \quad E° = 1.5 \text{ volts.})$$

20. One solution is 1 formal in ferric chloride, 1 formal in ferrous chloride, and 1 formal in hydrochloric acid; another is 0.01 formal in ferric chloride, 0.01 formal in ferrous chloride, and 1 formal in hydrochloric acid. How would the potentials of these two solutions compare with one another? Do you think that the definition of *formal potential* given on page 196 is satisfactory?

12

Methods of potentiometric titration

The scope of potentiometric titrations. Any titration can be performed potentiometrically in which one or more of the ions or molecules taking part in the reaction determines the potential of an electrode. Obviously, all inorganic oxidation-reduction titrations can be done potentiometrically; all that is needed is an indicator electrode, usually a platinum wire,[1] which dips into the solution being titrated, and a reference half-cell, such as the standard hydrogen or calomel half-cell, which makes electrical contact with the same solution through a salt bridge. The apparatus shown in Figure 1 is satisfactory for such titrations; one would start with, say, a ferrous salt solution in the right-hand compartment, and run in an oxidizing agent, plotting the electromotive force of the cell against the volume of oxidant added. A graph of the form shown in Figure 2 would be obtained.

To titrate an acid with a base potentiometrically, one could replace the platinum wire by a platinized platinum gauze over which hydrogen gas is passed. In the absence of other oxidation-reduction systems, the potential of the platinized platinum is determined by the equilibrium

$$2H^+ + 2e \rightleftharpoons H_2.$$

As the hydrogen ions in the solution are removed by combination with the added base, this electrode becomes more negative, and again

---

[1] Mercury is used where the oxidation-reduction potential of the solution falls below that of the hydrogen electrode.

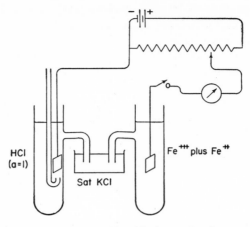

Fig. 12-1.   Measurement of oxidation-reduction potentials.

a curve something like Figure 2 is obtained if the cell electromotive force is plotted against the volume of added base. In this case the right-hand electrode (Figure 1) becomes more *negative*, instead of more positive, as the titration proceeds. The electromotive force is directly proportional to the pH of the solution being titrated [Equation (1b), Chapter 11].

The hydrogen gas-platinized platinum electrode may be replaced

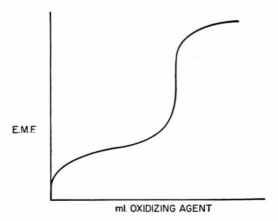

Fig. 12-2.   A typical emf-titration curve.

by other electrodes whose potentials depend on the hydrogen ion concentration, and which are more convenient to use. Examples of such electrodes are discussed below.

Electrodes of the second kind (page 188) are useful in titrations involving precipitation or complex formation. Thus an electrode of silver will follow the titration of chloride ions by silver nitrate. Its potential is determined by the equilibrium

$$Ag^+ + e \rightleftharpoons Ag.$$

At the start of the titration, the Ag^+ concentration is extremely low, but as silver nitrate is added and chloride precipitated, the silver ion concentration rises slowly, being governed by the solubility equilibrium

$$Ag^+ + Cl^- \rightleftharpoons AgCl \text{ (solid)}.$$

Near the equivalence point of the titration, the silver ion concentration rises extremely rapidly, and so does the potential of the silver indicator electrode. In the presence of solid silver chloride, the potential of the silver electrode against the standard hydrogen half-cell at 25°C is given by (see page 187):

$$
\begin{aligned}
E &= 0.7995 + 0.0592 \log a_{Ag^+} \\
  &= 0.7995 + 0.0592 \log (K_{sp}/a_{Cl^-}) \\
  &= 0.2222 - 0.0592 \log a_{Cl^-}.
\end{aligned}
$$

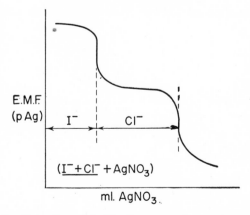

Fig. 12-3.   Potentiometric titration curve for a mixture of iodide and chloride, titrated with silver nitrate, using a silver indicator electrode.

If a mixture of chloride and iodide is titrated potentiometrically in the same way, the potential of the silver indicator electrode is at first extremely low on account of the low solubility product of silver iodide. When all the iodide is precipitated as silver iodide, the potential rises sharply, and when all the chloride is precipitated, it rises again. A curve with two inflection points is obtained (Figure 3).

Cyanide ions, which form a soluble complex with silver ions, can be titrated in the same way. The curve obtained is shown in Figure 4. Two inflection points are obtained, the first corresponding to

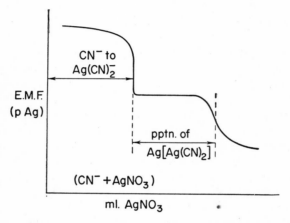

Fig. 12-4.   Titration of cyanide with silver nitrate, using a silver indicator electrode.

the completion of the reaction $2CN^- + Ag^+ \rightarrow Ag(CN)_2^-$. In the interval between the first and the second inflection points, the precipitation reaction $Ag(CN)_2^- + Ag^+ \rightarrow Ag[Ag(CN)_2]$ takes place.

Electrodes of the third kind are theoretically possible, but they are little used as they take a long time to come to equilibrium. An example which has been used in the potentiometric titration of calcium ions by oxalate[2] is amalgamated lead coated with a mixture of lead oxalate and calcium oxalate:

$$Pb - Hg \mid PbC_2O_4 + CaC_2O_4, \quad Ca^{++}.$$

[2] H. J. C. Tendeloo, *Rec. trav. chim.*, **59**, 681 (1940).

The potential of this electrode depends on the calcium ion activity of the solution, for the calcium ion activity determines the oxalate ion activity through the solubility product of calcium oxalate, and the oxalate ion activity similarly determines the lead ion activity, and hence the potential of the lead electrode.

Reference half-cells used in potentiometric titrations. In a cell used in potentiometric titrations, one electrode maintains a relatively constant potential with respect to the solution while the other changes its potential as the titration proceeds.   The first is called the *reference electrode,* the second the *indicator electrode.*   Contact between the two is generally made through a salt bridge.   The reference electrode assembly, namely the metallic conductor and the solution surrounding it, is properly called the reference half-cell, though the term "electrode" is often applied to the entire half-cell.

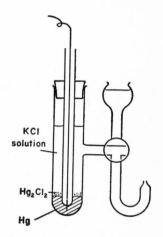

The standard hydrogen half-cell, illustrated in Figure 1, is the primary standard of reference for all electrode potential measurements.   It is an inconvenient standard for practical use, however, because of the need for a supply of pure hydrogen gas and the need for knowing accurately the partial pressure of hydrogen at the surface of the platinized platinum electrode.

Fig. 12-5.   Calomel half-cell.

In potentiometric titrations it is practically never used.   Instead, secondary standards are used, half-cells which are more easily assembled and maintained.   One such half-cell is the so-called calomel electrode (Figure 5).   A pool of mercury is in metallic contact with the external circuit; the solution above it is potassium chloride, saturated with mercurous chloride (calomel); above the mercury surface is a sludge of calomel and finely divided mercury.   The half-cell reaction is

$$Hg_2Cl_2 \text{ (solid)} + 2e \rightarrow 2Hg \text{ (liquid)} + 2Cl^-.$$

The potential depends on the chloride ion activity.   For a 1 normal KCl solution ($a = 0.59$), E_H is 0.2812 volt at 25°C.   Oxidation-reduction potentials referred to the normal calomel electrode are therefore less positive by 0.2812 volt than the same potentials referred to the standard hydrogen electrode.

Another form is the saturated calomel electrode. Here the solution is saturated with potassium chloride, and potassium chloride crystals are put in the cell to keep it so. The value of E_H for the saturated calomel electrode is +0.2458 volt at 25°C. The saturated calomel electrode is convenient because the salt bridge of saturated potassium chloride solution can be a part of the half-cell assembly, as in the half-cell shown in Figure 5. The solution in the salt bridge can be renewed when necessary by turning the stopcock.

Where a reference electrode having a more positive potential than the calomel electrode is desired, the mercury-mercurous sulfate electrode with $E°_H = 0.6151$ volt at 25°C may be used. This is exactly like the calomel electrode except that sulfate replaces chloride. With certain commercial instruments for potentiometric titration it is desirable to keep the cell electromotive force within a certain range during titration and not to have it change sign; hence it is convenient to use different reference electrodes for different titrations.

A very convenient reference electrode is the silver-silver chloride electrode. It consists of a surface of silver which is coated with silver chloride. Placed in a solution containing chloride ions, this takes up a definite potential in accordance with the reaction

$$AgCl \text{ (solid)} + e \rightharpoonup Ag + Cl^-.$$

For this reaction $E°_H$ is +0.2222 volt at 25°C. The advantage of this electrode is its simplicity. An electrode adequate for analytical purposes can be made by silver-plating a 2-cm. spiral of platinum wire, then making it anodic in hydrochloric acid for a short time. This can be immersed in a chloride solution in a device like that of Figure 5 and used as a reference electrode, or it can be dipped in a chloride solution which is to be titrated and used as the indicator electrode to follow the potential changes during titration. A silver-silver bromide electrode can be made and used similarly.

Finally, the glass electrode (see below) can be used for reference in cases where the pH of the solution does not change appreciably during titration. For example, in titrating an acid solution of a ferrous salt with ceric sulfate, or an acid solution of a chloride with silver nitrate, a glass electrode dipping in the solution can serve as the reference electrode, the indicator electrode being a platinum wire in the first case and a silver-silver chloride electrode in the second case. This is a very convenient arrangement to use in adapting a commercial glass electrode pH meter for general potentiometric titration. One simply removes the calomel half-cell from the pH meter and substitutes the appropriate indicator electrode.

The glass electrode.[3] Measurements of pH with the glass electrode are far more popular today than they were fifteen years ago. This is because of the simple, portable, reliable instruments which are now available. These pH meters have facilitated not only pH measurements, but all potentiometric measurements.

The glass electrode is not an electrode in the sense we have been discussing, for glass is not a metallic conductor, and no electrons are given up by, or to, the glass. However, in thin films glass acts as a membrane electrode, which permits certain kinds of ions to penetrate it, but not others. Glass consists of a dense, negatively charged silicate network in which are small positively charged ions, mainly sodium ions. It is possible for other positive ions to enter the glass from outside, by displacing these sodium ions, but electric repulsion makes it almost impossible for negative ions to enter. A glass membrane is therefore selectively permeable to cations. Owing probably to its dense structure, it is even more selective than this. Under ordinary conditions, the only cations which can penetrate the glass are hydrogen ions. This results in a special liquid junction potential being set up, which depends on the hydrogen ion activities on either side of the glass.

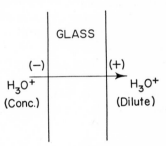

Fig. 12-6. Glass electrode (schematic).

Figure 6 indicates what is thought to happen when two solutions of different hydrogen ion concentrations are separated by a thin glass membrane. Hydrogen ions (solvated or otherwise) pass from the concentrated side to the dilute side by diffusion or osmosis, but

[3] M. Dole, *The Glass Electrode*, New York, Wiley, 1940.

since no negative ions can pass through with them, they build up a positive charge on the dilute side of the glass. The electronic charge is so large that it does not take many hydrogen ions to build up a positive charge large enough to prevent (by electrostatic repulsion) any more ions from diffusing through. By adding the free energy increase in transferring a mole of ions from activity a_1 to activity a_2 to the electric work necessary to move the charges of these ions against a potential difference E, and equating to zero, since equilibrium exists, we have:

$$\Delta F_{12} = RT \ln \frac{a_2}{a_1} + E_{12}\mathfrak{F} = 0,$$

or,

$$E_{12} = \frac{RT}{\mathfrak{F}} \, ln \, \frac{a_1}{a_2}, \tag{1}$$

where ΔF_{12} is the increase in free energy and E_{12} is the increase in positive potential in passing from side 1 to side 2. If we now insert reference electrodes, such as calomel half-cells, into the solutions on each side, and arrange to keep the hydrogen ion activity a_1 constant while a_2 can be varied, we have a pH meter. For,

$$E = E' + E_{12} = E' + \frac{RT}{\mathfrak{F}} \ln a_1 - \frac{RT}{\mathfrak{F}} \ln a_2$$

$$= E^\circ + \frac{2.303RT}{\mathfrak{F}} \cdot (\text{pH})_2, \tag{2}$$

since $\text{pH} = -\log_{10} a$. In this equation E' is the part of the cell electromotive force which is due to differences in the two reference electrodes, plus potentials at liquid junctions between different solutions; it also includes a small term for the "asymmetry potential" of the glass membrane, a potential difference which exists across it even when the solutions on both sides are the same, and is due to strains in the glass. The value of E° is constant for a given assembly at a given temperature.

The glass electrode assembly which is used in practice is illustrated in Figure 7. A is a silver-silver chloride electrode; B is the thin glass bulb which forms the membrane, and contains, usually, 1 N hydrochloric acid. This provides a constant hydrogen ion activity (a_1) as well as a constant chloride ion activity. C is a compact type of saturated calomel electrode. The junction between it and the test solution (in D) can be flushed out by removing the stopper E.

A disadvantage of the glass electrode is that the membrane B must be very thin, and therefore fragile. Special glasses have been developed having a relatively high electric conductivity, and by using them it is possible to make B thick enough to withstand ordinary shocks in use. Even so, it should never be touched except with wet filter paper or lens tissue. Its resistance is usually in the range 1 to 10 megohms. This means that the simple type of potenti-

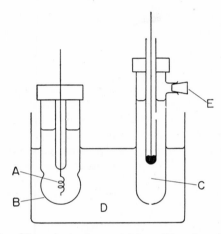

Fig. 12-7.   Glass electrode assembly, with calomel half-cell.

ometer circuit shown in Figure 1 cannot be used with the glass electrode; the resistance of the cell is so high that the galvanometer will not register. A direct current amplifier is therefore introduced which magnifies the cell current up to a level where it will easily deflect the pointer of a portable microammeter when the potentiometer is not in balance.

The glass electrode pH meter is subject to errors in highly alkaline solutions. Above pH 10, the pH indicated with the usual type of glass is less than the true pH. This is because the hydrogen ion concentration is so small that other cations besides the hydronium ion have a chance to penetrate the glass, diffusing from the outside of the bulb towards the inside in Figure 5, and so reducing the potential across the glass. The cation which diffuses most easily is the lithium ion, and after it the sodium ion. Such errors are, fortunately, reproducible, and a sodium ion correction can be applied to pH measurements in sodium salt solutions if the sodium ion concentration is known.   Figure 8 is a nomograph which gives the correction for a general purpose glass.   Above pH 12.5 these corrections become so large that the measurements are almost worthless, but other glasses are available which permit measurements up to pH 14.

Failure to correct for the sodium ion penetration of the glass electrode at high pH may result in errors, not only in the actual pH, but in the titer of solutions.   Figure 9 shows an experimental curve for the titration of a weak acid, succinimide, with sodium hydroxide, using a pH meter with a Corning 015 glass electrode.   The equivalence point comes at pH 11.8.   The lower curve is a graph of the observed pH readings, uncorrected for sodium ion penetration; the upper curve gives the corrected pH readings.   The lower curve is very distorted, and shows an inflection point with 0.2 to 0.3 ml. less sodium hydroxide than the corrected curve.   In a case like this, the error could be reduced by using potassium hydroxide for the titration instead of sodium hydroxide, but then the difficulty arises that the base must be carbonate-free, which is more difficult to accomplish with potassium hydroxide than with sodium hydroxide.

In very strongly acid solutions, an interesting effect appears. Not only the acid concentration, but also the water concentration affects the potential.   This is excellent evidence that the hydrogen ion is *hydrated*, and is really H_3O^+ in aqueous solutions.

Recently an extensive study has been made of the influence of chemical composition of glasses upon their pH response and electric resistance.[4]   It was found that the sodium ion error at high pH could be reduced considerably by substituting lithium for sodium in the composition of the glass, yet if the glass contained potassium instead of sodium the error was increased.   The sodium ion error diminished with increasing atomic weight of the alkaline earth metal used in the glass, and the addition of small amounts of rare earth metals decreased the sodium ion error somewhat and at the same time improved the chemical stability.   Unfortunately the factors which reduced the sodium ion error also tended to increase the electric resistance; some of the glass electrodes prepared had resistances over 5000 megohms, as compared with 10 megohms for Corning 015 soda-lime glass.   One of the best glasses, combining low sodium

[4] G. A. Perley, *Anal. Chem.*, **21**, 391, 394, 559 (1949).

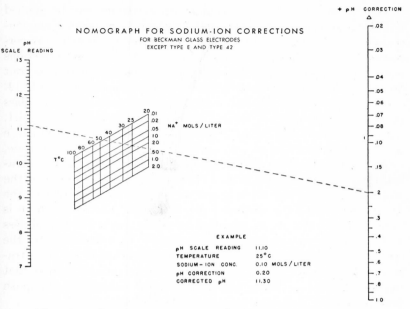

Fig. 12-8.   Nomograph for sodium ion corrections for Beckman General Purpose glass electrodes.   By courtesy of Beckman Instruments, Inc.

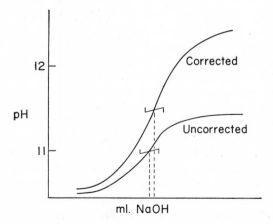

Fig. 12-9.   Effect of the sodium ion correction on the inflection point at high pH (schematic).

error with low resistance, had the following composition (moles per cent): Li_2O, 28; Cs_2O, 2; BaO, 4; La_2O_3, 3; SiO_2, 63.   Placed in a 2 N sodium salt solution of pH 12.8, the apparent pH measured by the electrode was only 0.12 unit less than the true pH.   The resistance was 70 megohms.   This glass also responded to changes in pH more rapidly than soda-lime glass, making it possible to use this electrode in conjunction with high-speed recording devices.   It is thought that the special properties of lithium glasses in pH electrodes are connected with the low coordination number of lithium (four) and its low ionic radius.

Special glasses are also available for pH measurements at high temperatures, though more work needs to be done in this respect.

Other electrodes for **pH** *measurement.*   The *quinhydrone electrode* is probably the most used after the glass electrode.   The electrode proper is a wire of platinum or gold.   It is dipped into the solution under test, and quinhydrone crystals are added to this solution.   The cell is completed with a calomel half-cell or other reference half-cell.

Quinhydrone is a solid compound containing one mole of hydroquinone to one mole of quinone.   It is sparingly soluble in water, and dissociates in solution.   The solution can be oxidized or reduced according to the reaction

$$O=\!\!\left\langle\!\!\begin{array}{c}=\\=\end{array}\!\!\right\rangle\!\!=O + 2H^+ + 2e \rightleftharpoons HO\!\!-\!\!\left\langle\!\!\!\!\!\!\right\rangle\!\!-\!\!OH.$$

The value of $E°_H$ for the forward reaction is 0.6994 volt at 25°C.   It is clear from the Nernst equation that

$$E = E° + \frac{RT}{2\mathfrak{F}}\ln a_H{}^2 = E° - \frac{2.303RT}{\mathfrak{F}}\cdot pH,$$

so long as the ratio of quinone to hydroquinone remains 1:1.   This is a simple case of an oxidation-reduction potential which depends on the pH of the solution.

Since hydroquinone is a weak acid, it will dissociate appreciably if the pH is high enough.   Its anion, moreover, is easily oxidized by air.   Therefore the quinhydrone electrode is seldom used above pH 8.   It is subject to small *salt errors*, since electrolytes change the activity coefficients of quinone and hydroquinone unequally.

A variant on the quinhydrone electrode is the *chloranil electrode*. Chloranil is tetrachloroquinone.   The solution under test is saturated with solid chloranil and also with solid hydrochloranil (tetrachloro-hydroquinone).   This pair is superior to quinhydrone in glacial acetic acid solutions, and has been used for potentiometric titration of weak bases by sulfuric or perchloric acid in glacial acetic acid.[5]

The *antimony electrode* has also proved useful in titrations in non-aqueous solvents.[6]   It consists of a rod of pure antimony which has been cast in air, and is superficially oxidized.   It, too, is an oxidation-reduction electrode whose potential depends on pH; the reaction is:

$$Sb_2O_3 + 6H^+ + 6e \rightarrow 2Sb + 3H_2O.$$

The activities of the solid antimony and antimony trioxide are constant, so the potential at a given temperature depends on the pH alone.   Deviations arise in aqueous solutions at pH values less than 2 or more than 8, owing to the solubility of antimony trioxide. Within this range, in aqueous solutions at 25°C,[7]

$$E = 0.2552 - 0.05893 \text{ pH at } 25°C.$$

Other electrodes which respond to the hydrogen ion activity of a solution by reason of an equilibrium (metal oxide plus H^+ plus electrons $\rightleftharpoons$ metal plus water) are tellurium, tungsten, and iron which has been made passive by fuming nitric acid.   Of these, the tellurium electrode is the best.[8]

Membrane electrodes.   Membrane electrodes are permeable to certain ions and not others.   An electric potential is set up across the membrane when it is placed between two solutions in which the concentrations of these ions are different, and if the ion concentration on one side of the membrane is known, the concentration on the other side can be calculated from the measured potential.   The glass electrode is a membrane electrode, but an unusually selective one, as it is far more permeable to hydrogen ions than to any others.

The selective action of membrane electrodes is due to a combination of electrostatic and steric effects.   The material of the membrane is ionized, consisting of a continuous framework carrying ionic groups of one sign, counterbalanced by small mobile ions of opposite

[5] N. F. Hall and J. B. Conant, *J. Am. Chem. Soc.*, **49**, 3047 (1927); N. F. Hall and T. H. Werner, *J. Am. Chem. Soc.*, **50**, 2367 (1928); O. Tomicek, *Collection Czechoslov. Chem. Commun.*, **13**, 116 (1948).

[6] M. L. Moss, J. H. Elliott, and R. T. Hall, *Anal. Chem.*, **20**, 784 (1948).

[7] F. Hovorka and G. H. Chapman, *J. Am. Chem. Soc.*, **63**, 955 (1941).

[8] O. Tomicek and F. Pupe, *Collection Czechoslov. Chem. Commun.*, **8**, 520 (1936).

sign. Essentially their structure is like that of an ion exchange resin (Chapter 8). If the framework is negatively charged, then, clearly, the concentration of free positive ions within the framework will far exceed the concentration of free negative ions, in accordance with the Donnan equilibrium. The lower the concentration of the external solution, the more selectively permeable the membrane becomes, and the more nearly is the potential difference across the membrane given by the ideal equation

$$E_{12} = \frac{RT}{n\mathfrak{F}} \ln \frac{a_1}{a_2}.$$

[Compare Equation (1) above.] The theory of membrane electrodes is discussed by Meyer and Sieverts[9] and by Marshall.[10]

The membrane electrodes which have been studied experimentally fall into three classes; oxidized collodion,[11] modified clay membranes,[10] and plasticized films of ion exchange resins.[12] Most of them have a negatively charged framework and are therefore permeable to cations. A cell of the following type:

Hg, Hg_2Cl_2, KCl (sat.) | KCl (a_1) | membrane | KCl (a_2)

| KCl (sat.), Hg_2Cl_2, Hg

has an electromotive force given by equation (1). If a_1 is known, a_2 can be calculated from the measured electromotive force.

The membranes are usually permeable to *all* ions of a given charge i.e., to all cations or to all anions, though the ionic radius affects the permeability somewhat. Marshall found that membranes made from montmorillonite clay containing hydrogen ions were permeable to alkali metal cations but not to alkaline earth metal cations,[10] but in general these membranes are not at all specific, and their use is limited to cases where only one kind of cation (or anion) is present— a very serious limitation indeed. Consequently they have been used only as research tools in special problems, such as determining

[9] K. H. Meyer and J. F. Sieverts, *Helv. Chim. Acta*, **19**, 649, 655 (1936).

[10] C. E. Marshall and W. E. Bergman, *J. Am. Chem. Soc.*, **63**, 1911 (1941); C. E. Marshall, *The Colloid Chemistry of the Silicate Minerals*, New York, Academic Press, 1949, Chap. 14.

[11] L. Michaelis, *Kolloid-Z.*, **62**, 2 (1933); K. W. Sollner, I. Abrams, and C. W. Carr, *J. Gen. Physiol.*, **24**, 467 (1941); **25**, 7 (1941); Sollner *et al.*, *J. Gen. Physiol.* **25**, 411 (1941), **26**, 17, 309 (1942).

[12] W. Juda and W. A. McRae, *J. Am. Chem. Soc.*, **72**, 1044 (1950).

the activity of free potassium ions in clay suspensions.[13] With reference to the membranes made from ion exchange resins, we must note that these are very new, and further developments are to be anticipated.

Differential potentiometric titration. In potentiometric titration, a graph is made of the electromotive force of the experimental cell against volume of the added reagent. The end point of the titration is taken as the volume of reagents for which the slope of this graph is the steepest.

In differential titration, one does not measure the electromotive force of the cell directly, but instead the increase or decrease in electromotive force for a certain small increment of added titrant.

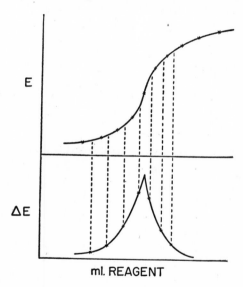

Fig. 12-10.   Differential titration curve.

This increase or decrease, plotted against the mean volume of titrant (the average of the total volumes added before and after the increment in question), gives a graph with a sharp peak at the end point, as shown in Figure 10. From such a graph the end point can usually be located with greater accuracy than from the conventional

[13] C. E. Marshall and W. E. Bergman, *J. Phys. Chem.*, **46**, 52, 327 (1942).

titration curve. Titrations can be made faster, for in favorable cases there is no need to draw a graph at all.

One very simple device for differential titration, devised by E. Muller, is shown in Figure 11. In the form used for oxidation-reduction titrations, two platinum wires are mounted, one inside, the other outside a narrow glass tube which dips into the solution

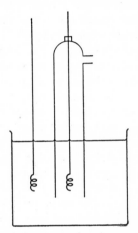

Fig. 12-11.   Apparatus for differential titration (Muller).

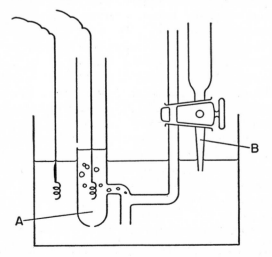

Fig. 12-12.   Apparatus for differential titration (McInnes and Dole).

and is used as a stirring rod. The tube is first withdrawn from the solution and immediately replaced; the solution is now the same inside and outside the tube, and there is no potential across the two wires. If a small amount of titrant is now added and the solution stirred *without* withdrawing the tube, the solution inside the tube remains the same as before while the solution in bulk has been changed by the addition of the titrant. The potential difference which now exists between the wires is the ΔE of Figure 10.

A more elaborate device whose principle is essentially the same is that of McInnes and Dole,[14] shown in Figure 12. A current of nitrogen or other gas keeps the solution in the pocket A mixed with the main solution in the titration vessel, as long as the buret stopcock B is closed, and it also protects the solution from atmospheric oxidation. When titrant is added through B, the solution in A is isolated, and between an electrode mounted in A and another similar electrode in the bulk of the solution a potential difference ΔE is set up. The apparatus is clearly adaptable to any type of electrode. It is claimed that ferrous iron can be titrated with potassium dichromate to a precision of 0.004%.

A different principle in differential titration is demonstrated by an electric circuit with a delayed response, arranged so that a sudden change in the electromotive force caused by adding a drop of titrant causes a capacitor to be charged, which then discharges slowly through a high resistance, giving a current which lasts long enough to be read on a microammeter. The current is proportional to ΔE. Such circuits are described by Baker and Muller[15] and Delahay.[16] In cases where the potentiometric titration curve gives a sharp break at the end point, a precision of 0.1% to 0.2% can be obtained.

Bimetallic electrode pairs. Half-cells such as the calomel half-cell, or any that require contact to be made with the test solution through a salt bridge, are distinctly cumbersome. A great advance in practical convenience was made when Hostetter and Roberts[17] discovered that oxidation-reduction titrations can be carried out by using as electrodes two dissimilar metals, both immersed in the test solution. One of these metals is generally platinum, which follows

[14] D. A. McInnes and M. Dole, *J. Am. Chem. Soc.*, **48**, 2831 (1927); **51**, 1119 (1930); **53**, 555 (1932).

[15] H. H. Baker and R. H. Muller, *Trans. Electrochem. Soc.*, **76**, 75 (1939).

[16] P. Delahay, *Anal. Chem.*, **20**, 1212 (1948).

[17] J. C. Hostetter and H. S. Roberts, *J. Am. Chem. Soc.*, **41**, 1337 (1919); see also H. H. Willard and F. Fenwick, *J. Am. Chem. Soc.*, **44**, 2504, 2516 (1922).

the potential of the solution rapidly, the exchange of electrons between it and the solution being fast and reversible.[18] The other is a metal such as tungsten, which does *not* exchange electrons reversibly with the solution, or if it does, is influenced by processes other than the oxidation and reduction going on in the solution, for example the tungsten-tungstic oxide-hydrogen ion reaction. In a typical oxidation-reduction titration, such as permanganate plus ferrous ion, the tungsten and the platinum indicate the same potentials when an excess of reducing agent is present, but widely different potentials when an excess of oxidizing agent is present. If, therefore, a galvanometer is connected between the platinum and the tungsten electrodes a current will flow so long as the oxidant is in excess, but as soon as enough reducing agent is added to combine with the oxidant, the current drops suddenly to zero. Figures 13 and 14 show the experimental arrangement used by Furman and Wilson[19] and the titration curves they obtained. Titration can be done in either direction; at the end point, the current indicated by the galvanometer shows a sharp rise or a sharp drop, depending on the direction of titration.

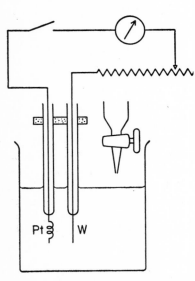

Fig. 12-13.   Titration with platinum-tungsten electrode pair.

The most popular pair of electrodes for this purpose is platinum and tungsten. Other good combinations are platinum and palladium, platinum and nickel, platinum and rhodium, platinum and platinum-iridium alloy. Platinum and gold give a sharp potential change at the end point, but its magnitude is not at all reproducible.

Among the titrations which can be done in this manner are Fe^{++}

[18] Even the platinum electrode may take a few minutes to reach equilibrium with the solution; see the work of P. K. Winter and H. V. Moyer (*J. Am. Chem. Soc.*, **57**, 1402 (1935) on ferrous iron-dichromate titrations.

[19] N. H. Furman and E. B. Wilson, *J. Am. Chem. Soc.*, **50**, 277 (1928).

plus $Ce(SO_4)_2$, $KMnO_4$, $K_2Cr_2O_7$, HVO_3; $S_2O_3^=$ plus $KMnO_4$, directly; $KMnO_4$ and $ZnSO_4$ plus $K_4Fe(CN)_6$; $Na_2C_2O_4$ plus $Ce(SO_4)_2$. It is even possible to perform acid-base titrations with bimetallic electrode pairs.[15]

The maximum current, or potential difference, usually comes just to one side of the equivalence point and not at the equivalence point itself. However, this error is reproducible and can be compensated by proper standardization. The great advantage of this technique is not its accuracy, but its simplicity. The only equipment needed is a galvanometer and the two electrodes. No curve need be plotted; the end point is found by watching for the permanent deflection of the galvanometer. The change in current can be made to actuate a relay which will turn the buret off automatically at the end point,[20] so that the operator does not even have to watch the titration.

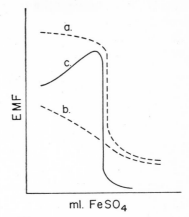

Fig. 12-14. Titration curves with platinum-tungsten pair. (a), potential of platinum electrode (reversible); (b), potential of tungsten electrode (irreversible); (c), difference between the two potentials. Curves are for $K_2Cr_2O_7$ titrated with $FeSO_4$.

Polarized electrode pairs: the dead-stop method. The same effect of a pair of electrodes, one acting reversibly and the other not, can be produced by making both electrodes of platinum and impressing a small potential difference (about 20 millivolts) upon them. This method, like the bimetallic electrode pair method, is not strictly speaking a potentiometric method, since it is a current which is measured and not an electromotive force. Rather it is an example of amperometric titration (see Chapter 20). Current flows between the electrodes on one side of the titration end point but not the other; the end point is marked by a sudden drop of the current to zero, or a rise from zero to a fairly steady value.

A typical dead-stop titration is that of iodine with thiosulfate. Figure 15 shows the apparatus, and Figure 16 shows the potential of each electrode against a reference electrode during titration.[21]

[20] W. E. Shenk and F. Fenwick, *Ind. Eng. Chem., Anal. Ed.,* **7**, 194 (1935).
[21] C. W. Foulk and A. T. Bawden, *J. Am. Chem. Soc.,* **48**, 2045 (1926); see also R. G. Van Name and F. Fenwick, *J. Am. Chem. Soc.,* **47**, 19 (1925).

While iodine is in excess, the electrodes are not polarized, and they have almost the same potential due to the high conductivity of the solution; current flows between them on account of the external electromotive force. As soon as thiosulfate is in excess, however, the current drops nearly to zero as the cathode becomes polarized, that is, the electrochemical reaction there is obstructed in some way. The potential difference between the electrodes rises, just as does

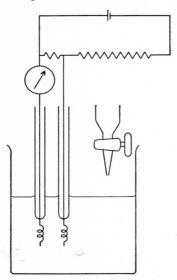

the potential difference across a light switch when the switch is turned off. A similar effect is found in the titration of ferrous iron with permanganate or dichromate, or of zinc sulfate with ferrocyanide. The sudden rise or fall in current does not always coincide exactly with the equivalence point, but the precision is good, about 0.1% in some cases. The method is specially useful in titrating iodine (or, indirectly, cupric ion) in very dilute solutions, where it is much more accurate than the starch indicator method,[22] and in titrations with the Karl Fischer reagent.[23]

Fig. 12-15. Apparatus for dead-stop titration.

The theory of bimetallic electrode pairs and dead-stop titrations is obscure, as is most of the theory of irreversible electrode processes, but it is related to the theory of concentration polarization and "amperometric titrations" (see Chapters 5 and 20).

Summary and conclusion. Electromotive force measurements are sometimes applied to determine the activity of an ion directly, by a single measurement. The most important application of this kind is in pH determination. More usually, however, electromotive force measurements are used in connection with titrations.

Potentiometric titration is a versatile technique. It can be used in every case where an indicator electrode can be found which is

[22] W. A. Schroeder, L. M. Kay, and R. S. Mills, *Anal. Chem.*, **22**, 760 (1950); N. H. Furman and E. B. Wilson, *J. Am. Chem. Soc.*, **50**, 277 (1928).

reversible to one of the substances consumed or added in the titration, which means in effect that it can be used for the great majority of titrations. It is the standby when indicators are not available, or are unsuitable because of the indistinctness or gradualness of their color change. It is particularly appropriate where two or more substances react successively in the same titration, since each reaction gives its own inflection point to the titration curve.

Where the indicator electrode is truly reversible, very high accuracy can be obtained by potentiometric titration. Even where the inflection is not sharp, the simpler kinds of titration curves, such as pH curves, can be subjected to mathematical analysis and the equivalence point located very accurately. This is especially valuable in titrations involving weak acids or weak bases or buffered solutions. The accuracy can often be increased by using a differential titration method. Even where the behavior of the electrode is not reversible, good precision can usually be obtained.

The basic equipment for potentiometric titration is simple, though an amplifier will be needed if the experimental cell has a high resistance. The simple equipment, however, takes

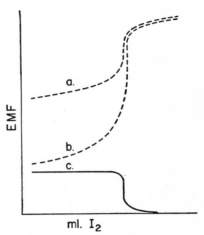

Fig. 12-16. Titration curves by dead-stop method. (a), potential of anodic wire; (b), potential of cathodic wire; (c), potential difference, i.e., polarization of anode. The *current* is nearly zero before the end point and rises sharply after it. $Na_2S_2O_3$ titrated with I_2; Van Name and Fenwick, *J. Am. Chem. Soc.*, **47**, 23 (1925).

time to operate. More elaborate equipment is available commercially which makes potentiometric titrations easier and better suited to routine work. Reference electrodes are streamlined or eliminated altogether, as in differential or dead-stop methods; where dead-stop

[23] G. Wernimont and F. J. Hopkinson, *Ind. Eng. Chem. Anal. Ed.*, **15**, 272 (1943).

methods are used, streamlining is carried to the point where the two wire electrodes are mounted on the glass stirrer blades. An electric eye, with its virtually instantaneous response, may replace a galvanometer as the null point detector. Instruments are available which can be adapted to any desired pair of electrodes, including the glass electrode, and to conventional, differential, or dead-stop procedures.

Perhaps the ultimate in timesaving is an instrument[24] which delivers the titrant from a calibrated syringe with a motor-driven plunger, while a self-balancing potentiometer traces the electromotive force with a pen on a roll of chart paper. The paper drive is synchronized with the plunger of the syringe, so that the whole titration curve is plotted automatically. Or the instrument may be set to stop delivering the titrant when a predetermined electromotive force is reached and maintained; a counter on the syringe drive registers the volume of solution used. An instrument of this type is now made commercially.

PROBLEMS

1. (a) AgCl and AgBr form solid solutions. Can Br^- be titrated potentiometrically by $AgNO_3$ in presence of Cl^-? Suggest an alternative method (potentiometric or otherwise) for determining Br^- in presence of Cl^-.

(b) Why do AgCl and AgI not form solid solutions? Would you expect AgBr and AgI to form solid solutions? Would it be feasible to titrate I^- potentiometrically with $AgNO_3$ in presence of Br^-?

2. Explain the sharp bend which occurs immediately after the first inflection point in titrating CN^- with $AgNO_3$ (Figure 4).

3. Calculate the electromotive force of the following cell, assuming the glass electrode has no asymmetry potential:

Ag, AgCl $\mid$ HCl ($a = 1.0$) $\mid$ glass $\mid$ solution of pH 5.0 and chloride ion activity 0.1 $\mid$ AgCl, Ag

4. The potentiometric titration of fluoride ions by means of a ferric salt has been proposed (see Chapter 7). Describe the experimental procedure that would be necessary, and comment critically on the merits of such a titration.

[24] J. J. Lingane, *Anal. Chem.*, **20**, 285 (1948).

13

Acid-base titrations

Introductory; the significance of pH. We saw in the preceding chapter that acid-base reactions can be studied potentiometrically, since the potential of a hydrogen electrode or glass electrode depends on the hydrogen ion concentration of the solution in which it is placed. The potential depends linearly on the *logarithm* of the hydrogen ion activity, hence a more useful quantity than the hydrogen ion concentration or activity itself is the logarithm of the activity, or the *pH*, which is the negative logarithm. Another reason for emphasizing the pH rather than the actual concentration of hydrogen ions is that the latter can vary over such wide limits—over a factor of 10^{15} or more in aqueous solutions—that the logarithm is easier to handle.

Defined as $-\log_{10} a_{H^+}$, the pH is directly proportional to the work needed to transfer hydrogen ions reversibly from the solution in which they are found to a standard solution in which hydrogen ions have unit activity. This is a very satisfactory theoretical concept, but as a practical definition of pH it is valueless, for no experiment can be performed in which hydrogen ions are transferred without at the same time transferring negative ions. It is better to define pH in terms of the way it is measured, which is by the electromotive force of a cell consisting of a hydrogen electrode immersed in the solution under test, a suitable reference half-cell, and a salt bridge connecting the two. Then the equation

$$E = E^\circ + \frac{2.303RT}{\mathfrak{F}} \cdot \mathrm{pH} \tag{1}$$

defines the pH, where E° is zero if the reference half-cell is the standard hydrogen electrode, and E is counted positive if the reference

223

electrode is positively charged with respect to the hydrogen electrode in the test solution.

This definition is identical with the definition

$$pH = -\log_{10} a_{H^+} \tag{2}$$

if, and only if, the net junction potential across the salt bridge of the cell is zero. There is good reason to believe this is very small, but liquid junction potentials cannot be determined without knowledge of single ion activities, and vice versa.

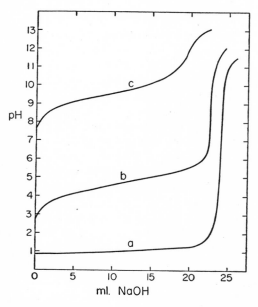

Fig. 13-1. Titration curves of strong, weak and very weak acids. (a), hydrochloric acid; (b), acetic acid; (c), succinimid. At end points, molar anion concentrations, a, are 0.4.

During acid-base titration, the pH of the solution changes in a characteristic manner. Typical graphs of pH against the volume of added base or acid are shown in Figures 1, 2, and 3. They all show a sharp change in pH with volume of titrant at the equivalence point, and the reason for this will become clear as we study acid-base equilibria. However, the pH at which this inflection is found

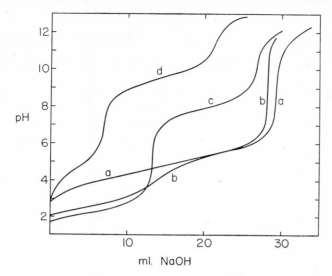

Fig. 13-2. Titration curves of dibasic acids and a mixture of acids. (a), succinic acid $(K_1/K_2 = 24)$; (b), malonic acid $(K_1/K_2 = 700)$; (c), selenious acid $(K_1/K_2 = 5 \times 10^5)$; (d), mixture of succinic acid $(K_2 = 2.7 \times 10^{-6})$ and succinimid $(K = 3.3 \times 10^{-10})$. The anion concentration, a, is 0.05 at the second equivalence for malonic and selenious acids, 0.4 for the others. (Curves for succinic acid and succinimid are by courtesy of Arapahoe Chemicals, Inc., Boulder, Colorado.)

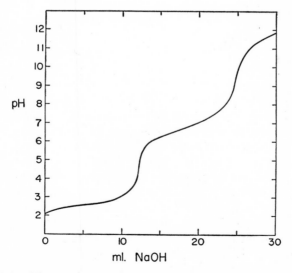

Fig. 13-3. Titration of phosphoric acid with sodium hydroxide. Anion concentration a at second equivalence = 0.05.

varies considerably from one curve to another, and so does the
steepness of the curve at this point. The analyst is interested in
the pH at the equivalence point, so that he may know when to stop
his titration, and what indicator, if any, to use. He also wants to
know how much error he will make if he does not stop at the right
pH, as for example when the observed color change of an indicator
comes at a pH different from that at the equivalence point. Therefore he is also interested in the slope of the titration curve in the
neighbourhood of the equivalence point.

The analyst should know what kind of pH titration curve to
expect from the composition of his solutions and the ionization constants involved; therefore this chapter will be devoted largely to
showing how to calculate the pH at equivalence and the slope of
the titration curve. He should also know how to modify the shape
of the curve when necessary; therefore we shall also include some
discussion of nonaqueous solvents in acid-base titration.

Acid-base equilibria. We shall use Bronsted's definition of the
terms "acid" and "base." According to this definition, an acid is a
proton donor, a base is a proton acceptor. Acid-base reactions are
analogous to oxidation-reduction reactions; in the former, protons
are transferred from one molecule to another, while in the latter,
electrons are so transferred. *Free* protons, H^+, do not exist to any
significant extent in any solvent. In water they are solvated to
form hydronium ions, H_3O^+. The use of the symbol H^+ to represent
the hydrogen ion in solution is therefore incorrect. It has the advantage of brevity, however, and it is entirely permissible so long
as its shorthand character is clearly understood.

Water, our most common solvent, is both an acid and a base.
It can lose a proton, leaving behind OH^-, or it can gain one, forming
H_3O^+. This latter is the symbol for the hydrogen ion in water
that we shall use in this chapter.

All acid-base reactions are reversible. The interaction of an acid
HA, and of a base B, with water are represented as follows:

$$HA + H_2O \rightleftharpoons H_3O^+ + A^-.$$

$$B + H_2O \rightleftharpoons BH^+ + OH^-.$$

The fragment A^- remaining after the acid HA has lost a proton
can take a proton back again to form HA; it is therefore a base,
and similarly BH^+, which can give up a proton, is an acid. They

are called, respectively, the *conjugate base* to the acid HA, and the *conjugate acid* to the base B. In general, every acid-base reaction can be written in the form

Acid + base $\rightleftharpoons$ conjugate base + conjugate acid.

Examples are:

$$CH_3COOH + H_2O \qquad \rightleftharpoons CH_3COO^- + H_3O^+.$$
$$NH_4^+ \qquad + CH_3COO^- \rightleftharpoons NH_3 \qquad + CH_3COOH.$$
$$H_2O \qquad + CH_3COO^- \rightleftharpoons OH^- \qquad + CH_3COOH.$$
$$HCO_3^- \qquad + HCO_3^- \qquad \rightleftharpoons CO_3^= \qquad + H_2CO_3.$$

We note in passing that acid molecules may be neutral, positively charged, or negatively charged, and the same is true of base molecules. Also, many substances are at the same time acidic and basic, for example HCO_3^-, $NH_2NH_3^+$, H_2O.

These equilibria obey the law of mass action. For example, in the interaction of the acid HA with water,

$$\frac{a_{H_3O^+}a_{A^-}}{a_{HA}a_{H_2O}} = K,$$

or more simply, since in dilute solution the water activity is almost constant,

$$\frac{a_{H_3O^+}a_{A^-}}{a_{HA}} = K_A \tag{3}$$

where the a's stand for activities. K_A is called the *ionization constant* of the acid, and it is a measure of its strength, or ability to give up protons to water.

In aqueous solution the equilibrium $2H_2O \rightleftharpoons H_3O^+ + OH^-$ is always present, so

$$a_{H_3O^+}a_{OH^-} = K_W. \tag{4}$$

Putting (3) and (4) together, we get the following expression for the ionization constant of the conjugate base, A^-:

$$K_B = \frac{a_{HA}a_{OH^-}}{a_{A^-}} = \frac{a_{HA}}{a_{A^-}a_{H_3O^+}} \cdot a_{H_3O^+}a_{OH^-} = \frac{K_W}{K_A}. \tag{5}$$

This is a very useful relation which will appear often in the derivations to follow.

Titration of an acid **HA** *with a base* **B**; *calculation of* **pH** *at equivalence.* Every acid-base reaction can be written in the form $HA + B$, where it is understood that no restrictions are placed on the charge which the acid or base may carry, nor on the strength of the acid or base. All special cases, such as the reaction of a weak acid with a strong base, or a mixture of two weak acids with a strong base, or the half neutralization of a dibasic acid, can be derived from the general case we are about to discuss.

For any mixture of HA, B, and water the following equations apply:

$$\frac{a_{H_3O^+} a_{A^-}}{a_{HA}} = K_A. \tag{6}$$

$$\frac{a_{BH^+} a_{OH^-}}{a_B} = K_B. \tag{7}$$

$$a_{H_3O^+} a_{OH^-} = K_W. \tag{8}$$

$$[HA] + [A^-] = a. \tag{9}$$

$$[B] + [BH^+] = b. \tag{10}$$

$$[BH^+] + [H_3O^+] = [A^-] + [OH^-]. \tag{11}$$

Here the symbols in square brackets, $[HA]$ and so on, stand for molar concentrations; a and b are the total numbers of moles of acid and base, respectively, per liter of solution, and are known from the proportions in which the solutions were mixed. For example, if equal volumes of 0.1 M acid and 0.1 M base were mixed, $a = b = 0.05$. Equation (11) follows from the condition of electric neutrality.

These six equations contain twelve unknowns, but the twelve unknowns may be reduced to six if the activities are considered equal to the concentrations. This is the first, and most serious, approximation which we shall make in these calculations.

Substituting $[A^-]$ for a_{A^-}, and so on, in equation (6), and combining (6) and (9),

$$\frac{[H_3O^+][A^-]}{K_A} + [A^-] = a.$$

$$[A^-] = \frac{aK_A}{[H_3O^+] + K_A}. \tag{12}$$

Similarly, $$[BH^+] = \frac{bK_B}{[OH^-] + K_B}. \tag{13}$$

Introducing these into (11),

$$[A^-] - [BH^+] = \frac{aK_A}{[H_3O^+] + K_A} - \frac{bK_B}{[OH^-] + K_B} = [H_3O^+] - [OH^-]$$

$$\frac{aK_A[OH^-] + aK_AK_B - bK_AK_B - bK_B[H_3O^+]}{([H_3O^+] + K_A)([OH^-] + K_B)} = [H_3O^+] - [OH^-]. \tag{14}$$

This equation may be expanded, substituting $[OH^-] = K_W/[H_3O^+]$; it is then a quartic in $[H_3O^+]$, from which the whole course of the titration curve can be calculated, although such a calculation would be extremely laborious. At present we are interested only in the equivalence point. At equivalence, $a = b$, and also $[H_3O^+] \ll K_A$, and $[OH^-] \ll K_B$. Substituting into (14) and approximating,

$$a\left(\frac{K_A[OH^-] - K_B[H_3O^+]}{K_AK_B}\right) = [H_3O^+] - [OH^-].$$

$$a(K_AK_W - K_B[H_3O^+]^2) = K_AK_B([H_3O^+]^2 - K_W)$$

$$[H_3O^+]^2 = \frac{aK_AK_W + K_AK_BK_W}{K_AK_B + aK_B} = \frac{K_AK_W(a + K_B)}{K_B(a + K_A)}.$$

or,

$$[H_3O^+] = \sqrt{\frac{K_AK_W(a + K_B)}{K_B(a + K_A)}}. \tag{15}$$

This is the general equation. From it, simplified equations may be derived which are valid within a very small error for special cases, as follows:

Strong Acid Plus Strong Base. Where the acid is very strong, as for example HCl, or H_2SO_4 in its first stage of dissociation, we can write $K_A \gg a$. Likewise for a base as strong as sodium hydroxide, $K_B \gg a$. Equation (15) then reduces to

$$[H_3O^+] = \sqrt{K_W}. \tag{15a}$$

Weak Acid Plus Strong Base. The vast majority of acids are either very strong, like hydrochloric, or relatively very weak, like acetic, and K_A is either greater than 1 or less than 10^{-4}. There are exceptions, of course, such as trichloracetic ($K_A = 10^{-1}$) and HSO_4^- ($K_A = 10^{-2}$), but these are not numerous. For most titrations involving a weak acid, $K_A \ll a$, and equation (15) becomes

$$[H_3O^+] = \sqrt{\frac{K_AK_W}{a + K_A}} \doteq \sqrt{\frac{K_AK_W}{a}}. \tag{15b}$$

Weak Base Plus Strong Acid.   Analogous to (15b), we have:

$$[H_3O^+] = \sqrt{\frac{K_W(a + K_B)}{K_B}} \doteq \sqrt{\frac{K_W a}{K_B}}. \tag{15c}$$

Weak Base Plus Weak Acid.   Here K_A and K_B are both much smaller than a, and

$$[H_3O^+] = \sqrt{\frac{K_A K_W}{K_B}}. \tag{15d}$$

The last case, weak acid plus weak base, would appear to have little practical significance.   Where one has to titrate a weak acid, he would not use a weak base unless the titration were to be done conductometrically, when this might have certain advantages; he would choose a strong base.   Equation (15d), however, is applicable to the half neutralization of a dibasic acid, or to the first equivalence point in titration of a mixture of two weak acids of different strengths. Consider what really determines the pH at equivalence.   It is the resultant of the hydrolysis of the conjugate base A^- and the hydrolysis of the conjugate acid BH^+.   These are the main species present at the equivalence point, apart from water itself.   Now equation (15d) may be put in another form:

$$[H_3O^+] = \sqrt{K_A K_A'}, \tag{15e}$$

where $K_A' = K_W/K_B$ = the dissociation constant of the acid BH^+, which is conjugate to the base B [see Equation (5)].   That is, *the hydronium ion concentration is the geometric mean of two acid dissociation constants, that of the acid which is present at equivalence* (BH^+), *and that of the acid which has been neutralized in reaching equivalence* (HA), provided further that the stoichiometric concentrations of these two acids are equal.   We have this very case in the titration of a dibasic acid, H_2A, to its first equivalence point.   The acid which is present is HA^-; the acid which has been neutralized is H_2A.   Their dissociation constants are K_2 and K_1, respectively. Therefore,

$$[H_3O^+] = \sqrt{K_1 K_2}. \tag{15f}$$

The same equation holds for the neutralization of a weak acid HA_1 in presence of a weaker acid HA_2, so long as their initial concentrations are equal.   Where these concentrations are not equal, it is best to apply the special treatment given on page 232.

Special derivations for special cases. In the foregoing we have attempted a treatment which shall be perfectly general, making appropriate approximations to obtain the equations which apply to special cases. We could also approach each special case separately, taking account of the concentrations of the species present in each particular case. This approach may be easier to understand, and it has the advantage that it forces one to consider which species are abundant relative to others. It also brings home the fact mentioned above, that the pH of the solution results from two hydrolysis reactions, that of the conjugate acid and that of the conjugate base. If the conjugate acid is stronger than the conjugate base, the pH will be less than 7 at equivalence, and vice versa.

Strong Acid Plus Strong Base. At equivalence, a salt is present whose ions do not interact with water in any way except hydration; that is, there is no hydrolysis or proton exchange. The only hydronium and hydroxyl ions are those produced by the ionization of the water:

$$2H_2O \rightleftharpoons H_3O^+ + OH^-,$$

wherefore,
$$[H_3O^+] = [OH^-] = \sqrt{K_W}. \tag{15a}$$

Weak Acid Plus Strong Base. The only hydrolysis is that of the base A^- which is conjugate to the weak acid. This reacts with water as follows:

$$A^- + H_2O \rightleftharpoons HA + OH^-$$

At equivalence, a mole of OH^- has been added to every mole of HA. Therefore, $[HA] = [OH^-]$. (Actually, $[OH^-]$ is somewhat larger than $[HA]$. It is more accurate to say $[OH^-] = [HA] + [H_3O^+]$, since OH^- ions come from the ionization of water as well as from the hydrolysis reaction; however, $[H_3O^+]$ is so much smaller than $[HA]$ that it can generally be neglected.) Then

$$K_A = \frac{[H_3O^+][A^-]}{[HA]} = \frac{[H_3O^+][A^-]}{[OH^-]} = \frac{[H_3O^+]^2[A^-]}{K_W}$$

and
$$[H_3O^+] = \sqrt{\frac{K_A K_W}{[A^-]}}, \text{ equivalent to (15b)}.$$

Weak Base Plus Strong Acid. The development is exactly like the case of weak acid plus strong base. The equation is:

$$[H_3O^+] = \sqrt{\frac{[BH^+]K_W}{K_B}}, \text{ equivalent to (15c)}.$$

Weak Acid Plus Weak Base. At equivalence, we have the salt $BH^+ A^-$, and these ions are the chief species present, other than water. The interaction of either of these ions with water is subsidiary to the reaction

$$BH^+ + A^- \rightharpoonup B + HA,$$

since A^- is a stronger base than water and BH^+ a stronger acid. Therefore, $[B] = [HA]$, and likewise, $[BH^+] = [A^-]$. (More accurately, $[B] + [H_3O^+] = [HA] + [OH^-]$.) Then,

$$\frac{K_A}{K_B} = \frac{[H_3O^+][A^-]}{[HA]} \times \frac{[B]}{[OH^-][BH^+]} = \frac{[H_3O^+]^2}{K_W}$$

and
$$[H_3O^+] = \sqrt{\frac{K_A K_W}{K_B}}. \tag{15d}$$

Weak Dibasic Acid, Half Neutralized with Strong Base. When H_2A is half neutralized with NaOH we have the salt Na^+HA^-. Since HA^- is both acidic and basic, the principal reaction is the disproportionation

$$2HA^- \rightharpoonup H_2A + A^=$$

and accordingly, $[H_2A] = [A^=]$. (More accurately, $[H_2A] + [OH^-]$ $= [A^=] + [H_3O^+]$, since H_2A is also formed by $HA^- + H_2O \rightharpoonup H_2A$ $+ OH^-$, and $A^=$ by $HA^- + H_2O \rightharpoonup H_3O^+ + A^=$; but if the pH is between, say, 5 and 9, this is as accurate a statement as we need.) Then

$$K_1 K_2 = \frac{[H_3O^+][HA^-]}{[H_2A]} \cdot \frac{[H_3O^+][A^=]}{[HA^-]} = [H_3O^+]^2,$$

which is the same as equation (15f).

Weak Acid HA_1, Neutralized by Strong Base in Presence of a Weaker Acid, HA_2. Again, the chief reaction occurring at equivalence is the acid-base reaction

$$HA_2 + A_1^- \rightharpoonup HA_1 + A_2^-$$

and $[HA_1] = [A_2^-]$. However, $[HA_2]$ is not necessarily equal to $[A_1^-]$. Therefore

$$K_1 K_2 = \frac{[H_3O^+][A_1^-]}{[HA_1]} \cdot \frac{[H_3O^+][A_2^-]}{[HA_2]} = \frac{[H_3O^+]^2[A_1^-]}{[HA_2]}$$

and
$$[H_3O^+] = \sqrt{K_1 K_2 \cdot \frac{a_2}{a_1}}, \qquad (15g)$$

where a_1 and a_2 are the stoichiometric concentrations of acids HA_1 and HA_2.

Table I summarizes the expressions for the $[H_3O^+]$ at titration equivalence points and notes the various approximations which are made in deriving them.

TABLE I

EXPRESSIONS FOR $[H_3O^+]$ AT EQUIVALENCE

Case	$[H_3O^+]$	Approximation
General.	$\sqrt{\dfrac{K_A K_W (a + K_B)}{K_B (a + K_A)}}$	$K_A \gg [H_3O^+]$; $K_B \gg [OH^-]$
Strong acid, strong base.	$\sqrt{K_W}$	
Weak acid, strong base.	$\sqrt{\dfrac{K_A K_W}{a}}$	$[HA] = [OH^-]$
Strong acid, weak base.	$\sqrt{\dfrac{K_W a}{K_B}}$	$[B] = [H_3O^+]$
Weak acid, weak base.	$\sqrt{\dfrac{K_A K_W}{K_B}}$	$[B] = [HA]$
Weak dibasic acid, half neutralized.	$\sqrt{K_1 K_2}$	$[H_2A] = [A^=]$

The validity of approximations: numerical examples. The simple forms given in Equations (15a) to (15f) are adequate in nearly all practical cases to evaluate the pH at equivalence. The approximations made in deriving these forms generally introduce less error than does the neglect of activity coefficients. However, it will be of interest to see just how much error is introduced by these approximations in a few typical cases.

Weak Acid Plus Strong Base; "a" Not Large Compared to "K_A." The more accurate form of (15b) is

$$[H_3O^+] = \sqrt{\frac{K_A K_W}{a + K_A}}.$$

The lowest value of a usually encountered in titrations is 0.001. For most weak acids, K_A is less than 10^{-4}. For acetic acid it is

1.8×10^{-5}; for monochloracetic acid, 1.5×10^{-3}. When $a = 0.001$, K_A is small compared to a with acetic acid, but not with monochloracetic. For acetic acid, (15b) gives pH = 7.86, the more accurate form gives pH = 7.87; for monochloracetic acid, (15b) gives pH = 6.91, the more accurate form gives pH = 7.11. It is evident that even in the extreme case of an 0.001 M solution of sodium monochloracetate, little error in pH is caused by using the simple Equation (15b). The error is quite insignificant in titration because the titration curve at the end point is very steep, so that an error of 0.2 pH in locating the equivalence point makes almost no difference to the volume of base used.

Titration of Phosphoric Acid with Sodium Hydroxide. Phosphoric acid, H_3PO_4, is a tribasic acid. Its first and second equivalence points can be treated just like the first equivalence point of a dibasic acid. From Equation (15f), $[H_3O^+] = \sqrt{K_1K_2}$ at the first equivalence point, $\sqrt{K_2K_3}$ at the second. These formulas suppose that $[H_3PO_4] = [HPO_4^=]$ at the first equivalence point, and that $[H_2PO_4^-] = [PO_4^=]$ at the second; that is, that $[H_3O^+] \ll [H_3PO_4]$ in the first case, $[OH^-] \ll [PO_4^=]$ in the second case. Actually, at the first equivalence point, the principal reactions between $H_2PO_4^-$ and water are:

$$2H_2PO_4^- \rightleftharpoons H_3PO_4 + HPO_4^=,$$

$$H_2O + H_2PO_4^- \rightleftharpoons H_3O^+ + HPO_4^=,$$

so that it is more correct to say,

$$[HPO_4^=] = [H_3PO_4] + [H_3O^+],$$

while at the second equivalence point,

$$[H_2PO_4^-] = [PO_4^=] + [OH^-].$$

Equation (15) does not assume that $[H_3PO_4] = [HPO_4^=]$ at the first equivalence, i.e., that $[H_3PO_4] \gg [H_3O^+]$, but only that $a \gg [H_3O^+]$ It is therefore more exact than (15f). For 0.01 M salts, the calculated pH values are as follows:

| | pH calculated by: | |
Solution	eq. (15f)	eq. (15)
0.01 M NaH$_2$PO$_4$	4.67	4.80
0.01 M Na$_2$HPO$_4$	9.77	9.52

($K_1 = 7.5 \times 10^{-3}$; $K_2 = 6.2 \times 10^{-8}$; $K_3 = 4.8 \times 10^{-13}$.)

At the third equivalence point another error appears. Equation (15) assumes that $[OH^-] \ll a$, and the hydrolysis is so great that this is no longer the case. A calculation can be made using successive approximations, but it is hardly worth it as the activity corrections are so great, and the pH titration curve is so flat in this region that the $PO_4^\equiv$ end point is of no consequence in titration.

The most serious approximation we have made in these calculations is to consider the activity coefficients equal to unity. Let us get an idea of the extent of this error by calculating the pH of a solution of sodium acetate, taking activity coefficients into account.

The acetate ion is hydrolyzed according to the reaction

$$Ac^- + H_2O \rightleftharpoons HAc + OH^-$$

and $[HAc] = [OH^-]$. The equilibrium constant of the reaction is

$$\frac{a_{HAc} a_{OH^-}}{a_{Ac^-}} = \frac{K_W}{K_A} = \frac{f_{HAc}[HAc] \cdot f_{OH^-}[OH^-]}{f_{Ac^-}[Ac^-]}$$

$$= \frac{f_{HAc} f_{OH^-}[OH^-]^2}{f_{Ac^-}[Ac^-]}. \tag{16}$$

Now, $$pH = -\log a_{H_3O^+} = \log a_{OH^-} - \log K_W$$

(this is the theoretical definition of pH given at the beginning of this chapter); $f_{HAc} \doteq 1$, since HAc is uncharged; and, since OH^- and Ac^- have the same charge, $f_{OH^-} \doteq f_{Ac^-} = f_-$. Therefore,

$$\frac{K_W}{K_A} = \frac{f_{OH^-}^2[OH^-]^2}{f_{OH^-} f_{Ac^-}[Ac^-]} = \frac{(a_{OH^-})^2}{f_-^2[Ac^-]}$$

$$\log a_{OH^-} = \frac{1}{2} \log \frac{K_W[Ac^-]}{K_A} + \log f_-$$

and $$pH = \frac{1}{2} \log \frac{[Ac^-]}{K_W K_A} + \log f_-. \tag{17}$$

The first term on the right in Equation (17) is the pH as calculated by (15b); $\log f_-$ is the correction to be added to it. Calculating this for 0.1 M sodium acetate by Equation (8), Chapter 2, using 5Å. for the distance of closest approach of the ions, we get -0.11 for this term. That is, *the* pH *of* 0.1 M *sodium acetate, calculated with the aid of the Debye-Hückel second approximation, is* 0.11 *unit lower than that calculated assuming activity coefficients to be unity.*

In solutions of ions of higher charge than 1 the activity correction is much greater, and specific ionic interactions enter at high concentrations. Table II shows the observed pH of solutions of primary and secondary sodium phosphate, with and without added salt, and the pH calculated from Equation (15). Deviations of 0.5 pH, and more, from the calculated values are observed.

TABLE II

pH OF PHOSPHATE SOLUTIONS AND SALT CONCENTRATION

Salt	Concentration		Measured pH	Calculated pH; eq. (15)
NaH_2PO_4	0.1 M 0.01 M 0.01 M	 1 M NaCl	4.44 4.80 4.4	4.67
Na_2HPO_4	0.1 M 0.01 M 0.01 M	 1 M NaCl	8.90 9.10 7.8	9.77

Equivalence* pH *and temperature. Most titrations are performed at or near room temperature, but sometimes this is not so. For example, a solution is boiled to drive out carbon dioxide before titrating. It will save time if the solution can be titrated while it is still hot. Again, in kinetic or biochemical studies it may be necessary to titrate solutions which are ice-cold.

Temperature can affect acid-base titrations in two ways; first, the pH of equivalence is changed, and second, if an indicator is used, its color change will depend on temperature. These effects may cancel out, as in the titration of sodium carbonate to the bicarbonate end point, using phenolphthalein, or again they may not cancel, as in the titration of bicarbonate to the carbonic acid end point, using methyl orange. Both effects are, of course, due to the change of acid-base equilibria with temperature.

The temperature dependence of acid-base equilibria has been studied extensively, both experimentally and theoretically. A very useful summary of this subject is given by Everett and Wynne-Jones.[1] The ionization constants of acids which are neutral molecules, e.g., acetic acid, or negatively charged, e.g., HCO_3^-, rise with

[1] D. H. Everett and W. F. K. Wynne-Jones, *Trans. Faraday Soc.*, **35,** 1380 (1939).

temperature up to a certain maximum, then fall as the temperature is increased further. This is associated with the drop in dielectric constant of water with rising temperature, which makes it harder to separate the ionic charges. Where no charges have to be separated, e.g., in the ionization of NH_4^+ and positively charged acids in general, the ionization constant rises steadily with temperature.[2] The smaller the ionization constant, the more it depends on temperature, as a rule; that is, ΔH increases along with ΔF. The ionization constant of water increases very rapidly with temperature in the range 0° to 100°C.

Representative data to show the effect of temperature on ionization constants are given in Table III. Most of them are taken from the compilation of Everett and Wynne-Jones. The effect of temperature on acid-base indicators will be discussed in the next chapter.

TABLE III

IONIZATION CONSTANTS AND TEMPERATURE

| Acid | K_A | | $\Delta F°_{298}$ | ΔH_{298} |
	25°C	60°C		
H_2O	1.01×10^{-14}	9.62×10^{-14}	19,122	13,490
CH_3COOH	1.75×10^{-5}	1.54×10^{-5}	6,484	-100
C_6H_5COOH	6.67×10^{-5}	6.10×10^{-5}	5,682	40
C_6H_5OH	1.3×10^{-10}	$\ldots$	13,650	5,900*
HBO_2	5.79×10^{-10}	9.20×10^{-10}	12,591	3,370
HCN	7.2×10^{-10}	$\ldots$	12,920	11,100*
NH_4^+	6.04×10^{-10}	5.45×10^{-9}	12,562	12,400
$H_3PO_4: K_1$	7.52×10^{-3}	4.63×10^{-3}	2,895	$-1,790$
K_2	6.23×10^{-8}	6.30×10^{-8}	9,823	820
Glycine: K_1	4.47×10^{-3}	5.37×10^{-3}	3,304	1,100
K_2	1.67×10^{-10}	1.07×10^{-9}	13,328	10,600

* Determined calorimetrically at 15°C.

The slope of pH-titration curves. A glance at Figures 1, 2, and 3 will show that the pH rises or falls much more steeply in the equivalence region in some titrations than in others. In the titration of hydrochloric acid by sodium hydroxide, the analyst may stop his titration anywhere between pH 5 and pH 9 without making any

[2] H. S. Harned and N. D. Embree, *J. Am. Chem. Soc.*, **56**, 1050 (1934); E. C. Baughan, *J. Chem. Phys.*, **7**, 951 (1939).

serious error, but in titrating phosphoric acid he must come within 0.2 unit of the correct pH, or his error will be 1% or more. The slope of the titration curve at equivalence is therefore very important in practice. It may be calculated in two ways; first by a general method which can be applied to any practical case by making appropriate approximations; and second by an *ad hoc* procedure which will depend on the particular case considered. We present the general method first. It is applicable, not merely to the equivalence point, but to any point on the titration curve.

General Analytical Treatment. Consider an acid HA being neutralized by a base B. Combining equations (10) and (11) above,

$$[H_3O^+] - [OH^-] = [A^-] - [BH^+]$$
$$= [A^-] - b + [B], \qquad (18)$$

where b is the total concentration of the component B which has been added, i.e., $[B] + [BH^+] \cdot [A^-]$ can be expressed in terms of a by equation (12), and so can $[B]$ be expressed in terms of b, if we remember that B is the base conjugate to BH^+, just as A^- is the base conjugate to HA. Combining equations (12), (8), and (18), and assuming activity coefficients to be unity,

$$[H_3O^+] - \frac{K_W}{[H_3O^+]} = \frac{aK_A}{[H_3O^+] + K_A} - b + \frac{bK_2}{[H_3O^+] + K_2} \qquad (19)$$

where $K_2 = K_W/K_B =$ the ionization constant of the acid BH^+. Rearranging and differentiating,

$$\frac{db}{d[H_3O^+]} = -1 - \frac{K_W}{[H_3O^+]^2} - \frac{aK_A}{([H_3O^+] + K_A)^2} - \frac{bK_2}{([H_3O^+] + K_2)^2}$$
$$+ \frac{K_2}{[H_3O^+] + K_2} \frac{db}{d[H_3O^+]}. \qquad (20)$$

Thus far the only approximation has been to treat activity coefficients as unity. Equation (20) holds for any point on the titration curve and may be used, if desired, to calculate the efficiency of buffer mixtures. For the present we are interested in equivalence points. At equivalence, $a = b$, and $K_A \gg [H_3O^+] \gg K_2$; therefore equation (20) may be simplified as follows:

$$-[H_3O^+] \frac{db}{d[H_3O^+]} = -\frac{db}{d \ln [H_3O^+]} = [H_3O^+] + [OH^-]$$
$$+ \frac{a[H_3O^+]}{K_A} + \frac{aK_2}{[H_3O^+]} - \frac{K_2}{[H_3O^+]} \frac{db}{d \ln [H_3O^+]}. \qquad (21)$$

Since $K_2/[H_3O^+]$ is much less than 1, the last term can be neglected. Converting to logarithms to the base 10,

$$- \frac{db}{d \log_{10} [H_3O^+]} = \frac{db}{d \, pH}$$

$$= 2.3 \left\{ [H_3O^+] + [OH^-] + \frac{a[H_3O^+]}{K_A} + \frac{aK_2}{[H_3O^+]} \right\}. \quad (22)$$

By substituting equations (15) into equation (22), we can derive db/d pH for the various special cases we considered. A more significant quantity than db/d pH for titration end points is $(1/b)(db/d \, pH)$; this measures the percentage error in the titer b caused by a given small error in judging the equivalence pH. Expressions for $(1/b)(db/d \, pH)$ for special cases, together with sample numerical values, are given in Table IV. We note that the possible end-point error is greatest for the case of weak acid plus weak base, and for the analogous case of the half neutralization of a dibasic acid. Here the error is greater, the closer the two ionization constants are to one another. This is apparent also from curves a, b, and c of Figure 2; succinic acid, for which $K_1/K_2 = 24$, shows no discernible first end point at all, but only an extended buffering action. Another case

TABLE IV

SLOPES OF TITRATION CURVES AT EQUIVALENCE

Case	Constants	$\dfrac{1}{b}\dfrac{db}{d \, pH}$
Strong acid, strong base.................	. . .	9.2×10^{-6}
Weak acid, strong base.................	$K_A = 10^{-5}$	6.5×10^{-4}
Weak acid, strong base.................	$K_A = 10^{-9}$	6.5×10^{-2}
Weak acid, weak base..................	$K_A = K_B = 10^{-5}$	4.6×10^{-2}
Weak dibasic acid, strong base:	$K_1 = 10^{-3}, K_2 = 10^{-6}$	
first equivalence...........		1.5×10^{-1}
second equivalence........		2.5×10^{-3}

Note: Values are calculated by Equation (22), for 0.1 N base added to 0.1 N acid (0.1 M dibasic acid).

for which the possible end-point error is considerable is that of a very weak acid plus a strong base.   In the case cited, the equivalence point would come at about pH 11, and the hydroxyl ion concentration is large enough to cause smearing of the end-point region, according to equation (22).   This equation tells us that end points which fall outside of the pH range 4–10 are automatically rather poor.

There remain to be considered two further representative cases in which the end-point region of the titration curve is flattened.

Titration of a Weak Acid, HA, *by a Strong Base*, NaOH, *in Presence of a Large Amount of the Salt of the Weak Acid.*

The quantity db/d pH can be calculated exactly as in Equation (22).   However, b here equals, not the amount of base added from the buret during the titration, but the total amount of sodium salt present per liter of solution at equivalence, which is much larger; $b = a = [Na^+] = [A^-] + [HA]$.   To get the slope of the titration curve relative to the amount of sodium hydroxide added, we must divide the calculated db/d pH by a quantity m which is the number of moles of sodium hydroxide added during the titration divided by the number of liters of solution at equivalence.   The quantity m is much smaller than b, and the accuracy of the titration is correspondingly reduced.

Titration of a Weak Acid, HA_1, *by* NaOH *in Presence of a Weaker Acid*, HA_2.   (Cf. curve d, Figure 2.)   Here the equation of electrical neutrality (Equation 18, page 238) should read:

$$[Na^+] + [H_3O^+] = [OH^-] + [A_1^-] + [A_2^-]. \qquad (23)$$

If we define $\qquad\qquad a = A_1^- + [HA_1]$

and $\qquad\qquad\qquad b = A_2^- + [HA_2],$

we get an equation similar to (22):

$$\frac{d[Na^+]}{d\,pH} = 2.3\left\{[H_3O^+] + [OH^-] + \frac{a[H_3O^+]}{K_A} + \frac{bK_2}{[H_3O^+]}\right\}. \qquad (24)$$

Here a is not necessarily equal to b. $[H_3O^+]$ must be calculated from equation (15g).   The accuracy of the titration is measured by $(1/m)(d[Na^+]/d\,pH)$, where m is again the number of moles of base added per liter of solution at equivalence; m and $[Na^+]$ are equal if there were no sodium salts in the solution at the start.   The weaker acid, HA_2, smears the end point by making $[H_3O^+]$ greater than it would be if HA_1 were being titrated alone.

These two examples will show how the general treatment can be applied to complicated cases. Such cases are more common in practice than one sometimes thinks.[3]

Ad hoc calculation of end point errors. The previous method of calculation gives the slope of the tangent to the pH titration curve at equivalence. At this point the curve is steepest, and its slope is changing rapidly as b changes. For real, noninfinitesimal errors in pH, the corresponding error in titration volume will be more than this calculation indicates, as can be seen from Figure 4; OA is the error in

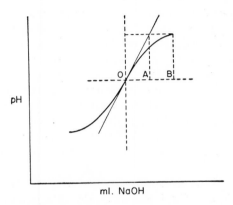

Fig. 13-4. Inflection in pH-titration curve; relation of slope to end point error.

volume calculated by multiplying the slope of the tangent by the error in pH; OB is the actual volume error. The calculations to be presented in this section give the actual error OB. The procedure is first to calculate the concentrations of all the relevant ionic and molecular species at the equivalence pH, then to recalculate them for the actual pH to which the solution is titrated, then from the differences in these concentrations to compute the amount of titrant needed to bring the solution from the equivalence pH to the actual pH. We shall illustrate this procedure by two examples.

(a) *Acetic acid* HAc, 0.1 *M*, *of* $K_A = 1.8 \times 10^{-5}$, *is titrated with* 0.1 *M sodium hydroxide. What percentage error is caused by stopping at a* pH *which is* 0.5 *unit too high?*

[3] F. Fenwick, *Ind. Eng. Chem., Anal. Ed.,* **4,** 144 (1932).

At equivalence, $[H_3O^+] = 1.9 \times 10^{-9}$, from equation (15b). The pH is 8.72. Also, $[Ac^-] = 0.05$, wherefore $[HAc] = [H_3O^+][Ac^-]/K_A = 5.3 \times 10^{-6} = [OH^-]$. At pH $(8.72 + 0.50)$, or 9.32, $[H_3O^+] = 4.8 \times 10^{-10}$. $[Ac^-]$ is still very nearly 0.05; it will not have changed by more than a fraction of a percent. The changes in $[H_3O^+]$, $[OH^-]$, and $[HAc]$ are proportionately much larger.

$$[HAc] = \frac{[H_3O^+][Ac^-]}{K_A} = 1.33 \times 10^{-6};$$

$$[OH^-] = \frac{K_W}{[H_3O^+]} = 2.1 \times 10^{-5}.$$

Tabulating,

pH	$[H_3O^+]$	$[OH^-]$	$[HAc]$
8.72	1.9×10^{-9}	5.3×10^{-6}	5.3×10^{-6}
9.32	0.5×10^{-9}	$21 \ \times 10^{-6}$	1.3×10^{-6}
Increase or decrease:	1.4×10^{-9}	$16 \ \times 10^{-6}$	4.0×10^{-6}

The amount of base which must be added to raise $[OH^-]$, and lower $[H_3O^+]$ and $[HAc]$, by the amounts given is the sum of these, or 2.0×10^{-5} equivalents per liter. The *percentage* excess of base $= (2.0 \times 10^{-5})/(0.05) \times 100 = 0.04\%$. Incidentally, by calculating $(1/b)(db/d\,\mathrm{pH})$ from equation (22) and multiplying by 0.5, we would have estimated this percentage excess to be 0.024%.

(b) 0.10 *molar* H_3PO_4 *is titrated to the first equivalence point with* 0.10 *N* NaOH. *What percentage error is caused by stopping the titration at a* pH *which is* 0.5 *unit too high?*

Using the approximate equation (15f), $[H_3O^+]$ at equivalence $= 2.14 \times 10^{-5}$, and pH $= 4.67$ (see page 234). The phosphoric acid is chiefly in the form $H_2PO_4^-$; approximately, therefore, $[H_2PO_4^-] = a = 0.05$. Thence $[H_3PO_4] = [H_2PO_4^-][H_3O]/K_1 = 1.43 \times 10^{-4}$, and similarly, $[HPO_4^=] = 1.43 \times 10^{-4}$ also. Calculating $[H_3PO_4]$ and $[HPO_4^=]$ at pH $(4.67 + 0.5)$, and tabulating as we did before;

pH	H_3O^+	OH^-	H_3PO_4	$HPO_4^=$
4.67	2.14×10^{-5}	4.7×10^{-10}	1.43×10^{-4}	1.43×10^{-4}
5.17	0.67×10^{-5}	1.5×10^{-9}	0.45×10^{-4}	$4.5 \ \times 10^{-4}$
Increase or decrease:	$1.5 \ \times 10^{-5}$	3.2×10^{-9}	0.98×10^{-4}	$3.1 \ \times 10^{-4}$

Summing these changes, the excess of base needed to raise the pH from 4.67 to 5.17 is 4.2×10^{-4} equivalents per liter; the percentage excess is 0.84%. The error estimated by calculating $(1/b)(db/d$ pH$)$ and multiplying by 0.5 is 0.67%.

These examples will show that the method can be applied to any titration end point. The principle is to decide which is (or are) the main ionic or molecular species present at equivalence, and then to calculate the changes in the concentrations of the *other* species as the pH is raised or lowered. Of course the concentration of the main species changes too; in the second example above, the concentration of $H_2PO_4^-$ falls as the pH is raised, but this decrease is so much less percentagewise than the decrease in H_3PO_4 concentration and the increase in $HPO_4^=$ concentration that it is simpler to calculate the changes in the latter.

Summary. We can summarize the conclusions of the two preceding sections briefly as follows. An acid-base titration gives a sharp enough end point to make it feasible with an indicator if *both* the following conditions are fulfilled: (1) the pH at equivalenc is within the range 4 to 10; (2) where two acids, or two bases, are present in approximately equal concentrations, the stronger may be titrated in presence of the weaker if the ratio of their dissociation constants is 10^4 or greater. Case (2) includes the titration of a dibasic acid, H_2A, to its first equivalence point. The "two acids" here are H_2A and HA^-. Thus selenious acid $(K_1/K_2 = 60,000)$ gives a very good first end point, while malonic acid $(K_1/K_2 = 1750)$ gives a poor one (Figure 2).

If the titration is done potentiometrically, even a poor end point can usually be located by inspection of the curve, or by a mathematical analysis based on the fact that the equation of the titration curve in the equivalence region is a cubic.[3] Acid-base titrations which have poor potentiometric end points often give better ones when done conductometrically (see Chapter 20).

The analytical treatment of the slope of pH titration curves which was given above can be applied with appropriate modifications to the calculation of the efficiency of buffer mixtures.

Titration of very weak acids and bases in nonaqueous solvents. We have seen that where extremely weak acids, having ionization constants of the order 10^{-10} or less, are titrated with strong

bases, flattened and indistinct inflection points are obtained in the
pH titration curve.   The reason is that the solvent, water, is nearly
as strong an acid as the acid which is being titrated.   To get a sharp
inflection point in aqueous solution, the equilibrium

$$HA + OH^- \rightleftharpoons A^- + H_2O$$

must lie overwhelmingly on the right.   This will only be so if HA
is a much stronger acid than water, or in other words, if A^- is a much
weaker base than OH^-.

If HA is a very weak acid, and we wish to titrate it, we must find
a solvent for it which is a much weaker acid.   It must be a weaker
acid than water, but at the same time it must be an ionizing solvent.
The titrant must be a base stronger than the hydroxyl ion.

A possible solvent is anhydrous ammonia, but this is hard to handle
on account of its low boiling point.   A better choice is ethylene diamine, $(CH_2NH_2)_2$; this boils at 117°C and is a stronger base than
ammonia.   The titrant could be a solution of $NaNH_2$ or its ethylene
diamine analogue, but in practice the compound $Na^+(OCH_2CH_2NH_2)^-$,
prepared from metallic sodium and ethanolamine, is found more
suitable; it is used as a solution in ethylene diamine.[4]   Acids as weak

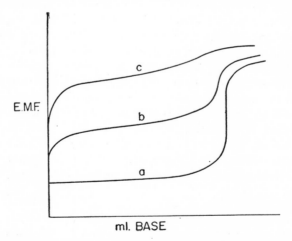

Fig. 13-5.   Titrations in nonaqueous solvents.   (a), benzoic
acid in ethylene diamine; (b), phenol in ethylene diamine; (c),
phenol in water.

[4] M. L. Moss, J. H. Elliott, and R. T. Hall, *Anal. Chem.*, **20,** 784 (1948).

as phenol and glycine have been successfully titrated in this way. The titration is done potentiometrically, using antimony electrodes. Phenol gives a titration curve shaped like that for acetic acid in water, while benzoic acid gives a curve like that for hydrochloric acid in water (see Figure 5). Phenol and benzoic acid can be titrated successively in the same solution. It is worth noting that the lower the dielectric constant of a solvent, the more difference there is between the ionization constants of two given weak acids or bases.[5]

Weak acids have also been titrated with sodium methoxide in butylamine, pyridine, piperidine, and benzene-methanol mixtures.[6] Thymol blue indicator can be used in some of these titrations.

For titrating very weak bases, glacial acetic acid is a good solvent.[7,8,9] The titrant is perchloric acid, made by dissolving 72% $HClO_4$ in glacial acetic acid, and adding just enough acetic anhydride to combine with the water in the perchloric acid solution. Anhydrous sulfuric acid can also be used as the titrant, but it is not so good. Again the titration is done potentiometrically, using a glass[8,9] or chloranil[7] electrode. Crystal violet indicator is also very satisfactory.[9,10] Bases as weak as urea can be titrated in this way, and so can amino acids and anions of weak acids such as acetate, benzoate, and the anion of sulfathiazole. The latter have been titrated using a propylene glycol-isopropanol mixture as the solvent.[11] *Formamide* is another solvent which gives promise of being useful.

In all these titrations it is important to exclude water completely. If water is present it will be titrated, as a weak acid or as a weak base, along with the main substance being titrated, and since its ionization constant will not be very different from that of the weak acid or base being titrated, it will smear the end point and introduce the very difficulty we are trying to avoid by using nonaqueous solvents. In potentiometric titrations care must be taken lest water from the reference electrode contaminate the solution. The type of calomel

[5] W. F. K. Wynne-Jones, *Proc. Roy. Soc., A*, **140**, 440 (1933); J. G. Kirkwood and F. H. Westheimer, *J. Chem. Phys.*, **6**, 506 (1938).

[6] J. S. Fritz and N. M. Lisicki, *Anal. Chem.*, **23**, 589 (1951).

[7] N. F. Hall and T. H. Werner, *J. Am. Chem. Soc.*, **50**, 2367 (1928); N. F. Hall, *J. Am. Chem. Soc.*, **52**, 5115 (1930).

[8] P. C. Markunas and J. A. Riddick, *Anal. Chem.*, **23**, 337 (1951).

[9] W. Seaman and E. Allen, *Anal. Chem.*, **23**, 592 (1951).

[10] O. Tomicek, *Collection Czechoslov. Chem. Commun.*, **13**, 116 (1948).

[11] M. W. Green, *J. Am. Pharm. Assoc.*, **37**, 240 (1948); S. R. Palit, *Ind. Eng. Chem., Anal. Ed.*, **18**, 246 (1946).

half-cell used in commercial pH meters does not introduce appreciable contamination.[8,9]

The use of nonaqueous media for acid-base titrations is a promising field of research in analytical chemistry. The titration of very weak acids and bases, and mixtures containing them, is important in the pharmaceutical and synthetic resin fields. It is to be hoped that more indicators will be found which will function in nonaqueous solvents.

The field has been reviewed by J. A. Riddick in *Anal. Chem.*, **24**, 41 (1952).

PROBLEMS

1. Calculate (a) pH, (b) pOH of buffers composed of equimolar concentrations of: (1) CH_3COOH and CH_3COONa; (2) Na_2HPO_4 and NaH_2PO_4; (3) NH_3 and NH_4Cl, all at 25° and at 60°C.

2. Calculate (a) pH, (b) pOH of 0.1 molar solutions of the following, at 25° and at 60°C; CH_3COONa, NH_4Cl, CH_3COONH_4, NaH_2PO_4.

3. Calculate the pH of 0.1 M $(NH_4)_2HPO_4$. *Note:* Go to first principles and do not depend upon a formula.

4. Make an estimate of the pH of 0.01 M NaH_2PO_4, allowing for activity coefficients by using the Debye-Hückel limiting law.

5. Calculate pH and dpH/db, the slope of the pH titration curve, at equivalence in the following titrations:

(a) 0.01 M acetic acid titrated with 0.1 M NaOH.
(b) A solution 0.01 M in acetic acid and 1 M in sodium acetate, titrated with 0.1 M NaOH.
(c) A solution 0.01 M in acetic acid and 0.01 M in HCl, titrated with 0.1 M NaOH to the point where only the HCl is neutralized.

Calculate also the percentage error which will be made in each case by titrating to a pH 1.0 unit too high, using the *ad hoc* method of page 241.

6. A solution is 1.0 M in NH_4Cl and 0.1 M in NH_3. It is titrated with 0.1 M HCl. Calculate the pH at the start of the titration, at equivalence, and halfway between; then calculate the slope of the titration curve at equivalence, using equation (22). Do the same for the titration of pure 0.1 M NH_3 with 0.1 M HCl. Plot the two titration curves, and compare them.

7. A solution is 0.02 M in acetic acid and 1.0 M in phenol. It is titrated with 0.02 M sodium hydroxide. Calculate (a) pH, (b) $(1/b)(db/dpH)$, at the equivalence point for neutralization of the acetic acid.

8. The ionization constants of ethylene diamine $(CH_2NH_2)_2$ as a base are $K_{B1} = 1.0 \times 10^{-4}$, $K_{B2} = 1.25 \times 10^{-7}$. Discuss the conditions to be used in titrating ethylene diamine solutions with hydrochloric acid, and in analyzing mixtures of H_3O^+ and $(CH_2NH_3)_2^{++}$ by titration with sodium hydroxide.

9. A sodium hydroxide solution contains carbonate. It is standardized against potassium acid phthalate, using phenolphthalein indicator. It is then used to titrate (a) hydrochloric acid, using methyl red indicator, (b) succinimide $(K_A = 10^{-10}$ approx.) potentiometrically. What errors will be introduced into these titrations?

10. How would you determine the carbonate content of a sodium hydroxide solution which has been exposed to air?

11. How would you prepare a carbonate-free solution of potassium hydroxide, starting with potassium hydroxide pellets?

12. A solution of ammonia, originally 0.1 M, has absorbed 0.01 mole of CO_2 per liter. This solution is titrated with 0.1 M HCl. *Calculate:* (a) the initial pH; (b) the pH at the first equivalence point; (c) the slope of the titration curve at this point. (*Note:* In equation (20), a and b are not equal.)

Would you use titration by hydrochloric acid to determine the carbonate content of an ammonia solution? Suggest an alternative method.

13. Calculate (a) the pH, (b) the percentage error caused by stopping at a pH 0.5 unit too high, in the titration of 0.02 M Na_2CO_3 with 0.02 M HCl. Assume that all the carbon dioxide liberated remains in solution, and use the *ad hoc* method described on page 241 to calculate the error.

14. Why is it nearly impossible to titrate amino acids, such as glycine, in aqueous solutions? Explain from the standpoint of acid-base equilibria why glycine can be titrated in ethylene diamine or in glacial acetic acid, but not in water.

15. Explain the use of (a) mannitol in titrating boric acid, (b) formaldehyde in titrating amino acids.

16. Give directions for titrating pyrophosphoric acid, a tetrabasic acid whose ionization constants are 0.14, 0.011, 2.1×10^{-7}, and 4.1×10^{-10}.

17. From the graph in Figure 2, estimate the ionization constants of selenious acid, and compare with the data given in the Appendix. Account for any differences.

18. Anhydrous perchloric acid is dangerously explosive, yet the solution in glacial acetic acid which is used for titrating weak bases is quite safe to use. Why?

14

Acid-base indicators

ACID-BASE INDICATORS are substances which change color or develop fluorescence or turbidity in a certain pH range. They are used to locate the equivalence point in acid-base titrations, and also to measure pH. For their color to depend on pH, these indicators must be acids or bases themselves. To show a marked color change without consuming appreciable quantities of the titrating agent in so doing, they must be strongly colored. Other requirements, such as adequate solubility and chemical stability, must be met also.

All practically useful acid-base indicators are organic in nature. One of the simplest is p-nitrophenol, which we shall use as an example to show how all acid-base indicators work. P-nitrophenol is a weak acid, and in its undissociated form it is colorless. Its anion, however, is yellow. This indicator is therefore colorless in acidic solutions and yellow in alkaline solutions:

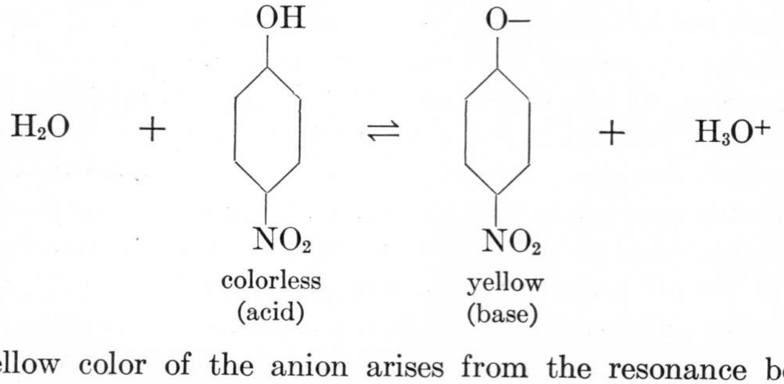

$$H_2O \quad + \quad \underset{\substack{NO_2 \\ \text{colorless} \\ \text{(acid)}}}{\overset{OH}{\bighexagon}} \quad \rightleftharpoons \quad \underset{\substack{NO_2 \\ \text{yellow} \\ \text{(base)}}}{\overset{O-}{\bighexagon}} \quad + \quad H_3O^+$$

The yellow color of the anion arises from the resonance between the structure shown above and an isomeric quinonoid structure in which the negative charge resides on the nitro group:

$$O^- \rightleftharpoons O$$

Oscillation of electrons between these two extreme forms is responsible for the absorption of light energy. In this case the oscillation frequency corresponds to the frequency of blue light; hence blue light is absorbed, and the color of the indicator is that complementary to blue, namely, yellow. Resonance due to electron isomerism of the kind shown here is responsible for the color of most, if not all, of the indicators we shall discuss in this chapter.[1]

The ionization constant of p-nitrophenol is 1.0×10^{-7} at 20°C. That is,

$$\frac{[H_3O^+][In^-]}{[HIn]} = 1.0 \times 10^{-7},$$

where HIn stands for the indicator acid and In^- for the anion or conjugate base. For a hydronium ion concentration of 1.0×10^{-7} (pH = 7.00) the concentrations of HIn and In^- are equal, that is, the yellow color of the indicator is half developed. At a higher pH than 7.00, the yellow basic form predominates; at a lower pH, the colorless acid form predominates. Below pH 6.00, at which the ratio basic form : acid form is 1:10, the yellow color of the basic form will be imperceptible to the eye. Likewise, the eye cannot distinguish between the yellow color at pH 8.00, when a fraction 10/11 of the indicator is in the basic form, and the color at higher pH values when conversion to the basic form is even more complete. The pH interval in which the color change of an indicator is apparent to the eye thus extends over about two pH units. This is perhaps an overestimate of the power of the eye to distinguish color intensities; a range of 1.6 or 1.8 pH units might be more realistic.

Different indicators have different ionization constants, and so

[1] For the connection between resonance and color, see G. E. K. Branch and M. Calvin, *The Theory of Organic Chemistry*, New York, Prentice-Hall, 1941, Chap. 5.

change color in different pH intervals.   At one extreme is methyl violet, which changes from violet to yellow as the pH falls below 1 and is used for rough adjustment of acidity in qualitative analysis, and at the other is nitramine (or tetryl), which is colorless at pH 11 and orange at pH 13.   Table I shows the pH range of a number of common indicators.   For certain indicators two ranges are listed.   These indicators are dibasic acids which show two color changes, in two dif-

TABLE I

COMMON ACID-BASE INDICATORS

Common name	Chemical type	Acid color	Base color	pH range
Methyl violet.....	Aminotriphenylmethane	Yellow	Blue	0.5– 1.5
Thymol blue.....	S. P.	Red	Yellow	1.2– 2.8
Tropeoline 00.....	Azo	Red	Yellow	1.3– 3.0
Methyl yellow....	Azo	Red	Yellow	2.9– 4.0
Methyl orange....	Azo	Red	Yellow	3.1– 4.4
Bromphenol blue..	S. P.	Yellow	Blue-violet	3.0– 4.6
Bromcresol green..	S. P.	Yellow	Blue	3.8– 5.4
Methyl red.......	Azo	Red	Yellow	4.2– 6.3
Chlorphenol red...	S. P.	Yellow	Red	4.8– 6.4
Bromthymol blue	S. P.	Yellow	Blue	6.0– 7.6
Paranitrophenol...	. . .	Colorless	Yellow	6.2– 7.5
Phenol red........	S. P.	Yellow	Red	6.4– 8.0
Cresol red........	S. P.	Yellow	Red	7.2– 8.8
Metanitrophenol..	. . .	Colorless	Yellow	7.8– 9.4
Thymol blue.....	S. P.	Yellow	Blue	8.0– 9.6
Phenolphthalein...	Phth.	Colorless	Red	8.0– 9.8
o-Cresolphthalein..	Phth.	Colorless	Red-violet	8.2–10.0
Thymolphthalein..	Phth.	Colorless	Blue	9.3–10.5
Alizarin yellow R	Azo	Yellow	Violet	10.1–12.0
Nitramine (Tetryl)	. . .	Colorless	Red-brown	10.8–13.0
Sodium indigo disulfonate.....	. . .	Blue	Yellow	11.4–12.8

Notes: 1. S. P. = sulfonephthalein; Phth. = phthalein.   2. Most of these data are taken from I. M. Kolthoff and H. A. Laitinen, *pH and Electrotitrations*, 2d ed., New York, Wiley, 1941.

ferent pH ranges, corresponding to two successive stages of ionization. These will be discussed in more detail below.

With the aid of tables such as Table I, and of calculations of the kind discussed in the last chapter, the indicator appropriate to any particular titration may be chosen.

Some indicators, like p-nitrophenol and phenolphthalein, are colorless in one form (acidic or basic) and colored in the other; other indicators, like methyl orange, have one color in the acid form and another color in the basic form. The former are called one-color indicators, the latter two-color indicators. Two-color indicators are preferred for titrations, because it is easier to tell visually when a desired pH has been reached; the eye is more sensitive to changes in hue than in color intensity, and the amount of indicator added is of little consequence. For accurate photometric measurement of pH, however, one-color indicators are better.

No attempt will be made in this chapter to describe the various acid-base indicators in detail. For such description the reader is referred to the treatises on the subject.[2] We shall try here to show the chemical structures of a few of the more common or representative indicators, and to discuss the effects of temperature, electrolytes, and solvent medium on their color changes.

Some typical indicators. The Phthaleins. These are made by condensing phthalic anhydride with phenols. The most familiar, and the simplest, is phenolphthalein, which has successive stages of ionization as shown below:

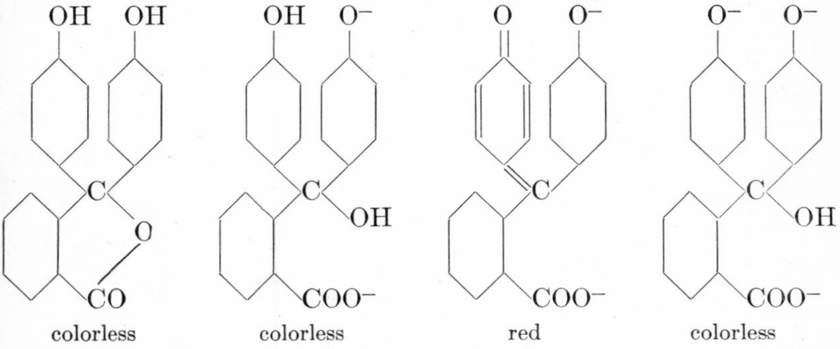

colorless   colorless   red   colorless

[2] For example, I. M. Kolthoff and C. Rosenblum, *Acid-Base Indicators*, New York, Macmillan, 1937.

Only one of the various resonance forms is shown for each stage of ionization, but it will be recognized that the red anion has two possible electronic structures of equal potential energy. The quinonoid structure can exist in either of the two phenolic residues, that on the left or that on the right.

Phenolphthalein changes color in the range pH 8.0 (colorless) to 9.8 (red). It is a very useful indicator for titrating weak acids with strong bases. Another important use is in titrating carbonate or carbon dioxide to bicarbonate; the pH of a dilute bicarbonate solution is about 8.4. The end point of the titration is not sharp, however, and the shade of pink at the end point must be gauged very carefully (see Chapter 13).

In 0.5 N sodium hydroxide, phenolphthalein slowly loses its red color to form the triply charged carbinol anion shown above. In more concentrated alkali the bleaching is faster. The red is only partly restored, if at all, by lowering the pH, for the triply charged anion suffers an irreversible breakdown.

Other phthaleins commonly used as indicators are o-cresolphthalein, thymolphthalein and α-naphtholphthalein. Like phenolphthalein, they are used as solutions of their colorless forms in alcohol. They suffer the same irreversible breakdown in strongly alkaline solutions.

The Sulfonephthaleins. This is a very important group and includes many common and useful indicators, all of which are of the two-color type, and are distinguished by the sharpness of their color changes. They are made by condensing phenols with the anhydride or chloride of o-sulfobenzoic acid. The simplest member of the group is phenolsulfonephthalein, or phenol red:

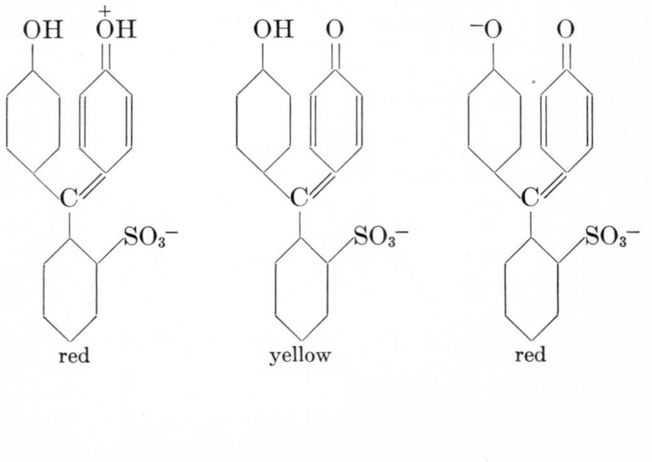

Again, only one of the resonance structures is shown for each form. pK for the first stage of ionization is 1.5, for the second 7.9. It is in the second stage of ionization that the practically useful color change occurs. A very interesting discussion of the color of the sulfonephthaleins is given by Schwarzenbach and his colleagues;[3] they point out that the two red forms shown above are symmetrical, as contrasted with the yellow form, which is unsymmetrical; in the symmetrical forms, the electrons have a longer period of oscillation, and therefore these forms absorb light of a longer wavelength (500–550 $m\mu$ for the red forms compared with 400–450 $m\mu$ for the yellow, or unsymmetrical, forms). This comparison is valid for a number of differently substituted sulfonephthaleins.

In the sulfonephthaleins we have a good opportunity to see the relationship between chemical constitution and the degree of ionization. Consider first the second stage of ionization of phenolsulfone-phthalein, shown above. The ionization is that of a phenolic group. Phenol, of course, is a very weak acid. Its ionization exponent, or negative logarithm of its ionization constant, pK, is 9.89 at 25°C. We might expect the phenolic group in the sulfonephthalein to ionize even more reluctantly than in phenol itself, because of the negative charge of the sulfonate group, which will oppose removal of the

TABLE II

IONIZATION EXPONENTS OF SULFONEPHTHALEINS

Systematic name	Common name	pK_1	pK_2
Phenolsulfonephthalein...........	Phenol red	1.5	7.9
m-Cresolsulfonephthalein.........	m-Cresol purple	1.51(30°)	8.32(30°)
Thymolsulfonephthalein..........	Thymol blue	1.65	9.20
Dichlorophenolsulfonephthalein...	Chlorphenol red	. . .	6.25
Dibromophenolsulfonephthalein...	Bromphenol red	. . .	6.8
Dibromothymolsulfonephthalein...	Bromthymol blue	. . .	7.10
Tetrabromophenolsulfonephthalein	Bromphenol blue	. . .	4.23
Tetrabromo m-cresolsulfonephthalein........	Bromcresol green	. . .	4.97
Tetrabromoanilinesulfonephthalein	. . .	8.48	. . .
Anilinesulfonephthalein..........	. . .	12.3	. . .

Notes: 1. All values are at 20°–25°C unless otherwise stated. 2. Aniline-sulfonephthalein has $pK = 1.6$ for the ionization of its singly charged cation (Schwarzenbach).

[3] G. Schwarzenbach *et al.*, *Helv. Chim. Acta*, **20**, 490, 498, 627, 654 (1937).

proton.   Instead, the phenolic ionization constant in the sulfone-phthalein is a hundred times as great as in phenol; the ionization exponent, pK_2, is only 7.9.   This shows how much the phenolate ion (the structure on the extreme right above) is stabilized by resonance.

Second, by comparing several differently substituted sulfonephthaleins we see very well the effect of substituents on the ionization constant of an acid.   Alkyl groups reduce the ionization, amino groups reduce it very greatly, and halogen atoms increase it, bromine having a greater effect than chlorine.   The effects are shown in Table II, which also provides a convenient summary of the sulfonephthalein indicators.

The sulfonephthaleins are more soluble in water than the phthaleins, and are generally used as aqueous solutions of their sodium salts.

The Azo Indicators.   These are made by reacting an aromatic amine with a diazonium salt.   The simplest example is methyl yellow, or *p*-dimethylaminoazobenzene:

red
(acid)

yellow
(base)

The most common azo indicators are listed below, with their structures and indicator exponents.   Again, the effect of structure on ionization is apparent.   Note that the acid forms of these indicators are given the formulas of zwitterions, or dipolar ions; part of the evidence for this formulation comes from the effects of temperature and electrolytes on their ionization.[4]

Theoretically, all these indicators except methyl yellow should show a color change in strongly acid solutions, corresponding to the addition of a proton to the acid forms listed in the table.   Such a change is observed with methyl red; its color changes from red to an orange-red as the acid concentration is raised above 1 normal.   This change is of no value analytically, but we mention it as we have known students to think their solution was neutral to methyl red when it was actually strongly acid.

[4] I. M. Kolthoff, *Rec. trav. chim.*, **44**, 68 (1925).

TABLE III

Azo Indicators

Formula (indicator acid)	Common name	Exponent, pK
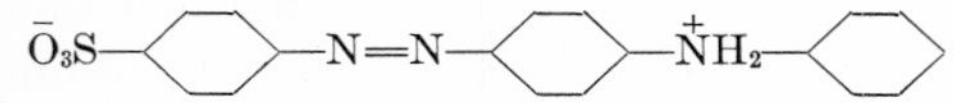 $\bar{O}_3S$—⟨ ⟩—N=N—⟨ ⟩—$\overset{+}{N}H_2$—⟨ ⟩	Tropaeolin 00	2.1
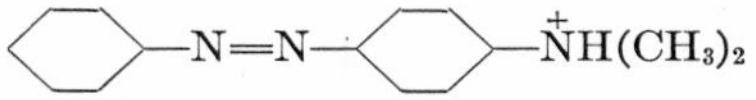 ⟨ ⟩—N=N—⟨ ⟩—$\overset{+}{N}H(CH_3)_2$	Methyl yellow	3.3
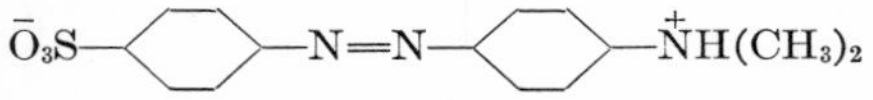 $\bar{O}_3S$—⟨ ⟩—N=N—⟨ ⟩—$\overset{+}{N}H(CH_3)_2$	Methyl orange	3.46
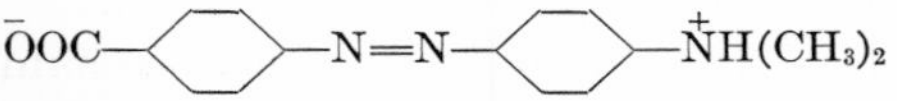 $\bar{O}OC$—⟨ ⟩—N=N—⟨ ⟩—$\overset{+}{N}H(CH_3)_2$	Methyl red	5.00

Except for methyl yellow, all these indicators are easily soluble in water, and are used as aqueous solutions of their sodium salts; or the acid form, which is less soluble than the basic form, may be dissolved in aqueous alcohol for reagent use.

Miscellaneous Indicators. The great majority of useful acid-base indicators have been covered in the three classes just listed. We shall give here a few examples of indicators of other chemical types.

Amino derivatives of triphenylmethane: malachite green, methyl violet, crystal violet.

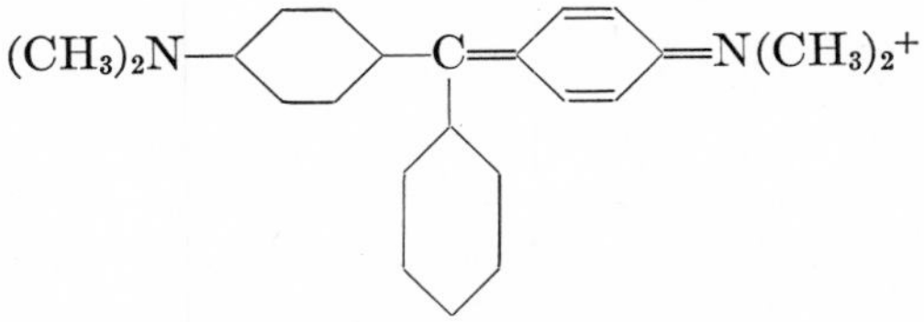

$(CH_3)_2N$—⟨ ⟩—C=⟨ ⟩=$N(CH_3)_2{}^+$

malachite
green

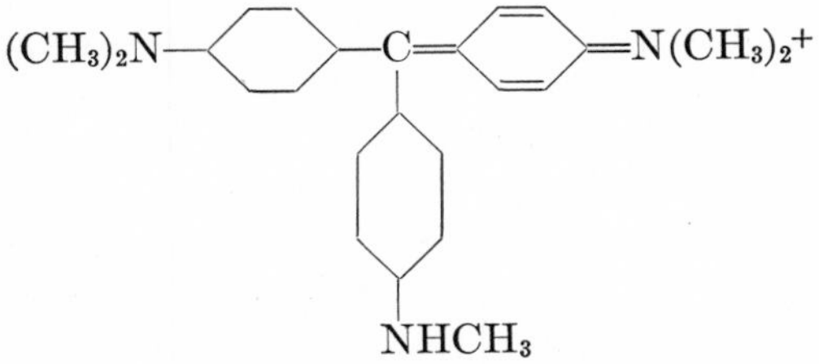

$(CH_3)_2N$—⟨ ⟩—C=⟨ ⟩=$N(CH_3)_2{}^+$

$NHCH_3$

methyl
violet

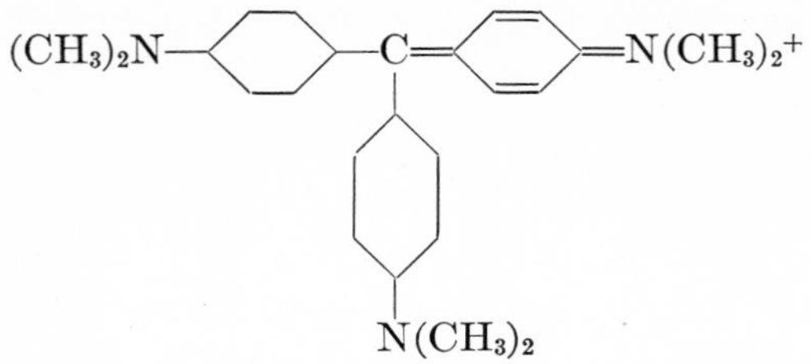

$$(CH_3)_2N - \overset{}{\underset{}{\bigcirc}} - C = \overset{}{\underset{}{\bigcirc}} = N(CH_3)_2{}^+$$

$$\overset{}{\underset{}{\bigcirc}}$$

$$N(CH_3)_2$$

crystal
violet

The possible structural changes are as follows, taking methyl violet as an example:

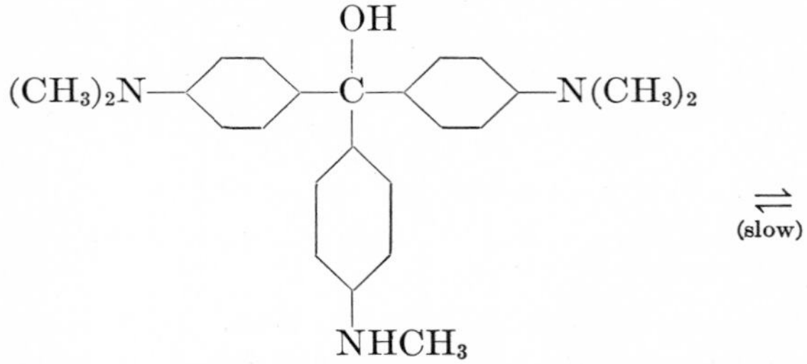

$$\overset{OH}{\underset{}{|}}$$

$$(CH_3)_2N - \bigcirc - \overset{}{\underset{}{C}} - \bigcirc - N(CH_3)_2$$

$$\bigcirc$$

$$NHCH_3$$

carbinol base
(colorless)

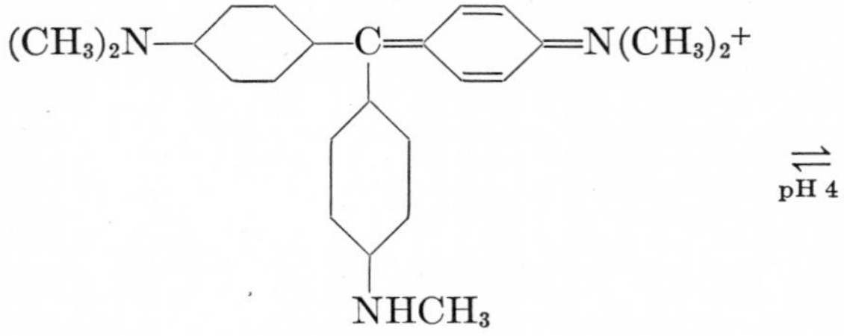

$\underset{(slow)}{\rightleftarrows}$

$$(CH_3)_2N - \bigcirc - C = \bigcirc = N(CH_3)_2{}^+$$

$$\bigcirc$$

$$NHCH_3$$

violet

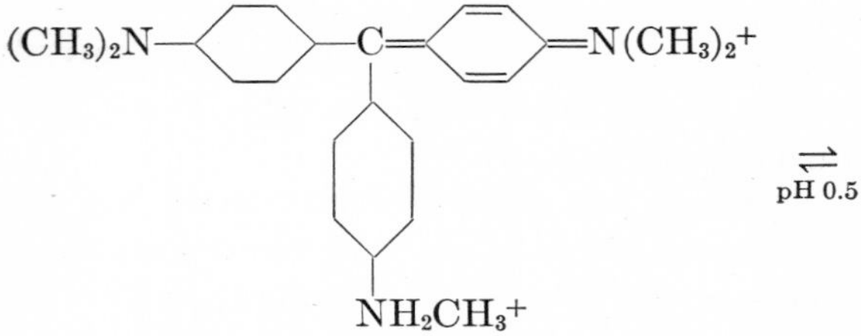

$\underset{pH\ 4}{\rightleftarrows}$

$$(CH_3)_2N - \bigcirc - C = \bigcirc = N(CH_3)_2{}^+$$

$$\bigcirc$$

$$NH_2CH_3{}^+$$

blue

$\underset{pH\ 0.5}{\rightleftarrows}$

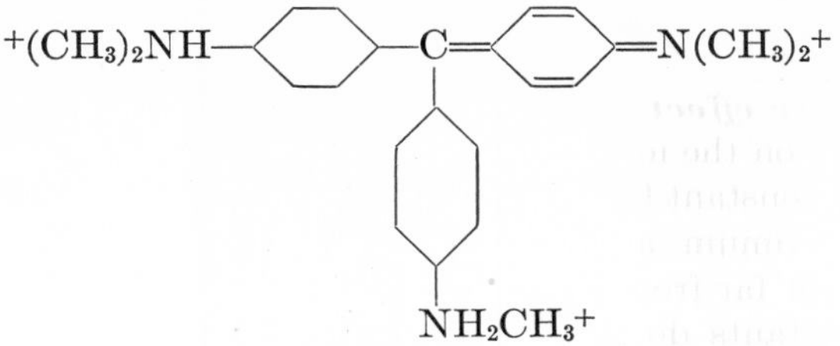

$$+(CH_3)_2NH—\langle\bigcirc\rangle—C=\langle\bigcirc\rangle=N(CH_3)_2^+$$

$$NH_2CH_3^+$$

yellow

Various resonance structures are possible, especially with the symmetrical molecule of crystal violet. Methyl violet is used for rough pH adjustment in the region of pH 0.5, while crystal violet is becoming a useful indicator for titrations in nonaqueous solvents (see page 245).

Nitramine (tetryl):

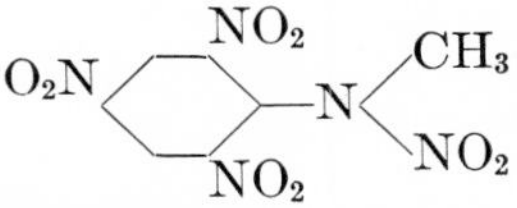

$$O_2N—\langle\bigcirc\rangle—N\begin{matrix}CH_3\\NO_2\end{matrix}$$

with NO₂ groups: NO_2 (top) and NO_2 (bottom).

This indicator is of interest only for rough pH measurements in the region of pH 12, and for its unusually weak acid properties, which are highly temperature-dependent (see Table III).

Sodium alizarin sulfonate:

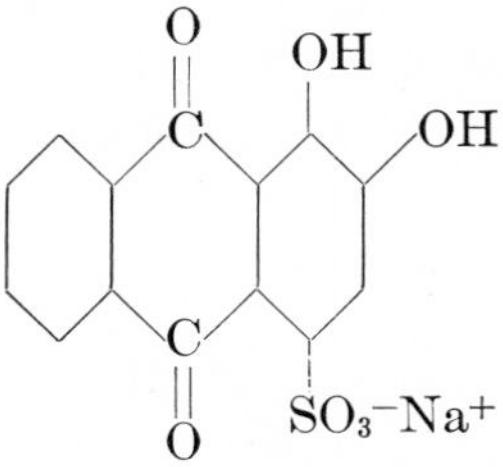

$$\begin{matrix}O\\||\\C\end{matrix}\quad OH\quad OH$$

$$\begin{matrix}C\\||\\O\end{matrix}\quad SO_3^-Na^+$$

This compound is little used as an acid-base indicator, but it is useful in colorimetric analysis and in titrating fluorides with thorium nitrate, since it forms colored lakes with a number of metal hydroxides and hydrous oxides (see page 107).

The nitrophenols and dinitrophenols. Being one-color indicators, these have a certain limited use in pH determination. The formula of *p*-nitrophenol was given at the beginning of this chapter to illustrate the action of acid-base indicators in general.

Temperature effects. In the last chapter we reviewed the effect of temperature on the ionization of acids, and saw that in most cases the ionization constant first rises with rising temperature, then passes through a maximum and falls again. For carboxylic acids this maximum is not far from room temperature, so that in general their ionization constants do not change much with temperature in the usual working range.

The main factor causing the fall in ionization with rising temperature is the effect of rising temperature on the dielectric constant of water, which is to decrease it. This is important in ionic dissociations where electric charges are separated, for the greater the dielectric constant, the easier it is to separate the charges. In an ionization such as

$$NH_4^+ + H_2O \rightleftharpoons NH_3 + H_3O^+$$

in which no separation of charges occurs, the dielectric constant is of minor importance, and the equilibrium constants for such ionizations generally increase steadily with rising temperature.

These same general considerations apply to the dissociation of the acid forms of indicators. Though accurate data are scanty, the following facts stand out.

The azo indicators, such as methyl orange and methyl yellow, show a considerable increase in dissociation as the temperature rises. It is common experience that a solution containing methyl orange which has been adjusted to give the orange-red transition color of the latter turns yellow on heating. The pH range for visible color change decreases from 3.1–4.4 at 18° to 2.5–3.7 at 100°C.[5] Now in the dissociation of the azo indicators, a proton is separated from a tertiary ammonium ion, leaving an uncharged residue, just as in the dissociation of the ammonium ion:

$$R\text{—}NH(CH_3)_2^+ \rightarrow R\text{—}N(CH_3)_2 + H^+.$$

There is no separation of charges, and so we should expect the dissociation to increase steadily with rising temperature. It is true that in methyl orange and methyl red the R group carries a negatively charged group at the end removed from the amino group, but this charge is so far away from the nitrogen atom—the methyl orange molecule is about 13 Å. long from the sulfur to the end nitrogen—

[5] I. M. Kolthoff, *Rec. trav. chim.*, **40**, 775 (1921).

that it has little influence in restraining the removal of the proton. In p-nitrophenol, on the other hand, where ionization of the phenolic group does cause a separation of charges, the dissociation changes very little with temperature. The same is true of the sulfonephthaleins in their second, or most generally useful, stage of ionization (see page 252). This means that the color change takes place in the same pH range at all temperatures between 0° and 100°C, although the pOH range will alter in accordance with the ionization constant of water.

The phthaleins and sulfonephthaleins should be analogous, yet the phthaleins show an appreciable change in ionization with temperature, connected probably with the fact that their ionization constants are in general smaller (see Chapter 13). The use of phenolphthalein in titrating carbonic acid or carbonate ion to bicarbonate was mentioned above; in this titration, the amount of base or acid taken to reach the end point is not affected by temperature. Evidently, the effect of temperature on the ionization constants of carbonic acid and on the ionization constant of the indicator just compensate one another.

Table IV summarizes the effect of temperature on the color changes of various common indicators.

TABLE IV

EFFECT OF TEMPERATURE ON INDICATORS

Indicator	(pH of half change at 70°C) −(pH of half change at 18°C)
Thymol blue (acid interval)	0.0
Bromphenol blue	0.0
Methyl orange	−0.3
Methyl red	−0.2
p-Nitrophenol	−0.5
Phenol red	−0.3
Thymol blue (alkaline interval)	−0.4
Phenolphthalein	−0.5
Nitramine	−1.45

Data from I. M. Kolthoff, *Rec. trav. chim.*, **40**, 775 (1921).

Salt effects. We noted in an earlier chapter that sparingly soluble salts are more soluble in solutions of electrolytes than they are in pure water, so long as the electrolyte and the sparingly soluble salt have no ions in common. This is due to the attractions between oppositely charged ions. The positive ions of the salt are surrounded by an atmosphere consisting predominantly of negatively charged ions, and the negative ions by an atmosphere consisting predominantly of positive ions. The attraction between unlike charges causes a lowering of potential energy, thus making it easier for the salt to go into solution where added electrolyte is present than where it is not.

Precisely the same effect operates in the ionization of a weak acid, HX. To form the ions H^+ and X^- (where H^+ is understood to stand for a *solvated* proton—in water, H_3O^+) and to separate them from one another, work must be done against the electrostatic attraction. If another electrolyte is present, its ions will form a negatively charged cloud around the H^+ and a positively charged cloud around the X^-, and the separation of H^+ from X^- will be made easier. Addition of a neutral salt will therefore increase the ionization of an acid of this type. The effect on the ionization of a negatively charged acid, HY^-, will be even greater, because of the double charge of the ion $Y^=$. This follows from the Debye-Hückel interionic attraction theory, as we shall now show.

The true, thermodynamic constant of ionization of a weak acid HX is:

$$K_a = \frac{a_{H^+} a_{X^-}}{a_{HX}} = \frac{c_{H^+} c_{X^-}}{c_{HX}} \cdot \frac{f_{H^+} f_{X^-}}{f_{HX}} \tag{1}$$

where the a's stand for activities, the c's for concentrations, and the f's for activity coefficients. The function pH relates to the *activity* of the hydrogen ion, not its concentration, for the potential of the hydrogen electrode, which is the definitive method of measuring pH, depends on the activity of the hydrogen ion. Introducing the relation $pH = - \log_{10} a_H$ into equation (1), we get:

$$\log K_a = \log a_{H^+} + \log \frac{c_{X^-}}{c_{HX}} + \log \frac{f_{X^-}}{f_{HX}}$$

$$pH = pK_a \quad + \log \frac{c_{X^-}}{c_{HX}} + \log \frac{f_{X^-}}{f_{HX}}$$

or $\qquad pK' = pK_a \quad + \log \frac{f_{X^-}}{f_{HX}} \tag{2}$

where pK' is the pH at which the indicator exists half in the acid and half in the basic form, in other words the pH of half color change. Now the activity coefficient f of an ion or molecule depends on its charge, and also on the charges and concentrations of all the ions present in the solution. At low concentrations the relationship approximates the Debye-Hückel limiting law (see Chapter 2):

$$\log f_i = -Az_i^2\sqrt{\mu} = -Az_i^2\sqrt{\frac{1}{2}\sum_j c_j z_j^2} \tag{3}$$

where z_i is the charge on the ion in question, and c_j, z_j are, respectively, the molar concentration and charge of every ion in the solution. The quantity μ is called the *ionic strength*. A is a constant which depends on the solvent and the temperature. For water at 25°C it is 0.506.

Equations (2) and (3) may easily be combined to give pK_c in terms of μ. Before doing so, however, we shall note that equation (2) is valid, not merely for an uncharged acid HX, but for charged acids such as HY^- and HZ^+. The activity coefficients are different in each case, however. Making the appropriate substitutions, and combining equations (2) and (3), we derive the following equations for the three different cases:

$$HX \rightleftharpoons H^+ + X^-; \quad pK' = pK_a - A\sqrt{\mu}. \tag{4a}$$

$$HY^- \rightleftharpoons H^+ + Y^=; \quad pK' = pK_a - 3A\sqrt{\mu}. \tag{4b}$$

$$HZ^+ \rightleftharpoons H^+ + Z; \quad pK' = pK_a + A\sqrt{\mu}. \tag{4c}$$

These equations are in the nature of first approximations, in which the ions are considered as point charges in a medium of uniform dielectric constant. Though they are only rough, they will serve as a guide to the effects to be expected.

Experimental studies of the effects of salts on indicators have been made by Kolthoff [6] and by Thiel and Coch.[7] Kolthoff worked with relatively dilute salt solutions, of ionic strength less than 1, while Thiel and Coch used ionic strengths of 1 and greater. Their experimental technique was more accurate than Kolthoff's, but the higher concentrations are difficult to treat theoretically, as the deviations

---

[6] I. M. Kolthoff, *J. Phys. Chem.*, **32**, 1820 (1928); see also I. M. Kolthoff and JI. A. Laitinen, *pH and Electrotitration*, 2d ed., New York, Wiley, 1941, p. 50.
[7] A. Thiel and G. Coch, *Z. anorg. Chem.*, **217**, 353 (1934).

from the simple Debye-Hückel activity equation are so large. Further, the higher concentrations are of less interest in analytical chemistry. We present the two sets of data separately. A selection of Kolthoff's results is given in Table V, a selection of Thiel and Coch's results in Table VI. The numbers given are $(pK'-pK_a)$; where this is negative, it means that a salt solution appears from the color of the indicator in it to be more alkaline than it really is.

TABLE V

SALT EFFECTS OF INDICATORS IN DILUTE SALT SOLUTIONS

			$pK' - pK_a$					
Ionic strength	Methyl orange	Methyl red	Thymol blue		Chlor-phenol red	Phenol-phthal-ein	p-Nitro-phenol	Triphenyl carbinol
			K_1	K_2				
0.01	0.02	0.00	0.00	−0.04	−0.02	−0.02	−0.02	. . .
0.05	0.04	0.00	0.00	−0.11	−0.10	−0.09	−0.03	0.08
0.10	0.04	0.00	0.00	−0.16	−0.15	−0.14	−0.06	0.17
0.5	0.04	0.00	0.00	−0.35	−0.34	−0.30	−0.22	. . .

Notes: 1. Data of I. M. Kolthoff, *J. Phys. Chem.*, **32**, 1820 (1928). Kolthoff's figures are referred to a buffer of $\mu = 0.1$ as standard; these figures are referred to a hypothetical buffer of $\mu = 0$. 2. In some cases these figures are interpolated from data at different ionic strengths. 3. The data for $\mu = 0.5$ refer to 0.5 M NaCl. 0.5 M KCl gave somewhat smaller deviations.

TABLE VI

SALT EFFECTS OF INDICATORS IN CONCENTRATED SALT SOLUTIONS

Salt and molarity	$pK' - pK_a$			
	Methyl orange	Methyl red	Cresol red	Phenol-phthalein
NaCl, 1.0 M	0.15	. . .	0.36	. . .
NaCl, 2.0 M	0.34	0.06	0.38	0.27
NaCl, 3.0 M	0.47	. . .	. . .	. . .
NaCl, 4.0 M	0.57	. . .	. . .	. . .
Na₂SO₄, 0.5 M	0.04	0.18	0.45	. . .
Na₂SO₄, 1.0 M	. . .	. . .	. . .	0.31

Notes: 1. Data of A. Thiel and G. Coch, *Z. anorg. Chem.*, **217**, 353 (1934). 2. Cresol red is o-cresolsulfonephthalein.

The data of Table V are qualitatively what we would expect from equations (4). The sulfonephthaleins, with a color change corresponding to a dissociation of the type of equation (4b), show the largest salt effect, and this is negative, as the equation predicts. The nitrophenols also show a negative salt effect, corresponding to equation (4a), which is smaller than that with the sulfonephthaleins. Both salt effects are quantitatively less than equations (4a) and (4b) predict, but that is to be expected. Hexamethoxytriphenylcarbinol illustrates equation (4c); its reaction is of the pattern

$$\underset{\text{carbonium ion}}{X^+} \quad + \quad H_2O \quad \rightleftharpoons \quad \underset{\text{carbinol}}{XOH} \quad + \quad H^+.$$

As expected, this indicator shows a positive instead of a negative salt effect.

Conspicuous for their negligibly small salt effect are the indicators methyl orange, methyl red, and thymol blue in its first stage of dissociation. In their acid forms, these are all zwitterions, or dipolar ions; their net charge is zero, and a proton leaving the acid molecule leaves behind an ion which is negatively charged. This is like the case $HX \rightarrow H^+ + X^-$, which would lead one to expect a negative salt effect. However, the negative charge of the zwitterion is some distance away from the removable proton—13 Å. in the case of methyl orange—and if we could neglect the attraction between these two charges, the ionization would be like that of an acid $ZH^+ \rightleftharpoons Z + H^+$, and the salt effect would be positive. *Can* we neglect this attraction? We may answer this question by calculating the Debye-Hückel parameter $1/\varkappa$, which is the effective radius of the ionic atmosphere. If this is much smaller than the distance apart of the two charged ends of the zwitterion, these charges are shielded from one another by their respective ionic atmospheres, and the attractive force between them is very small. If $1/\varkappa$ is much larger than the distance between the charges, they are not so shielded, and the attraction may not be neglected. For an ionic strength of 0.1 in water at 25°C, $1/\varkappa$ is 9.6 Å., of the same order as the length of the methyl orange molecule. A behavior intermediate to our two extreme cases is to be expected, and this is what we find; K' hardly changes at all between $\mu = 0.02$ and $\mu = 0.5$. The value of $1/\varkappa$ depends inversely on the square root of the ionic strength; at ionic strength higher than 0.5, $1/\varkappa$ is much less than the length of the molecule, and the behavior approaches that of case (4c), and likewise at very low ionic strengths the behavior is like case (4a). More precise measurements of the salt effects of indicators than those of Kolthoff have been made by Güntelberg and Schiödt,[8] Chase and Kilpatrick,[9] and Klotz;[10] these show the effects of ionic strength very well, but unfortunately they cover only a very few indicators.

Before leaving the effects of salts on indicators, we note that salts not only change the degree of dissociation, but may also modify the absorption spectra of indicators. For example, in 4 M NaCl the peak of absorption of the yellow form of methyl orange is shifted $4m\mu$ to the red, while the maximum extinction coefficient of the red form is increased by 5%.[7]

Effects of colloidal electrolytes, including proteins. Colloidal electrolytes such as soaps, detergents, proteins, or clays can have a very great influence on the color of indicators. They may combine preferentially with one form of the indicator, thus shifting the pH of half change, and may modify the color of the form they combine with, usually making it more intense.

With clays and such ionized precipitates as silver chloride the effect is one of surface adsorption, governed mainly by the charges on the colloid and on the indicator, and is analogous to the action of adsorption indicators (Chapter 18); in fact, several acid-base indicators function quite well as adsorption indicators too. The combination between proteins and indicators is more complicated. Attraction between indicator ions and proteins is greatest when the net charge of the protein is opposite to that of the indicator ion, but proteins carry both negative and positive charges in the same molecule, and binding may occur even when the net charges are similar.[10, 11] The protein errors of indicators have been known for a long time, because of the importance of pH measurements in sera or other media containing proteins, including living cells. They may be positive or negative, and may be quite large; for example, 0.5% of egg albumin lowers the pH of half change of methyl orange by 1.2 units.[10]

[8] E. Güntelberg and E. Schiödt, *Z. physik. Chem.*, **135**, 393–443 (1928).

[9] E. F. Chase and M. Kilpatrick, *J. Am. Chem. Soc.*, **54**, 2284 (1932).

[10] I. M. Klotz, *Chem. Rev.*, **41**, 373 (1947).

[11] I. M. Klotz, F. M. Walker, and R. B. Pivan, *J. Am. Chem. Soc.*, **68**, 1486 (1946).

In other cases the errors are much less. They depend on the indicator and on the protein.[12]

Colloidal electrolytes of the type of soap combine with indicators through a mechanism of their own. Soaps and detergents have long chain molecules with an ionized "head," such as —COONa or —SO₃Na, and a long hydrocarbon "tail." Individually these ions are of less than colloidal size, but above a certain critical concentration they associate to form colloidal aggregates or micelles. The interior of the micelle resembles a liquid paraffin, and can dissolve or solubilize nonpolar or weakly polar substances, giving dispersions which are so fine as to be clear to the eye. Indicator molecules can be solubilized in this way, that is, they can be taken out of the aqueous environment of their solutions and incorporated in the micelles instead. When this happens, their color can be modified profoundly, as the studies of Corrin and Harkins[13] show, and the acid-base equilibrium of the indicator may be shifted. Thus thymol blue, which normally changes from red to yellow in the pH range 1.2–2.8, is a much darker red in 0.01 M dodecanesulfonic acid (pH just over 2) than in 2 M HCl.[14] In trying to interpret these effects, it is well to remember that most indicators are colloidal electrolytes themselves, that is, their molecules associate to form large aggregates if their concentration is high enough or if other conditions are met.

Effects of alcohol. It is not surprising that a change of solvent, such as is produced by adding alcohol to an aqueous solution, changes the acid-base equilibrium of an indicator. The change in dielectric constant of the solvent would alone account for such a shift, but it cannot be the only factor, since the equilibrium

$$\text{zwitterion} \rightleftharpoons \text{negative ion} + \text{solvated proton}$$

is displaced to the right in methyl orange and methyl red, but to the left in thymol blue, by the addition of alcohol. Though the effects are specific and not easily systematized, they are practically important in testing the pH of tinctures. Table VII summarizes the

---

[12] I. M. Kolthoff and G. Rosenblum, *Acid-Base Indicators*, New York, Macmillan, 1937, pp. 351-353; I. M. Klotz, *Chem. Rev.*, **41**, 373 (1947).

[13] M. L. Corrin, H. B. Klevens, and W. D. Harkins, *J. Phys. Chem.*, **14**, 480 (1946).

[14] H. F. Walton, *J. Am. Chem. Soc.*, **69**, 469 (1947).

effects of alcohol on indicators.   The data are taken from the paper of Kolthoff.[15]

TABLE VII

EFFECT OF ALCOHOL ON INDICATORS

Indicator	Error, in pH units, for given alcohol content				
	10%	20%	30%	50%	70%
Thymol blue (pH 2).....	0.00	+0.02	+0.07	+0.21	+0.30
Bromphenol blue........	+0.06	+0.21	+0.35	+0.38	+1.0
Dimethyl yellow.........	−0.11	−0.24	−0.48	−1.1	−1.7
Methyl orange..........	−0.10	−0.20	−0.47	−1.2	−1.8
Phenolphthalein.........	+0.06	+0.10	+0.15	+1.0	+2.2
Thymol blue (pH 9).....	+0.15	+0.3	+0.5	+0.8	+1.0
Thymolphthalein........	+0.1	+0.3	+0.6	+1.3	+1.9
Nitramine..............	−0.25	−0.6	−0.9	−1.1	−1.25

Notes: 1. Data from I. M. Kolthoff, *Rec. trav. chim.*, **42**, 251 (1923).   2. Alcohol content is in volume per cent.   3. Temperature = 12°C.   The alcohol effects are strongly dependent on temperature.   4. The pH errors were computed from the amounts of acid or alkali needed to produce the color change.   Allowance was made for the change of K_W with alcohol content.

Mixed indicators.   In titration, it is sometimes necessary to locate the pH of an end point within close limits to obtain the desired accuracy.   Common examples of such titrations are bicarbonate plus a strong acid, and phosphoric acid plus a strong base.   The necessary pH control may be obtained in such cases by using a comparison flask containing a solution at the desired pH, with the same indicator concentration as the solution being titrated.   The same close adjustment of pH may be obtained, however, by using a suitable mixture of two indicators, chosen to produce a definite and characteristic color change within a very narrow range of pH.   For example, bromcresol green ($pK = 4.97$) and methyl red ($pK = 5.00$) together give a red color in acid and a green color in alkali, with a sharp transition through grey at pH 5.1.   At this pH the green color of the one indicator and the orange-red of the other are complementary, so the solution has no color, only a general light absorption over the whole spectrum.   One can devise many such pairs by choosing two indi-

[15] I. M. Kolthoff, *Rec. trav. chim.*, **42**, 251 (1923).

TABLE VIII

MIXED INDICATORS

Indicators		Ratio by wt.	Solvent	Acid color	Alkaline color	pH of change
I	II					
Methyl yellow	Methylene blue	1:1	Alcohol	Blue	Green	3.25
Methyl orange	Xylene cyanol FF	2:3	Alcohol	Red	Green	3.8
Methyl orange	Indigo carmine	2:5	Water	Violet	Green	4.1
Methyl orange	Bromcresol green	1:5	Water	Orange	Blue-green	4.3
Methyl red	Bromcresol green	2:3	Alcohol	Red	Green	5.1
Bromcresol green	Chlorphenol red	1:1	Water	Yellow-green	Blue-violet	6.1
Neutral red	Methylene blue	1:1	Alcohol	Violet	Green	7.0
Phenol red	Bromthymol blue	1:1	Water	Yellow	Violet	7.5
Cresol red	Thymol blue	1:3	Water	Yellow	Violet	8.3
Thymol blue	Phenolphthalein	1:3	Alcohol 50%	Yellow	Violet	9.0
Phenolphthalein	Nile blue	1:2	Alcohol	Blue	Red	10.0

Notes: 1. Total concentration of indicator is about 0.1% in each case. 2. Taken from I. M. Kolthoff and V. A. Stenger. *Volumetric Analysis,* New York Interscience, 1947, Vol. II, p. 58.

cators which have complementary colors at a certain pH. Actually it is not necessary for both components of the mixture to be indicators. A popular mixed indicator is the so-called "modified methyl orange," a mixture of methyl orange with the dye xylene cyanol FF. The blue color of the latter complements the orange-yellow of the former near the half-change point of methyl orange. The mixed indicator is purple-red in acid, green in alkali, and, of course, grey at an intermediate point, which happens to be pH 3.8. This is also the pH of 0.05 M carbonic acid, and this indicator is used in bicarbonate titrations.

A few representative mixed indicators are listed in Table VIII. A more extensive list is given in Kolthoff and Stenger, *Volumetric Analysis*, Vol. II (New York, Interscience, 1947).

Another type of mixed indicator is the so-called "universal indicator." This is intended, not for titrations, but for approximate pH measurements over a wide range. Table IX gives the composition of some universal indicators. The first of these shows colors in the order of the spectrum, starting with red at pH 3, and passing through orange at pH 5, yellow at pH 6, green at pH 7.5, blue at pH 9, to violet at pH 10. Accurate pH measurements may be made with such mixtures if they are calibrated with known buffer solutions. Test papers are available which are impregnated with universal indicator mixtures, and for rough pH tests these are extremely useful.

TABLE IX

UNIVERSAL INDICATORS

Constituent	Indicator Number		
	1	2	3
Methyl yellow..................	...	0.02	0.01
Methyl orange.................	0.03	...	...
Methyl red....................	0.15	0.03	0.013
Bromothymol blue..............	0.30	0.40	0.16
Naphtholphthalein.............	...	0.40	0.16
Cresolphthalein...............	...	0.40	0.24
Phenolphthalein...............	0.35	0.20	0.40
Alizarin yellow G.............	...	...	0.30

Notes: 1. Proportions given in grams per liter of 60% alcohol. 2. Table taken from T. B. Smith, *Analytical Processes*, 2d ed., London, Arnold, 1940.

pH *measurements with indicators*. Indicators are less used for
pH measurements today than they were ten years ago, because commercial glass electrode pH meters have become generally available
and are not subject to salt errors, protein errors, and the like.   However, these pH meters are still fairly expensive, whereas indicator
solutions are very cheap and easy to use.

The chief use of indicators is in rapid, relatively rough pH measurements.   We have referred to the use of universal indicator paper.
This paper is moistened with the solution to be tested, and its color

Fig. 14-1. Hellige color comparator. (By courtesy of Hellige, Inc.)

is compared with a chart. Readings valid to 0.3 pH are made in
this way.   Better accuracy is obtained by adding a measured amount
of indicator solution to the solution to be tested, mixing, and comparing the color visually with solutions of the indicator in standard
buffer solutions.   Colored glasses may be used instead of the buffer
solutions.   A very convenient device for matching indicator colors
is the comparator illustrated in Figure 1.   The colored glass disks
are mounted on a wheel.   The instrument is held up to the light, and
the wheel turned until the color of the glass in the line of sight matches
that of the solution under test, which is contained in a test tube or a

rectangular glass cell. The eyepiece contains a prism which brings the two beams of light from the solution and from the colored glass together, and so permits easier comparison. To allow tests to be made with colored solutions, the comparator has places for two more cells. One, containing some of the original solution, is placed behind the colored glass, while the other, containing water, is placed behind the test solution. Sets of glasses are available for several different indicators, and are generally made to simulate colors at intervals of 0.2 pH. By interpolation, readings to 0.1 pH or better can be obtained.

A comparator of this type can obviously be used for all kinds of colorimetric determinations where a quick, routine method of medium accuracy is desired.

Instead of comparing indicator colors visually with standards, one can measure the intensity of the light transmitted with a photocell. The best instrument to use is a spectrophotometer, for with this, the fraction of light transmitted can be measured at any desired wavelength, and the absorption spectrum of the solution can be plotted. Figure 2 shows the absorption spectrum of bromcresol green in the visible region, found by means of a spectrophotometer. Curve a is that for the acid form (singly charged anion), measured at pH 2; curve b is that for the alkaline form (doubly charged anion), measured at pH 10; curve c is that for a solution of pH 4.00. The indicator concentration is the same in all three cases. The ordinates of the graph are *optical densities*, not percentage transmission. Optical density is defined as log I_0/I, where I is the intensity of the transmitted light, and I_0 that of the incident light. (More precisely, I_0 is the intensity of the light transmitted by a cell similar to that containing the solution but containing pure water or buffer. This allows for the loss of light by reflection from the cell walls, which is assumed to be the same fraction in the test cell as in the solvent cell.) From Beer's law, the optical density is directly proportional to the concentration of the substance absorbing the light. Where only one light-absorbing substance is present,

$$\log \frac{I_0}{I} = D = \epsilon \cdot d \cdot C, \qquad (5)$$

where ϵ is the *extinction coefficient* of the substance for the particular wavelength used, d is the thickness of the cell, and C the concentration of the substance. Where a constant cell thickness is used, as is usual in spectrophotometric work, it is convenient to combine the constants ϵ and d into a single constant k.

Where two light-absorbing substances are present, as is the case in curve c of Figure 2, where we have both the acid and the alkaline form of the indicator, the optical density is

$$\log \frac{I_0}{I} = D = k_1 C_1 + k_2 C_2, \tag{6}$$

where C_1 and C_2 are the concentrations of the two forms, and k_1 and k_2 the corresponding absorption constants.

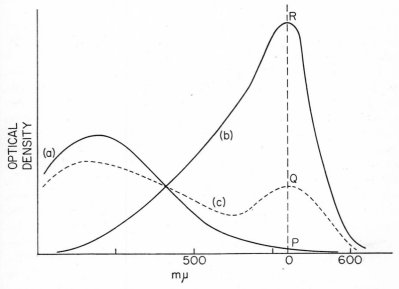

Fig. 14-2. Absorption spectrum of bromcresol green. (a), acid form, pH 2; (b), basic form, pH 12; (c), mixed acid and basic forms in a buffer of pH 4.00.

Referring now to Figure 2, and considering the absorption at its peak for the alkaline form, in the red,

OQ = optical density of indicator mixture $\Big\} = k_1 C_1 + k_2 C_2.$ (7a)

OR = optical density of alkaline form of indicator $\Big\} = k_2 (C_1 + C_2).$ (7b)

OP = optical density of acid form of indicator $\Big\} = k_1 (C_1 + C_2).$ (7c)

C_1 is the concentration of the acid form, C_2 that of the alkaline form, at pH 4.00. We recall that the *total* concentration of acid and alkaline forms combined is the same in all cases; hence equations (7b) and (7c). We now note that

$$QR = OR - OQ = (k_2 - k_1)C_1.$$
$$PQ = OQ - OP = (k_2 - k_1)C_2.$$

Therefore
$$\frac{QR}{PQ} = \frac{C_1}{C_2}. \tag{8}$$

Thus by the use of the spectrophotometer, we can measure the ratio of the acid to the alkaline form of the indicator. We should find this same ratio whatever wavelength we choose for comparing our optical densities, but the experimental error is least if the wavelength of maximum absorption of one of the forms is chosen.

Knowing the ratio of acid to alkaline form of the indicator, we can *either* calculate the ionization constant of the indicator if the pH of the solution is known, *or* we can calculate the pH if the ionization constant of the indicator is known.

The spectrophotometer is a very accurate instrument, and this is one of the most accurate ways of studying acid-base equilibria. It was used by Kilpatrick and his co-workers[16] in their researches on acid strengths and the ionization constants of indicators. We must note, of course, that the optical method gives us *concentrations* of the indicator forms, and not activities. If true thermodynamic equilibrium constants or true pH values are to be obtained, measurements must be made which permit extrapolation to infinite dilution.

Fluorescent indicators. One of the limitations of conventional acid-base indicators is that they cannot be used in strongly colored or highly turbid solutions. This limitation can be overcome by using as indicator a weak acid or base which fluoresces in the acid form but not in the base form, or vice versa. An example of such an indicator is α-naphthylamine. The free amine shows a blue fluorescence in ultraviolet light, whereas the salts of the amine do not. The value of K_a for the α-naphthylammonium ion is about 10^{-4}; therefore α-naphthylamine fluoresces above pH 4, but shows little or no fluorescence below pH 4. Theoretically, the intensity of the fluorescence could be used to measure the pH within a certain

[16] M. Kilpatrick *et al.*, *J. Am. Chem. Soc.* **54**, 2284 (1932); **55**, 4430 (1933); **59**, 572 (1937); *J. Phys. Chem.*, **43**, 259 (1939).

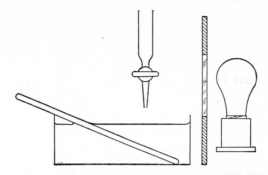

Fig. 14-3. Apparatus for titrating with fluorescent indicators. The glass screen on the right transmits only in the near ultraviolet.

TABLE X

FLUORESCENT INDICATORS

Substance	pH range	Acid fluorescence	Base fluorescence
Eosin	0.0–3.0	none	green
4-Ethoxyacridone	1.2–3.2	green	blue
Salicylic acid	2–4	none	blue (weak)
β-Naphthylamine	2.8–4.4	none	violet
α-Naphthylamine	3.4–4.8	none	blue
Dichlorofluorescein	4.0–6.6	none	green
3,6-dihydroxyxanthone	5.4–7.6	none	blue
Umbelliferone	6.5–7.6	none	blue
Coumaric acid	7.2–9.0	none	green
β-Naphthol	8–9	none	blue
Quinine	9.5–10	blue-violet	none
5-Aminonaphthalene-2-sulfonamide	*	none	blue

* This indicator is used in glacial acetic acid; O. Tomicek, *Collection Czechoslov. Chem. Commun.*, **13**, 116 (1948).

Note: Data in this table were taken from W. Holthof, *Z. anal. Chem.*, **91**, 263 (1933), and K. A. Jensen, *Z. anal. Chem.*, **94**, 177 (1933). See also R. Robl, *Ber.*, **59**, 1725 (1926); M. Haitinger, *Mikrochemie*, **11**, 429 (1932); E. A. Kocsis, *Z. anal. Chem.*, **124**, 45, 274 (1942).

range, and this has in fact been done, but the only practical use of fluorescent indicators is in titrations.

A good technique for titrating with fluorescent indicators is that due to Holthof.[17] This is illustrated in Figure 3. The solution to be titrated is placed in a shallow dish in a dark enclosure which is irradiated by ultraviolet light of wavelength 380–400 mμ, whose source is a tungsten filament lamp with a suitable filter. About 0.1 ml. of 0.1% indicator solution is added per 10 ml. of the solution being titrated. The solution is stirred with a glass rod during titration.

A list of fluorescent indicators is given in Table X. We may note, incidentally, that it should be possible to find fluorescent adsorption indicators and oxidation-reduction indicators, as well as acid-base indicators. Umbelliferone has been used as a fluorescent adsorption indicator in titrating lead salts with potassium ferrocyanide.[18] Quercitin is used in titrating fluorides with thorium nitrate (page 353).

Turbidity indicators. Certain weak acids and bases are highly insoluble, while their salts are soluble. Such substances can be used as indicators, for a precipitate will appear or disappear as the pH is changed over the appropriate range. The practical value of such indicators lies in the fact that the turbidity can be made to appear or disappear very sharply, in a very narrow pH range.

An example of a turbidity indicator is m-tolueneazonitrosoacetyl-o-toluidine,

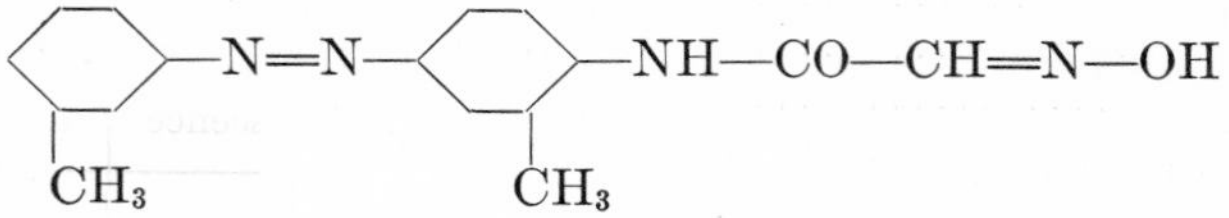

whose change is in the region pH 9.30 (turbid) − 9.40 (clear).[19] The salts of this acid, and of the other acids used as turbidity indicators, are colloidal electrolytes. We expect this from their structure, for the anion is a long hydrocarbon chain with a charged group at one end. It is characteristic of such ions that above a certain critical concentration they aggregate to form micelles. The onset of

[17] W. Holthof, *Z. anal. Chem.*, **91**, 263 (1933).

[18] A. del Campo and F. Sierra, *Chem. Abstracts*, **30**, 7058 (1936).

[19] C. Naegeli, *Kolloidchem. Beihefte*, **21**, 306 (1925); C. Naegeli and A. Tyabji, *Helv. Chim. Acta.* **15**, 403, 758 (1932).

this aggregation is very sharp, as is to be expected from the law of mass action where the number of ions coming together is large. These micelles contain a certain proportion of "counter-ions," i.e., small ions of opposite charge to the micelle, and the counter-ions influence greatly the size of the micelles and the concentration at which they are formed.[20] The hydrogen ion is a special kind of counter-ion, since it forms covalent bonds with the anion and precipitates an insoluble compound, but the *sudden* appearance of turbidity within a very narrow pH interval is certainly reminiscent of the sudden aggregation of long-chain ions to form micelles as the concentration of counter-ions is increased.

The pH at which turbidity indicators form a precipitate is influenced by all the factors which influence micelle formation, such as total salt concentration, alcohol, presence of other colloids, and temperature. Their usefulness is quite limited, but they may have a place in routine titration of very weak acids, where the slope of the pH-titration curve at the equivalence point is small and the pH of the end point must be located with corresponding accuracy. Naegeli obtained good results in the titration of boric and arsenious acids, also phenol, veronal, glycine, and alanine.

PROBLEMS

1. In a determination of pK_2 for phenol red, the following data were obtained: Optical density in 0.01 M NaOH, 1.760; in 0.01 M potassium acid phthalate, 0.005; in a buffer of pH 7.60, density is 0.575. The wavelength was 560 mμ, and the indicator concentration and cell thickness the same in every case. Calculate pK_2.

2. Dodecanesulfonic acid $C_{12}H_{25}SO_3H$ is a colloidal electrolyte in aqueous solution. It is a strong acid. Would you anticipate any difficulty in titrating it with an indicator, and how would possible difficulties be avoided?

3. Phosphoric acid may be titrated in the presence of strong acids like hydrochloric by using two indicators, one to change color when $H_2PO_4^-$ is formed, the other to change color when $HPO_4^=$ is formed. Discuss the experimental conditions necessary to obtain reliable results, and suggest suitable indicators.

[20] P. Debye, *J. Colloid Sci.*, **3**, 407 (1948); M. M. Corrin and W. D. Harkins, *J. Am. Chem. Soc.*, **69**, 683 (1947).

15

Oxidation-reduction titrations

Introduction. Oxidation-reduction titrations are probably the largest class of titrations, in the sense that almost every element can be determined directly or indirectly by a titration involving oxidation and reduction. So also can certain classes of organic compounds. A range of indicators is available which is wide enough so that there is usually no difficulty in locating the equivalence point, and potentiometric methods are always applicable. Most of the inorganic oxidation-reduction reactions used in titrations are very rapid, or can be made so by a suitable catalyst. The oxidation or reduction of organic compounds is generally slower, and the usual procedure there is to add an excess of the oxidant or reductant, allow time to react, and then back-titrate.

In this chapter we shall review the mode of action and applications of the more important volumetric oxidizing and reducing agents, and the methods for pretreating a sample so as to convert the element to be determined into a known state of oxidation. The application of oxidation-reduction titrations to organic compounds will be reserved for another chapter.

I. Volumetric Oxidizing Agents

Compounds of tetrapositive cerium
$$[Ce(IV) + e \rightarrow Ce(III)].[1]$$

These are probably the most versatile and useful group of volumetric oxidizing agents which we have. A main reason for their

[1] G. F. Smith, *Cerate Oxidimetry*, Columbus, G. Frederick Smith Chemical Co., 1942.

importance is that they can be used in conjunction with the phenanthroline indicators. These indicators are distinguished by the sharpness, clearness, and reproducibility of their color change.

Cerium is element 58, the second of the rare earth series. Its atom includes two 6_s, one 6_p, and one 4_f electron, all four of which can be removed by strong oxidation. The 6_s and 6_p electrons are removed easily, so that the element cerium is very reactive, forming compounds in which its oxidation number is $+3$. More powerful oxidation removes the 4_f electron, giving an oxidation number of $+4$. These are the only two oxidation states of cerium. Therein lies one great advantage of cerium (IV) as an analytical reagent; it is reduced cleanly to one product, without the possibility of such side reactions as in the reduction of manganese (VII), where oxidation states of $+2$, $+3$, $+4$, or $+6$ may be obtained.

Another advantage of cerium (IV) as an analytical reagent is that it is a powerful oxidant. Before we can state its oxidation-reduction potential, however, we must specify the form in which the cerium is combined. To represent its reduction by an equation

$$Ce^{++++} + e \rightarrow Ce^{+++}$$

is too simple. Ions of high charge are prone to form complex ions or covalent molecules, and this tendency is stronger, the greater the charge on the ion, because of the greater deformation produced in ions of opposite charge. Thus Ce^{++++} forms more stable complex ions than does Ce^{+++}. The effect of such complex ion formation is to depress the oxidizing power of cerium (IV), i.e., to shift the above equilibrium to the left. Perchlorate, nitrate, sulfate, and chloride ions combine with Ce^{++++} as follows:

$$Ce^{++++} + 6ClO_4^- \rightleftharpoons Ce(ClO_4)_6^=$$

$$Ce^{++++} + 6NO_3^- \rightleftharpoons Ce(NO_3)_6^=$$

$$Ce^{++++} + 3SO_4^- \rightleftharpoons Ce(SO_4)_3^=$$

$$Ce^{++++} + 6Cl^- \rightleftharpoons CeCl_6^=$$

The lengths of the arrows indicate the extent of the reactions; the chloride complex is the most stable, the perchlorate complex, the least. This order of stability of anionic complexes is the usual one, and is found in many elements. It is the order of polarizability of the anions, the chloride ion being the most polarizable of the four and the perchlorate ion the least. It is questionable whether the ion $Ce(ClO_4)_6^=$ exists at all to any measurable extent; some evidence, e.g., the fact that cerous perchlorate can be oxidized electrolytically to ceric perchlorate in a cell without a diaphragm, indicates that it does exist, while other evidence, e.g., the fact that ceric perchlorate solutions obey Beer's law while other ceric salt solutions do not, suggests that complex ion formation is inappreciable.[2] The anionic complexes are very stable in salts other than the perchlorate, however; hence the names "sulfatocerate," "hexanitratocerate," and "cerate oxidimetry."

The stability of the cerate complexes, over and above the stability of cerite ($+3$) complexes if such exist, is shown by the oxidation-reduction potentials listed in Table I. The perchlorate of cerium

TABLE I

OXIDATION-REDUCTION POTENTIALS OF CERIC COMPOUNDS

Anion	$E°$ in acid of concentration		
	$1 N$	$4 N$	$8 N$
ClO_4^-	1.70	1.75	1.87
NO_3^-	1.61	1.61	1.56
$SO_4^=$	1.44	1.43	1.42
Cl^-	1.28	...	...

Reference: G. F. Smith, *Cerate Oxidimetry*, Columbus, G. Frederick Smith Chemical Co., 1942; G. F. Smith and C. A. Getz, *Ind. Eng. Chem., Anal. Ed.*, **10**, 191 (1938).

(IV) is a very powerful oxidizing agent, much more so than potassium permanganate ($E° = +1.5$ volt), while the chloride is a rather weak oxidizing agent, weaker even than chlorine. These relationships have obvious advantages in analytical chemistry. First, ceric salt solutions have a wide range of oxidizing power, the perchlorate being one of the strongest oxidizing agents obtainable in aqueous solution. Second, ceric sulfate solutions do not oxidize dilute hydrochloric acid to chlorine; the relatively stable $CeCl_6^=$ complex is formed instead. (Ceric perchlorate or nitrate solutions containing perchloric or nitric acids *will* oxidize hydrochloric acid, however, owing to the reaction

[2] R. L. Moore and R. C. Anderson, *J. Am. Chem. Soc.*, **67**, 167 (1945).

between these acids and hydrochloric acid.) The insensitivity of ceric sulfate solutions to hydrochloric acid is very valuable in inorganic analysis, because hydrochloric acid is usually the fastest solvent for metals and alloys.

Ceric salt solutions are usually prepared either from the acid sulfate (sulfatoceric acid) or from ammonium ceric nitrate (hexanitrato ammonium cerate). The latter compound, $(NH_4)_2Ce(NO_3)_6$, can be obtained in primary standard purity by simple recrystallization. Sulfate solutions may be obtained from this salt by stirring it with concentrated sulfuric acid, then adding water gradually until the salt is all dissolved. Perchlorate solutions may be made in the same way, starting with 72% perchloric acid. These solutions contain ammonium ions and nitrate ions, however, which make the sulfate solution somewhat less stable and make the perchlorate solution a slightly less powerful oxidizing agent than if they were absent.

Solid ceric sulfate, either the normal or the acid salt, may be dissolved in dilute sulfuric acid to prepare volumetric ceric sulfate solutions. The disadvantage of this procedure is that the sulfate salts are usually impure; they contain traces of phosphates, which form a precipitate of ceric phosphate in the solution on standing, and they also contain some 10% of rare earths other than cerium. These latter do not interfere with the analytical applications, but the ceric sulfate solutions so prepared must be standardized before use. Once the phosphates have settled out, ceric sulfate solutions which are free from nitrate and ammonium ions will keep their strength for years; they are extraordinarily stable.

Ceric perchlorate solutions are usually prepared from ammonium hexanitratocerate as described above. Where the maximum oxidizing power and purity are needed, they may be made by the electrolytic oxidation of cerous perchlorate solutions. A solution of ceric perchlorate in 4 N perchloric acid is useful for organic oxidations on account of its high oxidizing power.

All volumetric ceric salt solutions must be at least 0.5 N in the appropriate acid to prevent hydrolysis.

Ceric salt solutions may be standardized, where necessary, as follows:

(a) *Against iron wire.* The conventional procedure is used involving reduction of the iron to the ferrous condition with stannous chloride, oxidation of the excess of stannous chloride with mercuric chloride, and addition of phosphoric acid and diphenylamine sulfonic acid indicator. Ferroin may also be used.

(b) *Against sodium oxalate.* Ceric perchlorate and nitrate solutions may be used directly in the cold, but sulfate solutions need a catalyst to react rapidly enough with oxalate ions for titration below 100°C. Osmic acid may be used as the catalyst at room temperature,[3] or iodine monochloride in hydrochloric acid at 50°C,[4] using ferroin indicator; or, the titration may be done potentiometrically, without catalyst, in 1 N HCl at 100°C. (Ferroin is destroyed at this temperature.)

(c) *Against arsenious oxide.* This is dissolved in sodium hydroxide to give a standard sodium arsenite solution. The conditions of titration are the same as for sodium oxalate.

(d) *Potassium ferrocyanide* has been suggested as a standard. Titration is done in 1 M HCl at room temperature.[4]

We are now ready to summarize the advantages and disadvantages of tetrapositive cerium solutions as volumetric oxidizing agents, by comparison with permanganate and dichromate solutions. They are, in approximate order of importance:

Advantages

1. *Stability.* Ceric sulfate solutions have almost the same oxidizing power as permanganate solutions, yet unlike permanganate solutions they are stable almost indefinitely.

2. *Oxidizing power.* The oxidizing power depends on the anion present, and a wide range of oxidation-reduction potentials, from 1.87 volts to 1.28 volts, can be obtained. Ceric perchlorate has the strongest oxidizing power, and is used in 4 N perchloric acid solution for the quantitative oxidation of organic compounds.

3. *Inertness to chloride ion.* Ceric sulfate solutions, like dichromate but unlike permanganate solutions, do not attack dilute (1 N) hydrochloric acid, yet ceric sulfate is a more powerful oxidant than dichromate.

4. *Single reduction step.* Since the only possible reduction is Ce(IV) + $e \rightarrow$ Ce(III), there can be no side reactions.

5. *Primary standard.* Ceric salt solutions of determinate concentration can be made from the primary standard, $(NH_4)_2Ce(NO_3)_6$.

[3] K. Gleu, *Z. anal. Chem.*, **95**, 305 (1933).
[4] H. H. Willard and P. Young, *J. Am. Chem. Soc.*, **55**, 3260 (1933).

6. *Indicator.* Ferroin can be used with ceric sulfate, nitroferroin with the nitrate and perchlorate. These indicators are distinguished by their sensitivity, sharp color change, and reversibility. They are better than diphenylamine and its derivatives, which are used with dichromate, and the end point is sharper than that in potassium permanganate titrations.

7. *Color of solution.* Ceric salt solutions are a light orange color, almost identical with that of potassium dichromate solutions. The buret can therefore be read more accurately than with dark-colored permanganate solutions.

Disadvantages:

1. *Speed of reaction.* Ceric sulfate solutions do not react rapidly with oxalic acid and arsenious acid at room temperature, nor even at 50°C unless a catalyst is added. In this they are inferior to permanganate. Ceric perchlorate and nitrate react rapidly at room temperature, but their solutions are not so stable as the sulfate and must be restandardized weekly or oftener.

2. *Cost.* A mole of primary standard grade hexanitrato ammonium cerate costs about $10.00.

We shall close this discussion of cerate oxidimetry by giving a few examples of inorganic analytical procedures which use ceric compounds.

(a) *Determination of* Fe, Cr *and* V *in steel.* Solutions containing Fe^{++}, Cr^{+++}, and VO^{++}, and 0.5 N—1 N in sulfuric or hydrochloric acid, can be titrated potentiometrically at 50°–60°C. Distinct inflections are obtained successively for the oxidation of Fe^{++} and VO^{++}, but Cr^{+++} is not oxidized until all the vanadium has been oxidized, and then only slowly.[5] Chromium can be oxidized quantitatively to $Cr_2O_7^=$ by ceric sulfate in 3 M sulfuric acid in five minutes at 65°C; the excess of ceric sulfate is back-titrated potentiometrically with standard sodium nitrite solution.[6]

(b) *Determination of* As *and* Sb. Both As(III) and Sb(III) are oxidized by ceric sulfate in 5 N hydrochloric acid at 50°C, but arsenic reacts very slowly unless iodine monochloride is added as catalyst. Thus antimony can be titrated first without a catalyst, then iodine monochloride can be added and the arsenic titrated. The titration

[5] N. H. Furman, *J. Am. Chem. Soc.*, **50**, 1675 (1928).
[6] H. H. Willard and P. Young, *J. Am. Chem. Soc.*, **51**, 139 (1929).

is done potentiometrically.[7] Ferroin indicator can be used if antimony alone is titrated, but in this case a hydrochloric acid concentration of only 1 N is used, and iodine monochloride is added as catalyst.[8]

(c) *Determination of small quantities of calcium, potassium, or sodium.* Calcium is precipitated as the oxalate, which is then dissolved in cold 1 N perchloric acid and the oxalic acid titrated by ceric perchlorate in 1 N perchloric acid, using nitroferroin as indicator.[9] The ceric solution may be prepared from $(NH_4)_2Ce(NO_3)_6$. This method is faster than the conventional titration with permanganate at 50°C, and is much more satisfactory for the determination of small amounts, since the end point is clearer.

An analogous method can be used for potassium. This is precipitated as $K_2NaCo(NO_2)_6$; the precipitate is dissolved in dilute sulfuric acid containing excess ceric sulfate and the solution heated to 100°C for five minutes to oxidize the nitrous acid. It is then cooled and back-titrated with ferrous sulfate solution.[10] Sodium may be determined by precipitation as $NaMg(UO_2)_3(CH_3COO)_9 \cdot 6.5H_2O$, dissolution of the latter in dilute sulfuric acid, reduction of the solution to a mixture of $+3$ and $+4$ uranium with a zinc reductor, oxidation of $+3$ to $+4$ uranium by a stream of air; and titration of the uranium to the $+6$ condition with ceric sulfate at 50°.[11]

Potassium permanganate.

[Mn(VII) $\rightarrow$ Mn(II), Mn(III), Mn(IV), or Mn(VI)].

Potassium permanganate is the best known of all volumetric oxidizing agents and probably the most used. It is readily available and powerful. Its intense color makes indicators unnecessary, except in special cases; a drop of permanganate in excess makes the solution distinctly pink. The dark color of the solution has, however, the drawback that it makes it difficult to read the buret accurately.

[7] N. H. Furman, *J. Am. Chem. Soc.*, **54**, 4235 (1932).

[8] H. H. Willard and P. Young, *J. Am. Chem. Soc.*, **55**, 3260 (1933).

[9] G. F. Smith, *Cerate Oxidimetry*, Columbus, G. Frederick Smith Chemical Co., 1942, p. 79.

[10] D. S. Brown, R. R. Robinson, and G. M. Browning, *Ind. Eng. Chem., Anal. Ed.*, **10**, 652 (1938).

[11] G. F. Smith, *Cerate Oxidimetry*, Columbus, G. Frederick Smith Chemical Co., 1942, p. 67; H. H. Willard and P. Young, *J. Am. Chem. Soc.*, **55**, 3260 (1933).

Permanganate solutions must be prepared with some care, or they deteriorate rapidly on standing, with liberation of oxygen and hydrated manganese dioxide, for permanganate is a stronger oxidizing agent than oxygen.   Manganese dioxide catalyzes the decomposition, which is also accelerated by light and by acids.   Table II shows the effects of the different factors on the decomposition of permanganate solutions.   Knowing these, we can understand the directions which are always given for preparing standard permanganate solutions; the crystals (which always contain manganese dioxide on their surface) are dissolved in water, the solution is heated and kept hot for a while to destroy any oxidizable impurities in the water, and then filtered through asbestos, sintered glass, or porous porcelain.   The solution must then be standardized.

TABLE II

STABILITY OF POTASSIUM PERMANGANATE SOLUTIONS

Treatment	Drop in titer after 7 months
Pure solution in dark.............................	0.2%
Neutral solution plus MnO_2, in dark.................	4.5%
Neutral solution plus MnO_2, in light.................	6.0%
Solution 2 N in H_2SO_4, no MnO_2, dark...............	76%
Solution 2 N in H_2SO_4, no MnO_2, light...............	95%

Reference: I. M. Kolthoff and H. Menzel, *Volumetric Analysis*, translated by N. H. Furman, New York, Wiley, 1928, Vol. I, p. 230.

Permanganate can be reduced quantitatively to any one of four reduction stages.   We shall consider each reduction process in turn.

1. *Reduction of Manganese* (VII) *to Manganese* (II) *in Acid Solution*

$$MnO_4^- + 8H^+ + 5e \rightarrow Mn^{++} + 4H_2O; \quad E^\circ = 1.52 \text{ volts.}$$

This is the reduction process which is most frequently used.   It takes place best in solutions 0.1 N or more in hydrogen ion; if the solution is not acid enough, some MnO_2 is likely to be formed.   The reduction product, Mn^{++}, is almost colorless.   With most reducing agents the reaction is rapid, but not with all; oxalic acid requires a temperature of 50°C, and arsenious acid requires a catalyst.   The manganous ion has a catalytic effect; thus the reaction of permanganate with oxalate is slow at the start, but speeds up as soon as a little manganous salt has been formed.

The conditions of reaction can be seen from the procedures for standardizing permanganate in acid solution. These are as follows:

(a) *Against iron wire.* Iron is dissolved in dilute hydrochloric acid, and the solution reduced either with amalgamated zinc or with stannous chloride plus mercuric chloride to ensure that all iron is in the ferrous condition. "Preventive solution," containing phosphoric acid and manganous sulfate, is then added. The phosphoric acid makes it easier to oxidize the iron by complexing the ferric ion and so lowering its oxidation-reduction potential; the manganous sulfate catalyzes the reaction between permanganate and ferrous ion and at the same time lowers the oxidation-reduction potential of the permanganate. The net result is to prevent the permanganate from oxidizing the hydrochloric acid to chlorine by facilitating the oxidation of the ferrous ion. This prevention is the more necessary since ferric ions catalyze the reaction between permanganate and hydrochloric acid. Of course the prevention is not quite complete, and the titration is slightly in error, but if permanganate is used for determining iron, and both the standardization and the analysis are done in this way, the error more or less cancels. This is the well-known Zimmermann-Reinhardt procedure.

(b) *Against sodium oxalate.* The National Bureau of Standards recommends dissolving the sodium oxalate in 2 N sulfuric acid and adding 95% of the permanganate to the *cold* solution all at once. When this has reacted, the solution is heated to 60°C and the titration finished in the usual way. The intermediate stages of this reaction are complex.[12]

(c) *Against arsenious oxide.* Arsenious oxide is dissolved in sodium hydroxide, and the solution then acidified to 0.5 N in hydrochloric acid and about 1.5 N in total chloride. One drop of 0.0025 M potassium iodide is then added as a catalyst (it probably forms ICl), and the solution titrated in the cold. The hydrochloric acid is not oxidized, and the method is very reliable.[13]

The applications of permanganate titration in acid solution are

[12] R. M. Fowler and H. A. Bright, *J. Research Nat. Bur. Standards*, **15**, 493 (1935).

[13] H. A. Bright, *Ind. Eng. Chem., Anal. Ed.*, **9**, 577 (1937).

well known and need not be detailed here. It can be used for most of the purposes for which ceric sulfate titration is used, with one important qualification. Procedures which require adding an excess of permanganate, heating to complete the oxidation, and then back-titrating the excess permanganate are not recommended for exact work. Two side reactions can occur, as follows:

$$4MnO_4^- + 12H^+ \rightarrow 4Mn^{++} + 5O_2 + 6H_2O. \tag{1}$$

$$2MnO_4^- + 3Mn^{++} + 2H_2O \rightarrow 5MnO_2 + 4H^+. \tag{2}$$

That these reactions are thermodynamically possible is seen from the standard potentials:

$$O_2 + 4H^+ + 4e \rightarrow 2H_2O; \qquad E° = 1.23 \text{ volts.}$$
$$MnO_2 + 4H^+ + 2e \rightarrow Mn^{++} + 2H_2O; \quad E° = 1.28 \text{ volts.}$$

With ceric sulfate, no reaction analogous to (2) exists; the reaction analogous to (1) is thermodynamically possible but is indefinitely slow, even at boiling temperature. With permanganate, both reactions are appreciable.

As a rule, no indicator is needed in acid permanganate titrations. The exceptions are: first, when dilute solutions are used and extra sensitivity is needed; second, when there can be two successive oxidation reactions and it is desired to stop after the first, e.g., in titrating Fe^{++} in the presence of VO^{++}. Ferroin and erioglaucin are suitable indicators.

2. *The Reaction:*

$$MnO_4^- + 3H_2P_2O_7^= + 8H^+ + 4e$$
$$\rightarrow Mn(H_2P_2O_7)_3^\equiv + 4H_2O; \quad E° = 1.7 \text{ volts, approx.}$$

The simple manganic ion, Mn^{+++}, is unstable in water, disproportionating to Mn^{++} and MnO_2. It may be stabilized by complex formation, the best complex former being the pyrophosphate ion, although fluoride is also effective. The main use of this reaction is the titration of manganous ion by potassium permanganate. This is done in saturated sodium pyrophosphate solution at pH between 4 and 7, and the end point is found potentiometrically.[14] The pH must be in the range stated to obtain the necessary $H_2P_2O_7^=$ ions.

---

[14] J. J. Lingane and R. Karplus, *Ind. Eng. Chem.*, *Anal. Ed.*, **18**, 191 (1946).

3. *The Reaction:*

$$MnO_4^- + 4H^+ + 3e \rightarrow MnO_2 + 2H_2O; \quad E° = 1.67 \text{ volts.}$$

This reaction is favored over reaction (1) at high pH, and is the most probable reaction when permanganate is reduced in the pH range 2–12. This can be understood since the reaction

$$2MnO_4^- + 3Mn^{++} + 2H_2O \rightarrow 5MnO_2 + 4H^+$$

is spontaneous even in 1 N acid, and is the more likely to occur the lower the hydrogen ion concentration. The practical advantage of reaction (3) in titrating with permanganate is that it permits oxidations to be done in neutral or alkaline solution which in acid solution are indefinite or incomplete. Thus cyanide ion is oxidized cleanly to cyanate in alkaline solution, and sulfide, sulfite, and thiosulfate are oxidized cleanly to sulfate. (In acid solution, these give some dithionate and tetrathionate as well.) The reaction is also applied to determining manganese. The manganese salt solution is neutralized by adding zinc oxide, which aids in the precipitation of the manganese dioxide; the mixed precipitate settles well and allows one to see whether the supernatant liquid is pink or not. The end point in these titrations is usually found visually.

4. *The Reaction:*

$$MnO_4^- + e \rightarrow MnO_4^=; \quad E° = 0.54 \text{ volt.}$$

Permanganate can be reduced quantitatively to manganate only in strongly alkaline solution, 1 N or more in hydroxyl ion. In less alkaline solutions the disproportionation

$$3MnO_4^= + 2H_2O \rightarrow MnO_2 + 2MnO_4^- + 4OH^-$$

takes place.

The analytical uses of this reaction have been explored by Stamm.[15] Its great advantage is the strongly alkaline solution.

Most oxidations proceed better in alkaline solution than in acid solution, for the reason that when a substance loses electrons it usually loses protons too. Examples of such oxidations are the following:

[15] H. Stamm, *Z. angew. Chem.*, **47**, 191 (1934); **48**, 710 (1935); W. Bottger (ed.), *Newer Methods of Volumetric Analysis*, New York, Van Nostrand, 1938, Chap. III.

$$I^- + 4H_2O \rightarrow IO_4^- + 8H^+ + 8e.$$

$$HCHO + 2H_2O \rightarrow CO_3^= + 6H^+ + 4e.$$

These are accomplished easily by permanganate in strongly alkaline solution, but not at all with acid permanganate. Iodide can be determined in presence of bromide by alkaline permanganate, for bromide is not oxidized. Cyanide is oxidized to cyanate, sulfide and sulfite are oxidized to sulfate, phosphite and hypophosphite are oxidized to phosphate.

The technique is as follows: The substance to be determined is mixed with an excess of permanganate and enough sodium hydroxide to make the solution at least 1 N in hydroxyl ion, and allowed to stand for ten minutes at room temperature, or five minutes at 40°C (not more, or the permanganate solution decomposes). Barium chloride is then added, and the unreacted permanganate is back-titrated with standard sodium formate solution, a drop of nickel nitrate solution being added as a catalyst towards the end of the titration. The object of the barium chloride is to precipitate the manganate as insoluble $BaMnO_4$, so that the green color of the manganate will not interfere. The end point is that at which the pink permanganate color disappears from the supernatant solution. The formate is oxidized to carbonate.

Many organic substances, for example glycols, phenols, salicylic acid, are oxidized by alkaline permanganate to give a mixture of carbonate and oxalate. The applications of the Stamm procedures to organic compounds will be discussed in Chapter 16.

Potassium dichromate.

$$(Cr_2O_7^= + 14H^+ + 6e \rightarrow 2Cr^{+++} + 7H_2O; \quad E° = 1.36 \text{ volts}).$$

The advantages of potassium dichromate are that it is readily available in primary standard purity, that its solutions are stable indefinitely, and that it does not oxidize hydrochloric acid in dilute solution. Its disadvantages are its rather low oxidation-reduction potential and the fact that the indicators used with it are rather unsatisfactory. Most phenanthroline indicators cannot be used as their oxidation-reduction potentials are too high, although ferrous 4,7-dimethyl–1,10-phenanthroline promises to be a good indicator for dichromate titrations (page 334). Diphenylamine and diphenylamine sulfonic acid are usually used. The color change at the end point is obscured somewhat by the deep green or violet color of the chromic ion. The difficulty of the indicator can, of course, be avoided by potentiometric titration.

Potassium dichromate is too weak an oxidizing agent to be used for titrating oxalic acid or potassium ferrocyanide. It is used in organic oxidimetry, for example in the routine determination of glycerol, but it is much inferior to ceric perchlorate for this purpose. Its main use is in the titration of ferrous iron in solutions containing hydrochloric acid. A diphenylamine indicator is used, and phosphoric acid is added to depress the ferric-ferrous potential, so that the ferrous ion will be oxidized before the indicator. There is an appreciable indicator blank, so it is usual to standardize a dichromate solution against iron wire if it is to be used to determine iron, even though the dichromate itself may be of primary standard purity.

Potassium dichromate may be used to standardize thiosulfate solutions; a known quantity is made to liberate iodine from excess potassium iodide, and the iodine is then titrated with the thiosulfate. Again, the color of the chromic ion may obscure the end point in this titration.

Sodium periodate and periodic acid.

$$(H_5IO_6 + H^+ + 2e \rightarrow IO_3^- + 3H_2O; \quad E^\circ = 1.7 \text{ volts, approx.}).[16]$$

The outstanding property of periodic acid is the very high oxidation-reduction potential just quoted. Periodic acid oxidizes manganous salts to permanganic acid, and its main use in inorganic analysis is in the determination of manganese. It oxidizes 1,2-glycols, breaking the carbon chain and producing two aldehyde molecules from one molecule of glycol, under conditions where monohydroxy compounds have no action, and it has been used for organic structural determinations as well as for functional group analysis.

The most common laboratory source of periodic acid is sodium paraperiodate, $Na_3H_2IO_6$. This is dissolved in a solution containing sulfuric or nitric acid. The metaperiodates, $NaIO_4$ and KIO_4, are also available, the former being much more soluble in water than either $Na_3H_2IO_6$ or KIO_4. Periodic acid itself can be made from $Ba_3H_4(IO_6)_2$ by double decomposition with dilute sulfuric acid or

[16] G. F. Smith, *Analytical Applications of Periodic Acid and Iodic Acid*, Columbus, G. Frederick Smith Chemical Co., 1950.

concentrated nitric acid (in which barium nitrate is insoluble—see Chapter 9). Solid H_5IO_6 is hygroscopic. None of these compounds is suitable as a primary standard, but solutions are readily standardized against sodium arsenite.

Periodate can be titrated in the presence of iodate by the method of Barnebey.[17] This is based on the reaction

$$2H^+ + IO_4^- + 2I^- \rightharpoonup IO_3^- + I_2 + H_2O.$$

which goes quantitatively in 1 to 3 minutes at pH 9 to 10; a borate buffer is used, and the iodine titrated with thiosulfate or arsenite. Iodate, bromate, and chlorate ions do not interfere. A simpler method is to titrate the periodate with sodium arsenite in a bicarbonate buffer, adding a small amount of iodide as a catalyst:

$$H_3IO_6^= + AsO_2^- \rightharpoonup HAsO_4^= + IO_3^- + H_2O.$$

The usual procedure in periodate oxidations is to add an excess of periodate, allow time for the reaction (five minutes is usually sufficient), and then back-titrate the periodate remaining. Alternative methods are to titrate the excess periodic acid potentiometrically with a base (it titrates as a dibasic acid, with inflections at pH 5 and 10) and to determine it gravimetrically as $Hg_5(IO_6)_2$. This latter reaction can also be used to determine mercury.[18]

In the determination of manganese by periodate oxidation, the permanganate formed is usually measured colorimetrically. Alternatively, the excess of periodate can be precipitated as the mercury salt and the permanganate determined by adding excess ferrous sulfate and back-titrating.[18]

Potassium iodate and iodic acid.

$$(IO_3^- + Cl^- + 6H^+ + 4e \rightharpoonup ICl + 3H_2O; \quad E° = 1.20 \text{ volts}).[19]$$

Iodic acid is a moderately strong oxidizing agent, and is therefore selective, oxidizing some substances and not others. Thus bromide may be oxidized in the presence of chloride without oxidizing the chloride, and ferrous iron may be titrated without interference from

[17] O. L. Barnebey, *J. Am. Chem. Soc.*, **38,** 330 (1916).

[18] H. H. Willard and J. J. Thompson, *Ind. Eng. Chem., Anal. Ed.*, **3,** 398, 399 (1931).

[19] G. S. Jamieson, *Volumetric Iodate Methods*, New York, Chemical Catalog Co., 1926.

vanadium or from organic matter.[20]   The salt $KH(IO_3)_2$ is an excellent primary standard, and its solutions are stable indefinitely.

Titrations with iodate are usually made in 6 N hydrochloric acid, using a flask with a tightly fitting glass stopper.   A little carbon tetrachloride is added.   The first portions of iodate to be added are reduced to iodine, which colors the carbon tetrachloride violet, but later this iodine is oxidized to yellowish iodine monochloride.   The end point is that at which the violet color in carbon tetrachloride disappears, and it is very sharp.   Of course the flask must be vigorously shaken as the end point is approached.[21]   Alternatively, carbon tetrachloride may be replaced by a suitable organic dye which is oxidized as soon as all the iodine has been converted to iodine monochloride.   Such dyes are naphthol blue black, brilliant Ponceaux 5R, and amaranth.[22]

In these titrations the hydrochloric acid concentration must be high, or iodine monochloride disproportionates into iodine and iodic acid.   The high acid concentration makes it impossible to use starch indicator.   The acid concentration need not be so high if the iodine cyanide method of Lang is used.[23]   In this method, potassium cyanide is added in about a twofold excess to a solution which is 1–2 N in hydrochloric acid.   The very stable ICN is formed when the iodate is reduced.   Starch indicator is used, and the end point found by the disappearance of the blue color.   By this technique iodide may be titrated in the presence of bromide, and by a modification the bromide can be determined after the iodide has been oxidized.[24]   Also the iodine cyanide formed can be titrated with thiosulfate if desired, which makes it possible to determine I_2 and I^-, or I_2 and I^{+1}, in presence of one another.

Among the substances which can be determined conveniently by iodate titration are Fe(II), Sn(II), As(III), Sb(III), Tl(I), H_2O_2, Br^-, I^-, $SO_3^=$, $S_2O_3^=$, $S_4O_6^=$, CNS^-, N_2H_4, $C_6H_5NHNH_2$.   Sulfite, thiosulfate, and tetrathionate are oxidized to sulfate; thiocyanate is oxidized to sulfate and hydrocyanic acid.   The latter reaction can

[20] G. B. Heisig, *J. Am. Chem. Soc.*, **50**, 1687 (1928).

[21] L. W. Andrews, *J. Am. Chem. Soc.*, **25**, 756 (1903).

[22] G. F. Smith and C. S. Wilcox, *Ind. Eng. Chem.*, *Anal. Ed.*, **14**, 49 (1942).

[23] R. Lang, *Z. anorg. Chem.*, **122**, 332 (1922); **142**, 229, 280 (1925); chapter by R. Lang in *Newer Methods of Volumetric Analysis* (W. Bottger, ed.), New York, Van Nostrand, 1936.

[24] R. Lang, *Z. anorg. Chem.*, **144**, 75 (1925).

be used to determine copper, which is precipitated as cuprous thio-cyanate, the precipitate being then dissolved in 6 N hydrochloric acid, or 2 N acid containing cyanide, and titrated; mercury, zinc, cadmium, cobalt, nickel, and copper can be determined by precipi-tating $ZnHg(CNS)_4$, etc., and titrating this with iodate.

Potassium bromate.

$$(BrO_3^- + 6H^+ + 6e \rightarrow Br^- + 3H_2O; \quad E° = 1.44 \text{ volts}).$$

This reagent is used to determine arsenic and antimony; it oxidizes them from their +3 states to their +5 states in acid solution. An-timony is titrated in 1–2 N hydrochloric acid, which may be cold or hot; arsenic is titrated either in 2–3 N hydrochloric acid or in 5–6 N sulfuric acid. The acid concentration is rather important. The value of this method for titrating arsenic lies in the fact that it can be applied directly to the distillate obtained after separating arsenic from a mixture as its volatile trichloride (see Chapter 9). Potas-sium bromate is also used to titrate thallium (I) and hydrazine; the latter is oxidized to nitrogen in acid solution.

Potassium bromate is used to titrate phenolic compounds. These are mixed with excess potassium bromide and acid, then titrated with bromate, which liberates bromine according to the reaction $BrO_3^- + 5Br^- + 6H^+ \rightarrow 3Br_2 + 3H_2O$. This in turn reacts rapidly with the phenol, brominating it. Usually an excess of bromate is added, followed after a minute or two by potassium iodide; the iodine liber-ated by the unreacted bromine is then titrated with thiosulfate. One of the most important applications of this technique is the deter-mination of metals such as aluminum, magnesium, and zinc by titra-tion of their 8-hydroxyquinoline complexes; see Chapter 6, page 96.

In direct titrations with potassium bromate, the end point is marked by the appearance of free bromine. If the solution is per-fectly colorless the appearance of the yellow bromine color may be a sufficiently sensitive indication of the end point. Where additional sensitivity is needed, an indicator such as methyl red is added. This is bleached irreversibly by a trace of bromine, so the end point must be approached slowly and carefully; no back titration is possible. A better indicator is p-ethoxychrysoidin, whose color change is to some extent reversible (see Chapter 17).

Iodine.

$$(I_3^- + 2e \rightarrow 3I^-; \quad E° = 0.535 \text{ volt}).$$

Iodine is a relatively weak oxidizing agent, yet it is useful in volumetric analysis because of its selectivity and because of the sharp end points possible with starch indicator. The oxidation reactions used in analysis go to completion provided the pH is properly adjusted. Thus iodine reacts quantitatively with arsenic (III) and antimony (III) at pH 8–9. Latimer[25] quotes the following standard potentials:

$$H_3AsO_4 + 2H^+ + 2e \rightarrow HAsO_2 + 2H_2O; \quad E° = 0.56 \text{ volt.}$$

$$Sb_2O_5 + 6H^+ + 4e \rightarrow 2SbO^+ + 3H_2O; \quad E° = 0.64 \text{ volt.}$$

In 1 N acid, both arsenic (V) and antimony (V) are stronger oxidizing agents than iodine, so iodine would react hardly at all with arsenic (III) or antimony (III); the reverse reaction would predominate. But as the acidity is lowered, so is the oxidizing power of arsenic (V) and antimony (V). The effect of lowering the acid concentration is greater than the above equations indicate, for arsenic acid is a stronger acid than arsenious, and dissociates more as the hydrogen ion concentration is lowered. The result is that arsenic (III) and antimony (III) can be titrated easily with standard iodine solution in a sodium bicarbonate buffer.

Standard iodine solution is also used to determine tin. Tin alloys are dissolved in concentrated hydrochloric or sulfuric acid, and the solution made 3 M in hydrochloric acid, adding chloride if necessary. The tin is then reduced to the stannous state by boiling with excess of iron, adding a trace of antimony trichloride as a catalyst. The solution is then cooled to 10°C to prevent reduction of the iodine by the excess of iron, and the stannous salt is titrated with iodine, passing carbon dioxide to prevent oxidation by the air. Antimony and arsenic, if present, are reduced to the free elements and do not interfere.

Other uses of standard iodine solution are the titration of hydrogen sulfide, sulfurous acid, and thiosulfate ion. Applications in organic analysis are mentioned in Chapter 16.

Volumetric iodine solutions are prepared by dissolving iodine in water containing an excess of potassium iodide. Standard solutions *can* be made by adding pure iodine to a very concentrated potassium

[25] W. M. Latimer, *The Oxidation States of the Elements*, New York, Prentice-Hall, 1938, 1952 (second edition).

iodide solution, which is weighed before and after the addition, but it is easier to standardize the solutions against arsenious oxide, dissolving the latter in sodium hydroxide, then neutralizing and buffering with bicarbonate before titration. Iodine solutions are somewhat sensitive to light, and they must be kept tightly stoppered or some iodine will evaporate. For these reasons it is sometimes convenient to use a standard potassium iodate solution in place of iodine; thus the titration of stannous chloride, which is done in acid solution, may be performed with iodate, detecting the end point with starch in the usual way. This would not be possible in neutral or basic solution, since the reaction $IO_3^- + 5I^- + 6H^+ \rightarrow 3I_2 + 3H_2O$ could not take place.

Starch indicator is used with iodine wherever possible. For maximum sensitivity the solution should be cold, should not be more than 1–2 N in acid, and should contain iodide ions. An iodine concentration of 10^{-5} N then produces a blue color. The sensitivity is much less at temperatures above 50°C, in acid concentrations above 2 N, and in presence of more than 10% of alcohol. The starch should preferably be freshly made, but starch solutions may be stabilized by adding a fairly high concentration of cadmium chloride. Where starch indicator cannot be used, an alternative is to shake the solution with a few drops of carbon tetrachloride, which is colored violet with a trace of iodine.

Calcium hypochlorite.

$$(OCl^- + H_2O + 2e \rightarrow Cl^- + 2OH^-; \quad E° = 0.94 \text{ volt}).$$

This is an oxidizing agent for use in alkaline solutions. It performs oxidations which are not easily done in other ways, for example nitrite to nitrate, sulfide, thiosulfate, and tetrathionate to sulfate. It oxidizes bromide ions to hypobromite, which provides a very convenient way of liberating known amounts of hypobromite. Solutions of hypobromites are unstable, whereas calcium hypochlorite solutions prepared from the commercial H. T. H. calcium hypochlorites are very stable and need only infrequent standardization. Hypobromite reacts with urea to give carbon dioxide and nitrogen, and with ammonia to give nitrogen; urea and ammonia can therefore be directly titrated with standard hypochlorite solution in the presence of excess bromide.

The hypochlorite solution is conveniently standardized against sodium arsenite. Certain dyes, including Bordeaux and tartrazine, will serve as indicators.[26]

II. Volumetric Reducing Agents

Sodium thiosulfate.

$$(S_4O_6^= + 2e \rightarrow 2S_2O_3^=; \quad E° = 0.17 \text{ volt}).$$

Sodium thiosulfate solutions are used exclusively in titrating iodine. Titration must be done in acid solution, for in alkaline solution, sulfate is formed as well as tetrathionate, but the solution must not be too acid or the thiosulfate is decomposed to sulfur and sulfur dioxide. Fortunately this decomposition is slow, so thiosulfate titrations may be made in 1 N acid provided the solutions are kept well stirred as the thiosulfate is added.

Thiosulfate may be used to determine any oxidizing agent which liberates iodine from potassium iodide. Thus the ferric ion may be determined, even though the reaction

$$2Fe^{+++} + 3I^- \rightarrow 2Fe^{++} + I_3^-$$

is measurably reversible (equilibrium constant = 10^8), because the amount of I_3^- present at the end point is so small. (The reaction is slow, however, so a catalyst-cuprous-iodide must be added.) Other oxidizing agents which can be determined include chlorine and hypochlorites, chromates (hence, indirectly, metals which form insoluble chromates), lead dioxide and manganese dioxide (these are boiled with concentrated hydrochloric acid and the liberated chlorine dissolved in potassium iodide solution), cupric copper (see the discussion in Chapter 11), and oxygen itself; the list is very long.

Sodium thiosulfate solutions must be standardized. A convenient way of doing this is to add a measured volume of standard permanganate or ceric sulfate to an excess of acidified potassium iodide, and titrate the iodine which is liberated. Better still, a weighed amount

[26] I. M. Kolthoff and V. A. Stenger, *Ind. Eng. Chem., Anal. Ed.*, **7**, 79 (1935); R. Belcher, *Anal. Chim. Acta*, **4**, 468 (1950). See also I. M. Kolthoff and E. B. Sandell, *Textbook of Quantitative Inorganic Analysis*, 2d ed., New York, Macmillan, 1943, p. 587.

of primary standard potassium iodate is added to an excess of potassium iodide solution which contains enough acid for the reaction

$$IO_3^- + 5I^- + 6H^+ \rightarrow 3I_2 + 3H_2O.$$

Again the iodine is titrated. In all such titrations precautions must be taken against loss of iodine by evaporation, and also against gain of iodine by atmospheric oxidation. One can guard against the latter by throwing in a little sodium bicarbonate at the start, thus blanketing the solution with carbon dioxide.

Thiosulfate solutions decompose on long standing with liberation of sulfur, due to

$$S_2O_3^= + H_2O \rightarrow S + HSO_3^- + OH^-$$

and other reactions. These are encouraged by acid and by bacteria. It is therefore usual to add borax or sodium carbonate to thiosulfate solutions before standardization. They should also be made with boiled water and stored in the dark.

Titanous salts.

$$(TiO^{++} + 2H^+ + e \rightarrow Ti^{+++} + H_2O; \quad E° = 0.1 \text{ volt}).[27]$$

Titanous salts are strong reducing agents, whose solutions are sensitive to air, yet not so sensitive as to be hard to handle. They are prepared by reduction of titanic salts, either electrolytically or with amalgamated zinc, and 20% titanous chloride solution is available commercially. The electrolytic reduction of titanium tetrachloride solution is very easy;[28] however, solutions thus prepared have to be standardized. A solution of determinate concentration can be made from the primary standard, $K_2TiF_6 \cdot H_2O$, by evaporating a known weight with sulfuric acid in a platinum dish, diluting to a measured volume, and reducing with amalgamated zinc in an apparatus such as Lingane and Pecsok[29] used for preparing chromous salt solutions.

Before they are standardized, titanous salt solutions can be poured from one vessel into another without precautions, as the oxidation on brief contact with air is slight. Standard solutions, on the other hand, must be protected from air, both during storage and during

[27] E. Knecht and E. Hibbert, *New Reduction Methods in Volumetric Analysis*, London, Longmans, Green, 1918.

[28] H. F. Walton, *Inorganic Preparations*, New York, Prentice-Hall, 1948.

[29] J. J. Lingane and R. L. Pecsok, *Anal. Chem.*, **20**, 426 (1948).

transfer to the buret.   An arrangement for this is shown in Figure 1.
Another method in which the solution is stored under an inert gas at
more than one atmosphere pressure is described by Stone[30] (Figure 2).

Standardization is best done against metallic iron, the latter being
dissolved in aqueous perchloric acid, evaporated to fumes to oxidize
all the iron to the ferric state and to drive off all the chlorine formed

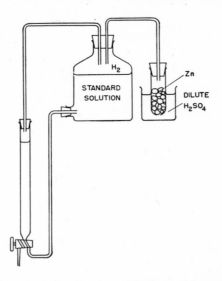

Fig. 15-1.   Apparatus for titrating with air-sensitive solutions, e.g.
titanous salts.

in this oxidation, and then diluted with water.   The ferric salt solution is titrated with titanous chloride or sulfate, using as indicator
methylene blue, indigo carmine, or potassium thiocyanate.   Titanous
salts are violet in color, but the color is not intense enough to dispense with an indicator.   At room temperature the reaction is rather
slow and the end point must be approached very slowly.   At 45°–
50°C it is virtually instantaneous.

The main use of titanous salt solutions is in titrating ferric iron.
Other inorganic applications are the titration of cupric ion (which is
reduced to CuCl in the presence of chloride—see Chapter 11), chromate, vanadate (reduced to VO^{++}), and chlorate (reduced in the

[30] H. W. Stone, *Anal. Chem.*, **20**, 747 (1948).

cold to Cl⁻). Perchlorates in dilute solution are not attacked. Stannic salts are reduced to stannous, but with methylene blue indicator, ferric chloride can be titrated in the presence of stannic chloride; the indicator is bleached before any stannic salt is reduced, so long as the acidity is high enough. This is apparent from the oxidation-reduction potentials concerned. Many indirect titrations suggest

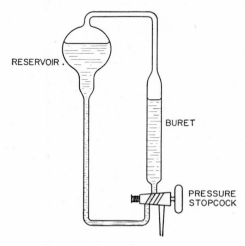

Fig. 15-2. Apparatus for titrating with air-sensitive solutions (Stone). The solution is forced in under pressure and stored under nitrogen or hydrogen.

themselves; for example, titanium itself can be determined by passing a solution of titanium (IV) through a zinc reductor into a known amount of standard ferric salt solution, then titrating the unreduced ferric salt with titanous chloride. Incidentally, solutions of potassium fluotitanate are reduced quantitatively by metallic zinc, in spite of the stability of the complex ion $TiF_6^=$, because titanium (III) forms a fluoride complex also.

Chromous salts.

$$(Cr^{+++} + e \rightarrow Cr^{++}; \quad E° = -0.41 \text{ volt}).[31]$$

Chromous salts are the strongest reducing agents used in volumetric analysis. Their solutions are oxidized extremely fast by air,

[31] E. Brennecke in W. Bottger (ed.), *Newer Methods of Volumetric Analysis*, New York, Van Nostrand, 1938.

and care is needed in their manipulation, but they are easy and convenient to use once the proper equipment has been assembled.[28, 29] The standard potential quoted shows that chromous salts will liberate hydrogen spontaneously from dilute acid solutions, but if catalysts are carefully excluded, the solutions can be kept several days without measurable concentration change Chromous salt solutions have these advantages over titanous salt solutions: they are more easily obtained pure, they are stronger reducing agents, and their reactions are generally faster. They are thus more suited than titanous salts to automatic potentiometric titration techniques.[32]

Chromous chloride or sulfate solutions of standard, determinate concentration can be prepared from pure potassium dichromate by reduction with hydrogen peroxide, followed by pure amalgamated zinc.[29] Purity of reagents is essential if the solutions are to be stable. An older method of preparation[31] purified the chromous salts by precipitating chromous acetate. If desired, the solutions can be standardized against $CuSO_4 \cdot 5H_2O$ by titrating in 2–6 N HCl ($Cu^{II} \rightarrow Cu^{I}$, as the soluble complex, $CuCl_4^=$; later this is reduced to Cu metal), or against standard dichromate to which a slight excess of pure ferrous salt has been added. (The direct reaction between dichromate and chromous ions is slow.)

All chromous salt titrations are done potentiometrically. A platinum indicator electrode is suitable so long as the potential at equivalence is more positive than that of the hydrogen electrode; if it is more negative, as in the titrations of titanium (IV) salts, the platinum catalyzes the reaction between chromous ions and hydrogen ions, and an indicator electrode of mercury is used.[32]

Many metallic elements have been determined by titration with chromous chloride or sulfate, including iron, titanium, copper, molybdenum, tungsten, uranium, vanadium (V or IV), mercury (II), selenium (IV), tellurium (IV), bismuth, gold, and silver. Cupric copper is reduced directly to copper metal in chloride-free solutions, but in solutions 1 N or more in chloride, a soluble cuprous chloride complex is formed. With metals which form chloride complexes, such as bismuth, mercury, gold, and silver, the potential range in which reduction occurs is quite different in chloride solutions from that in chloride-free solutions. Advantage is taken of this fact in titrating mixtures. For example, selenium and copper

[32] J. J. Lingane, *Anal. Chem.*, **20**, 797 (1948).

give separate inflections in 9 N hydrochloric acid, but not in sulfuric acid; the same is true of selenium and tellurium.[33] Iron and copper give separate and clearly distinct inflections in chloride-free solutions, but not in 1 N chloride solutions;[34] dichromate and tungstate are consecutively reduced in hydrochloric acid solutions, tungstate and ferric iron in chloride-free solutions.[35]

Chromous salts will reduce the same organic compounds which titanous salts reduce, and the action is faster.

Ferrous salts.

$$(Fe^{+++} + e \rightarrow Fe^{++}; \quad E^\circ = 0.78 \text{ volt}).$$

Solutions of ferrous sulfate and ferrous ammonium sulfate are among the most commonly used volumetric reducing agents. The salt $FeSO_4 \cdot (NH_4)_2SO_4 \cdot 6H_2O$ is obtainable in high purity, and even though it is not suitable as a primary standard, it is a very convenient standard where an accuracy of the order of 0.5% is sufficient. To make a standard ferrous salt solution, the appropriate weight of this salt is dissolved in freshly boiled and cooled distilled water *to which a little sulfuric acid has been added*. If this last precaution is not taken, the slightest trace of ferric salt produced by oxidation hydrolyzes, depositing hydrous ferric oxide, and deterioration by further oxidation is very rapid. A solution which has been prepared as described may be used without further standardization on the same day that it has been prepared, provided it is kept in a stoppered bottle. If it is to be used subsequently it should be restandardized.

Ferrous ammonium sulfate solution is used to titrate strong oxidizing agents, such as cerium (IV), chromium (VI), vanadium (V). It is often used in indirect titration, that is, the substance to be determined is added to a measured excess of ferrous salt, and the unreacted ferrous salt then titrated with a standard oxidizing agent.

[33] J. J. Lingane and L. Niedrach, *J. Am. Chem. Soc.*, **70**, 1997 (1948).

[34] E. Zintl and F. Schloffer, *Angew. Chem.*, **41**, 956 (1928); see also T. F. Buehrer and O. E. Schupp, *Ind. Eng. Chem.*, **18**, 121 (1926).

[35] R. Flatt and F. Sommer, *Helv. Chim. Acta*, **27**, 1518, 1522 (1944).

III. Methods for Preliminary Oxidation and Reduction

Where an element is to be determined by oxidation-reduction titration, it is first necessary for it to be in the appropriate oxidation state. Thus if the total iron in a sample is to be determined by dichromate, the iron must be completely converted into the ferrous condition before titration, while if the iron is to be determined by titanous chloride, it must first be completely converted into the ferric condition. The excess of the reducing or oxidizing agent used in such pretreatment must be destroyed or inactivated, or it will be titrated along with the substance which is to be determined.

There are certain reagents which are used for such preoxidation or prereduction because the excess can easily be removed or inactivated. They are listed and discussed below.

Perchloric acid.[36] The oxidizing power of perchloric acid depends on its concentration and temperature. The most concentrated perchloric acid which is available commercially is the vacuum-distilled constant-boiling mixture containing 70–72% $HClO_4$. This solution is a powerful oxidizing agent when hot, yet in the pure state it is perfectly stable and may be stored indefinitely. Perchloric acid which is more concentrated than 84.79% $HClO_4$ (the composition corresponding to "oxonium perchlorate," $H_3O^+ClO_4^-$), however, decomposes spontaneously on standing and eventually explodes. At the other end of the scale, solutions of perchloric acid which are less concentrated than 20% $HClO_4$ have virtually no oxidizing power whatever; the perchlorate ion in water is highly stable and reacts with reducing agents extremely slowly or not at all. Even 60% $HClO_4$ does not oxidize potassium iodide in the cold.

Because of these properties, analytical procedures such as the following are possible. In the determination of chromium in stainless steel, a sample is dissolved in hot 60% perchloric acid (or, which may be faster, in hot concentrated hydrochloric acid, adding the perchloric acid afterward). The solution is heated until no further color change

[36] G. F. Smith, *Perchloric Acid*, Columbus, G. Frederick Smith Chemical Co., 1940.

is seen, or else until fumes of perchloric acid are given off. Oxidation of chromium to the +6 condition is now complete, but the solution will contain a little chlorine due to decomposition of the perchloric acid. It is now cooled somewhat, diluted with twice its volume of water, boiled again for a few minutes to drive off chlorine, then cooled, diluted, and a measured excess of standardized ferrous sulfate added. The unreacted ferrous iron is titrated with permanganate or ceric sulfate, using ferroin indicator in either case.[37] *The diluted, cold perchloric acid is without action on the ferrous salt.* A similar procedure may be followed to convert primary standard iron wire into the ferric condition for standardizing a titanous chloride solution.

Perchloric acid is strong enough to oxidize chromium to chromic acid and vanadium to vanadic acid, but not strong enough to oxidize manganese to permanganic acid. Sulfur compounds are oxidized to sulfuric acid, and carbon and most carbon compounds are oxidized to carbon dioxide. Hot concentrated perchloric acid reacts with organic compounds very vigorously, and indeed explosively if proper precautions are not taken. Most of the serious explosions which have occurred with perchloric acid have been caused by contact with organic matter. Nevertheless, organic compounds may be oxidized perfectly safely with perchloric acid if this is mixed with another acid, such as sulfuric, nitric, or phosphoric acid, whose molecules break the reaction chains which would otherwise lead to explosion. Many standard methods for the determination of metallic elements in biological materials involve "wet ashing" by heating with mixtures of perchloric acid and one or more of the acids mentioned.[38] Arsenic and antimony are oxidized to the +5 oxidation state and therefore do not volatilize during this treatment.[39] When coal is heated with perchloric and nitric acid, together with a little vanadic acid as a catalyst, the sulfur it contains is all oxidized to sulfate.[40]

Ammonium persulfate or peroxydisulfate, $(NH_4)_2S_2O_8$. In acid solution, this is a powerful oxidizing agent, converting chromium compounds completely to chromic acid and manganese compounds incompletely to permanganic acid. Cerous sulfate is oxidized by peroxydisulfate to ceric sulfate. After the oxidation is complete,

[37] J. Birckel, *Ann. chim. anal.*, **24,** 170 (1942).

[38] G. F. Smith, *Mixed Perchloric, Sulphuric and Phosphoric Acids and Their Applications in Analysis*, Columbus, G. Frederick Smith Chemical Co., 1942.

[39] E. Kahane, *Compt. rend.*, **195,** 48 (1932).

[40] G. F. Smith and A. G. Deem, *Ind. Eng. Chem., Anal. Ed.*, **4,** 227 (1932).

the excess of peroxydisulfate is destroyed by boiling for a few minutes; it decomposes into sulfate and oxygen. These oxidations are catalyzed by silver salts, probably because of the intermediate formation of argentic compounds. In the absence of silver, manganous ion is oxidized only as far as manganese dioxide.

Ammonium persulfate is chiefly used in steel analysis, where it oxidizes not only the metallic constituents but also the carbon. Even graphitic carbon is slowly attacked, and the larger graphite particles which resist attack are easily filtered out.

Sodium peroxide and hydrogen peroxide. Sodium peroxide is used mainly in mineral analysis, for example in the analysis of chromite, where the powdered mineral is fused with sodium peroxide in a nickel crucible The chromium is converted to sodium chromate. It is also used, in conjunction with potassium perchlorate or nitrate, in the Parr bomb. This was designed primarily for the analysis of coal—the sulfur, for example, is oxidized to sulfate—but it is used for general elemental analysis of organic compounds, which are oxidized in the Parr bomb preparatory to the determination of chloride and other elements. The residue from the fusion in the crucible or Parr bomb is boiled with water for a few minutes before proceeding with the analysis, to decompose the excess of sodium peroxide into sodium hydroxide and oxygen.

Hydrogen peroxide is used in a similar way, except that 30% hydrogen peroxide is added to the boiling solution which is to be oxidized. Again, the excess hydrogen peroxide is destroyed by boiling. The solution may be either acid or alkaline, depending on the substance to be oxidized. It must be remembered, however, that hydrogen peroxide is a reducing as well as an oxidizing agent:

$$H_2O_2 \rightarrow 2H^+ + O_2 + 2e.$$

Manganese dioxide, for example, is reduced very rapidly by acidified hydrogen peroxide to give a manganous salt solution. In hot acid solution hydrogen peroxide reduces dichromates to chromic salts, although in alkaline solution, it oxidizes chromic salts to chromates. Thus in determining chromium by alkaline oxidation to chromate, the alkaline solution must always be boiled until all the excess hydrogen peroxide is decomposed before it is acidified, or some of the chromium will revert to the +3 condition.

Sodium bismuthate. So-called sodium bismuthate, which is really a mixture containing Bi_2O_4, is a yellow powder which in presence of dilute nitric acid oxidizes manganous salts to permanganates. This is its main use in analysis. The excess of sodium bismuthate is insoluble and is removed by filtration.

Metals and metal amalgams. These are used to reduce dissolved substances prior to titration. Three techniques are used; one, the most common, is to let the solution flow down a column containing the metal in granulated form; another is to dip the metal into the solution, the metal being in the form of a rod or wire spiral; the third is to shake the solution with a liquid amalgam.

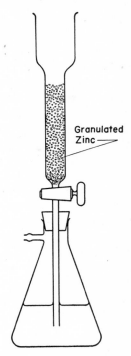

The first technique is that of the familiar Jones reductor (Figure 3), which uses granulated zinc that has been amalgamated by stirring with mercuric chloride solution before putting it into the column. Amalgamation retards the liberation of hydrogen from acid solutions, because of the high overvoltage of hydrogen on mercury; however, hydrochloric acid solutions will liberate hydrogen with zinc in spite of amalgamation, and solutions which are to be reduced with zinc should be acidified with sulfuric rather than hydrochloric acid.

Zinc is a very powerful reducing agent, and will reduce titanium salts to Ti^{+++}, chromium salts to

Granulated Zinc →

Fig. 15-3. Jones reductor.

Cr^{++}, vanadium salts to V^{++}, uranium salts to a mixture of UO^{++} and U^{+++}, and nitrates partially to hydroxylamine salts, for example. Where a milder reducing action is required, other metals may be used, for example cadmium, lead, and silver. A glance at a table of oxidation-reduction potentials will show that lead cannot reduce chromic salts to chromous, although it can reduce titanic salts to titanous. Silver is generally used in conjunction with chloride ion; this enhances the reducing power of the metal, because of the formation of insoluble silver chloride. ($E°$ for $AgCl + e \rightarrow Ag + Cl^-$ is $+0.222$ volt.) Hydrochloric acid is added to the solution to be reduced, and this is then passed through a column of spongy

Fig. 15-4. Apparatus for reduction with liquid amalgams (Someya). Amalgam and solution are introduced through A; B is for passing an inert gas. After reduction, the amalgam is run into C, which is previously filled with air-free water.

silver obtained by reduction of the chloride.[41] Ferric salts are reduced to ferrous, but titanic salts are unaffected.

In many cases the solution passing out of the reductor is sensitive to air. Where only a single substance is to be determined, for example titanium by a zinc reductor, the easiest technique is usually to let the solution from the reductor flow out under the surface of a measured excess of ferric salt solution. The titanous ion (for example) reacts to form its equivalent of ferrous ion, which is easily titrated without special precautions to exclude air.

The second technique mentioned above, that of reducing the solution by dipping a metal rod or wire spiral into it, is simpler than the column technique, but far less certain. There is no better way of ensuring a thorough contact between a solution and a solid than to have the solution percolate through a column of the solid in granular form.

The third technique—shaking the solution with a liquid amalgam—was developed by Someya.[42] Shaking is done in a special separating funnel (Figure 4), the

[41] G. H. Walden, L. P. Hammett, and S. M. Edmonds, *J. Am. Chem. Soc.*, **56**, 350 (1934).

[42] K. Someya, *Z. anorg. Chem.*, **138**, 291 (1924); **145**, 168 (1925); **148**, 58 (1925); **160**, 404 (1927); **169**, 293 (1928).

amalgam being run out into a side tube before titration. Different amalgams give different reducing powers, and the reducing power may be further controlled by varying the acidity and the temperature. In this way, complex mixtures may be completely analyzed through selective reduction. Table II summarizes some of the possibilities.

TABLE III

METAL AMALGAMS AS REDUCING AGENTS

Metal	Oxidation state obtained with amalgam of		
	Zn	Pb	Bi
Cu	0	0	1*
Sn	0	0	2*
Ti	3	3	4
V	2	4	4
Cr	2	3	3
Mo	3	3	5, 3*
W	3	3	5
U	3	3, 4	4
Fe	2	2	2

Notes: *In conc. HCl solution.
Standard potentials: $Zn + 2e \rightarrow Zn$, -0.76 volt;
$Pb + 2e \rightarrow Pb$, -0.12 volt;
$Bi + 3e \rightarrow Bi$, 0.23 volt.

A variant on the Someya technique is to shake the solution with a finely powdered metal, and filter this out afterwards. Thus Ti(IV) may be reduced with powdered iron, and Fe^{+++} may be reduced in presence of Ti(IV) with copper powder.[43]

The special use of Devarda's alloy to reduce nitrates to ammonium salts was noted in Chapter 9.

Sulfur dioxide. This is a rather weak reducing agent which in acid solution reduces Fe^{+++} without reducing Ti(IV), reduces VO_3^- to VO^{++} and no further, and reduces arsenic (V) and antimony (V) to the $+3$ condition. Excess of sulfur dioxide may be removed by boiling for ten minutes or more.

[43] L. Silverman, *Chemist-Analyst*, **33**, 8 (1944).

Stannous chloride. This is used to reduce ferric iron to ferrous in the well-known Zimmermann-Reinhardt method for determining iron. Reduction is done in a hot concentrated solution containing hydrochloric acid. A slight excess of stannous chloride is added, and this excess is afterwards removed by cooling, diluting, and adding all at once a large excess of mercuric chloride. The reaction is

$$Sn^{++} + 2HgCl_2 \rightarrow Sn^{++++} + Hg_2Cl_2 + 2Cl^-.$$

The solid mercurous chloride does not interfere with the subsequent titration of ferrous iron by permanganate, dichromate, or ceric sulfate, provided this titration is done rapidly. If insufficient mercuric chloride is added, free mercury will form as a greyish precipitate; this reacts with the oxidant during titration and spoils the determination.

PROBLEMS

1. Ferrous iron is to be titrated with permanganate in presence of vanadyl ion VO^{++}. Recommend a suitable method, including details of acidity, temperature, and indicator, if any.

2. The reaction $2Fe^{+++} + 2I^- \rightleftharpoons 2Fe^{++} + I_2$ is incomplete, yet it may be applied to the determination of ferric iron by thiosulfate titration. Why? What would be the best conditions for such a titration?

3. Write a comprehensive essay on the uses of perchloric acid in analytical chemistry.

4. Why is ferroin indicator used in titrating iron with permanganate in the presence of chromic salt (page 301)? What other indicators would be suitable?

5. In the destruction of organic matter with perchloric acid, what would you expect to happen to any nitrogen present?

6. A gas stream contains a little hydrogen chloride, the rest being chlorine. Devise a method for determining the amount of hydrogen chloride carried in the gas stream, using simple equipment and ordinary titrimetric techniques.

7. Devise a method for determining iron, aluminum, phosphate, and chromate in a solution used in the anodic treatment of aluminum, which contains all these.

8. When is phosphoric acid added in titrating ferrous ions, and when is its use unnecessary?

9. Using oxidation-reduction potentials, predict whether or not a neutral

0.1 N solution of potassium permanganate in water will be thermodynamically stable.

10. Cupric ions are to be titrated in presence of ferric ions, using a chromous salt. What conditions are necessary, and why?

11. Devise a method for determining copper, iron, and traces of lead in pyrites (a mineral which is mainly FeS_2 plus $CuFeS_2$, and may contain arsenic). The copper and iron should be determined volumetrically.

12. A method has been proposed for titrating cupric ions with standard ferrous sulfate. Under what conditions would you expect such a titration to be feasible?

16

Volumetric oxidation-reduction methods in organic chemistry

MANY ORGANIC COMPOUNDS can be quantitatively oxidized or reduced by the reagents described in the previous chapter. The reactions are generally not instantaneous, so the usual procedure is to add a measured excess of the oxidizing or reducing agent, allow time for reaction, and then back-titrate.

We shall begin this chapter with a brief discussion of the stoichiometry of organic oxidations and reductions, showing how to write balanced equations which will tell the number of equivalents of oxidizing or reducing agent required for a particular reaction. We shall then outline the uses of certain reagents of general application, such as ceric perchlorate, periodic acid, titanous chloride, and lithium aluminum hydride, in determining certain classes of organic compounds. Finally we shall discuss the Karl Fischer reagent. This reagent, which is used to determine water, is included here because the reaction on which the titration is based is one of oxidation and reduction.

Equation Balancing

Organic oxidation-reduction equations can be balanced by the method of oxidation numbers which is customarily used in inorganic chemistry. The method seems more arbitrary when applied to organic compounds, however, because the binding is predominantly covalent rather than ionic. Atoms generally share electrons with one another instead of losing or gaining them outright. It is perfectly natural to assign an oxidation number of $+2$ to copper in a cupric salt, since a copper atom loses two electrons to form Cu^{++}, but it seems highly artificial to call the oxidation number of the carbon atoms in oxalic acid $+3$. Nevertheless, a self-consistent scheme of oxidation numbers in organic compounds can be devised by taking hydrogen as $+1$, oxygen (except in peroxides and ozonides) as -2, amino nitrogen as -3, nitro nitrogen as $+5$, and so on, and then giving the carbon atoms whatever oxidation number is necessary to make all the oxidation numbers in a neutral molecule add up to zero. Thus in $H_2C_2O_4$, the H atoms are each $+1$, the O atoms -2, and the C atoms must therefore be $+3$. On oxidation to CO_2 these become $+4$, so that two equivalents of oxidant are necessary to convert a mole of oxalic acid to carbon dioxide. Likewise in ethylene glycol, $C_2H_6O_2$, each carbon atom must be $\frac{1}{2}(-6 + 4)$ $= -1$; in formic acid, CH_2O_2, the carbon must be $+2$. To convert a mole of ethylene glycol to two moles of formic acid, therefore, 6 equivalents of oxidant are necessary (see page 311).

A more natural and perhaps an easier way of balancing organic oxidation and reduction equations in aqueous solutions is to set up the half-cell reactions as follows:

Step 1. Write down the formula for the reactant, i.e., the substrate which is to be oxidized or reduced, and the formulas for the known products.

Step 2. Balance the carbon atoms on each side of the equation, and any atoms other than carbon, hydrogen, and oxygen which take part in the reaction.

Step 3. Balance the oxygen atoms by adding hydroxyl ions to the equation.

Step 4. Balance the hydrogen atoms by adding hydrogen ions to the equation.

Step 5. If the solution is *acid*, add equal numbers of hydrogen ions to both sides of the equation until the hydroxyl ions are neutralized. Combine the hydrogen and hydroxyl ions to form water. If the solution is *alkaline*, add equal numbers of hydroxyl ions to both sides of the equation until the hydrogen ions are neutralized, and combine the hydrogen and hydroxyl ions to form water.

Step 6. The equation is now balanced with regard to all the *atoms* taking part. Now balance the *electric charges* by adding the right number of electrons.

To illustrate this procedure let us consider the oxidation of urea in alkaline solution to carbonate ions and nitrogen.

Steps 1 and 2:

$$CO(NH_2)_2 \rightarrow CO_3^= + N_2$$

Step 3:

$$CO(NH_2)_2 + 2OH^- \rightarrow CO_3^= + N_2$$

Step 4:

$$CO(NH_2)_2 + 2OH^- \rightarrow CO_3^= + N_2 + 6H^+$$

Step 5:

$$CO(NH_2)_2 + 8OH^- \rightarrow CO_3^= + N_2 + 6H_2O$$

Step 6:

$$CO(NH_2)_2 + 8OH^- \rightarrow CO_3^= + N_2 + 6H_2O + 6e.$$

A mole of urea thus requires six equivalents of an oxidizing agent, such as hypobromite, to convert it to carbonate ions and nitrogen.

In many cases this procedure can be shortened; for example, all the equations listed on page 311–312 for ceric perchlorate oxidations were balanced by adding enough water molecules to the left-hand side to balance the oxygen atoms, balancing the hydrogen atoms by adding hydrogen ions to the right-hand side, then balancing the ionic charges by adding electrons to the right-hand side.

Oxidation Methods

Potassium dichromate. In acid solution this oxidizes a good many organic compounds, but the reactions are often slow and incomplete. One of the few uses of this reagent is the determination of glycerol. A standard method used in the soap industry for many years consists in heating the sample (after removing fatty acids, chlorides, and volatile alcohols) in a solution 0.5 N in dichromate and 12 N in sulfuric acid for at least two hours between 90° and 100°C. The solution is then cooled, diluted, an aliquot taken, potassium iodide added, and the liberated iodine titrated with thiosulfate.

Alternatively, the excess of dichromate can be titrated with ferrous sulfate, using a bimetallic electrode pair (page 217).[1]

Glycerol is oxidized quantitatively to carbon dioxide and water according to the reaction:

$$C_3H_8O_3 + 7H_2O \rightarrow 3CO_2 + 4H_2O + 14H^+ + 14e.$$

One mole of glycerol, therefore, consumes 14 equivalents of dichromate. Sugars, if present, are oxidized along with the glycerol, and a correction must be made for them. They are hydrolyzed to invert sugar, and this is determined by reduction of an alkaline cupric solution to cuprous oxide.

Ceric perchlorate. In Chapter 15 we noted the extremely high oxidizing power of ceric perchlorate, or perchloratoceric acid. In 1 N perchloric acid, the standard potential of the ceric-cerous system is $+1.7$ volts; in 8 N perchloric acid, $+1.87$ volts. It is not surprising, therefore, that ceric perchlorate oxidizes many organic compounds quickly and quantitatively. The main classes of compounds which are oxidized are glycols, sugars, α-hydroxyacids, dicarboxylic acids, and aldehydes. Typical reactions are:[2]

$$\begin{array}{l} CH_2OH \\ | \\ CH_2OH \end{array} + 2H_2O \qquad \rightarrow 2H \cdot COOH + 6H^+ + 6e.$$

$$\begin{array}{l} CH_2OH \\ | \\ CHOH \\ | \\ CH_2OH \end{array} + 3H_2O \qquad \rightarrow 3H \cdot COOH + 8H^+ + 8e.$$

$$\begin{array}{l} CHO \\ | \\ CHO \end{array} + 2H_2O \qquad \rightarrow 2H \cdot COOH + 2H^+ + 2e.$$

$$\begin{array}{l} COOH \\ | \\ CH_2 \\ | \\ COOH \end{array} + 2H_2O \qquad \rightarrow 2CO_2 + H \cdot COOH + 6H^+ + 6e.$$

[1] Procter and Gamble Company, *Ind. Eng. Chem., Anal. Ed.*, **9**, 515 (1937).
[2] G. F. Smith, *Cerate Oxidimetry*, Columbus, G. Frederick Smith Chemical Co., 1942.

$$\begin{array}{c} CH_2COOH \\ | \\ C(OH) \cdot COOH + 5H_2O \rightarrow 4CO_2 + 2H \cdot COOH + 14H^+ + 14e. \\ | \\ CH_2COOH \end{array}$$

$$\begin{array}{c} CH_3 \\ | \\ CO + H_2O \qquad\qquad \rightarrow CO_2 + CH_3COOH + 2H^+ + 2e. \\ | \\ COOH \end{array}$$

From these examples and others we can formulate the following rules:

1. Carbon-carbon bonds are broken between any two of the following: COOH, CHO, CO, CHOH, active CH_2. An active CH_2 group is defined as one which has one or other of the four preceding groups on each side of it (not including —CHOH·CH_2·CHOH—, however).

2. Where such a bond is broken, the products are such as would be expected if hydroxyl groups had attached themselves to the broken ends of the bond. Two hydroxyl groups attached to the same carbon atom will then lose water and form C=O.

3. If the product of this process is formaldehyde, it is immediately oxidized to formic acid. Other aldehydes are oxidized slowly and incompletely.

Consider glycerol, for example. The hypothetical intermediates, according to Rule 2, are $CH_2(OH)_2$ and $CH(OH)_3$. The latter loses water to form H·COOH, the former to form H·CHO; H·CHO is immediately oxidized to H·COOH. Another application of these rules is seen by comparing the oxidation of glucose, CHO·$(CHOH)_4$·CH_2OH, and fructose, CH_2OH·CO·$(CHOH)_3$·CH_2OH. The former gives 6H·COOH, the latter 5H·COOH + CO_2. An electronic interpretation of these reactions is given by Smith and Duke.[2,3]

These reactions are all rapid. Glycerol and ethylene glycol are oxidized in 15 minutes at 60°C, a great saving of time compared to the dichromate procedure. Other compounds, such as tartaric acid and biacetyl, are oxidized considerably faster. The reagent is 0.1 N ceric perchlorate in 4 N perchloric acid, prepared by adding $(NH_4)_2Ce(NO_3)_6$ to the appropriate quantity of 72% $HClO_4$, then adding water slowly with stirring. (The salt dissolves much faster

[3] G. F. Smith and F. R. Duke, *Ind. Eng. Chem., Anal. Ed.*, **15,** 120 (1943).

in 72% acid than in the diluted acid.)   The organic compound is dissolved in 4 N HClO$_4$, and enough reagent added to provide at least a 10% excess and to make the solution 0.025–0.05 N in ceric salt.   After reaction, the solution is cooled and titrated with 0.1 N sodium oxalate in 0.1 N perchloric acid, using nitroferroin indicator. The reaction with oxalate is instantaneous and the end point sharp; moreover, the oxalate solution keeps indefinitely.   The same solution is used to standardize the ceric perchlorate solution every week or so.[2, 4]

The question naturally arises whether formic acid, which is a product in all the reactions listed, is oxidized by the ceric perchlorate. Actually, it is oxidized, but the reaction is very slow.   The error introduced into the glycerol determination described above is 0.1% or less.   Above 60°C the oxidation of formic acid is fast enough to cause significant error in a one hour period, and so, too, is the oxidation of water:

$$2H_2O \rightarrow O_2 + 4H^+ + 4e.$$

Acetaldehyde and acetone are appreciably oxidized after 5 minutes at 10°C.

Periodic acid.   This compound is as strong an oxidizing agent as ceric perchlorate (see page 288), yet it is more selective in its reactions.   At room temperature it oxidizes only 1,2-glycols, or carbonyl compounds which by hydration could produce 1,2-glycols, or 1,2-aminohydroxy compounds.   Unlike ceric perchlorate, periodic acid does not oxidize formaldehyde appreciably, except at a temperature higher than that used in analytical work.   Typical reactions are the following:[3, 5, 6]

$$\begin{matrix} CH_2OH \\ | \\ CH_2OH \end{matrix} \quad \rightarrow 2H \cdot CHO + 2H^+ + 2e.$$

$$\begin{matrix} CH_2OH \\ | \\ CHOH \\ | \\ CH_2OH \end{matrix} + H_2O \rightarrow H \cdot COOH + 2H \cdot CHO + 4H^+ + 4e.$$

[4] G. F. Smith and C. A. Getz, *Ind. Eng. Chem., Anal. Ed.*, **10**, 304 (1938).

[5] G. F. Smith, *Analytical Applications of Periodic Acid and Iodic Acid*, 5th ed., Columbus, G. Frederick Smith Chemical Co., 1950.

[6] L. Malaprade, *Bull. soc. chim.*, **43**, 683 (1928).

$$\begin{matrix} CHO \\ | \\ CHO \end{matrix} + 2H_2O \;\rightarrow\; 2H \cdot COOH + 2H^+ + 2e.$$

$$\begin{matrix} CH_2OH \\ | \\ CHO \end{matrix} + 2H_2O \rightarrow 2H \cdot COOH + 4H^+ + 4e.$$

$$\begin{matrix} CH_2OH \\ | \\ CH_2NH_2 \end{matrix} + H_2O \rightarrow 2H \cdot CHO + NH_4^+ + H^+ + 2e.$$

Malonic acid, $CH_2(COOH)_2$, and malic acid, $\begin{matrix} CH(OH) \cdot COOH \\ | \\ CH_2 \cdot COOH \end{matrix}$, are not

oxidized, but tartaric acid, $\begin{matrix} CH(OH) \cdot COOH \\ | \\ CH(OH) \cdot COOH \end{matrix}$, is oxidized to glyoxylic acid, $CHO \cdot COOH$.

There is very clear evidence that an intermediate compound is formed between the 1,2-glycol and periodic acid before the carbon-carbon bond is broken,[7] and this intermediate is believed to be a cyclic ester:

$$\begin{matrix} | \\ CH-O \\ | \quad\;\; \diagdown \\ \qquad I-O^- \quad H^+ \\ | \quad\;\; \diagup \\ CH-O \\ | \end{matrix}$$

Periodic acid has proved useful in structure determinations. For example one can distinguish between 5-membered and 6-membered rings in the sugars:[8,9]

$$\begin{matrix} | \\ CH- \\ | \\ (CHOH)_2 \qquad O \;\rightarrow\; \\ | \\ CH- \\ | \end{matrix} \qquad \begin{matrix} | \\ CH \\ | \\ CHO \\ \qquad \diagdown \\ \qquad\quad O \\ \qquad \diagup \\ CHO \\ | \\ CH \\ | \end{matrix}$$

[7] G. Hughes and T. P. Nevell, *Trans. Faraday Soc.*, **44**, 941 (1948).
[8] E. L. Jackson and C. S. Hudson, *J. Am. Chem. Soc.*, **61**, 1530 (1939).
[9] B. Lythgoe and A. R. Todd, *J. Chem. Soc.*, 1944, p. 592.

$$
\begin{array}{c}
\overset{|}{C}H\!\!\!-\!\!\!\!\!\!\rule{0pt}{0pt} \\
\overset{|}{(C}HOH)_3 \quad O \\
\overset{|}{C}H\!\!\!-\!\!\!\!\!\!\rule{0pt}{0pt} \\
|
\end{array}
\qquad
\begin{array}{c}
\overset{|}{C}H \\
\overset{|}{C}HO \diagdown \\
\ O + H\cdot COOH \\
\overset{|}{C}HO \diagup \\
\overset{|}{C}H \\
|
\end{array}
$$

The latter yield formic acid while the former do not. The formic acid can be titrated with standard base if a solution of sodium metaperiodate $NaIO_4$ is used as the oxidant. Sodium periodate is a better choice than the potassium salt, for it is ten times as soluble.

The reduction of periodate proceeds by the equation

$$IO_4^- + 2H^+ + 2e \rightharpoonup IO_3^- + H_2O$$

or, since IO_4^- is hydrated in aqueous solution,

$$H_4IO_6^- + 2H^+ + 2e \rightharpoonup IO_3^- + 3H_2O.$$

One proton is consumed for each electron consumed, and in the oxidation of glycols, one proton is released for every electron released; therefore if we start with a neutral periodate solution, any acidity at the end of the reaction is due to formic acid. In this way one can distinguish qualitatively between ethylene glycol and glycerol, for glycerol produces formic acid and ethylene glycol does not. The reaction can be used to determine glycerol and ethylene glycol quantitatively in presence of one another; a measured amount of 0.05 M H_5IO_6 is added, and after an hour the solution is titrated potentiometrically with sodium hydroxide.[10] Two end points are obtained; the first, at pH 5, gives $H\cdot COOH + HIO_3 + H_5IO_6$; the second, at pH 10, gives $H_4IO_6^-$ alone.

The phrase, "neutral periodate solution," needs amplification. In aqueous solution, the only stable periodic acid is paraperiodic acid, H_5IO_6 (note the effect of the large atomic radius of iodine). This titrates as a dibasic acid, with $K_1 = 2.30 \times 10^{-2}$, $K_2 = 4.35 \times 10^{-9}$ ($pK_1 = 1.63$, $pK_2 = 8.36$). A solution of $H_4IO_6^-$, therefore, has a pH of $\frac{1}{2}(1.63 + 8.36) = 5.00$ (see Chapter 13). This is what we have called the "neutral" solution.

Ethylene glycol is oxidized completely by a small excess of peri-

[10] N. Allen, H. Y. Charbonnier, and R. M. Coleman, *Ind. Eng. Chem., Anal. Ed.*, **12**, 384 (1940).

odate in a solution of pH < 3 in less than five minutes at 25°C; the reaction is catalyzed by acid.[11]   Not all glycols are oxidized as rapidly as this, however.   The usual reaction time recommended is 1–2 hours at 25°C; Malaprade[6] recommends this time even for glycol and glycerol.   Certain glycosides may need three days with neutral periodate.[9]   After reaction, an excess of sodium bicarbonate is added and the periodate remaining is determined by adding a measured excess of sodium arsenite, then back-titrating with standard iodine, using starch indicator:

$$H_4IO_6^- + AsO_2^- + OH^- \rightarrow IO_3^- + HAsO_4^= + 2H_2O.$$

$$I_2 + AsO_2^- + 3OH^- \rightarrow HAsO_4^= + 2I^- + H_2O.$$

Alternatively, the solution is acidified, potassium iodide is added, and the liberated iodine titrated with thiosulfate.   This has the drawback that iodate is titrated as well as periodate, and the quantity desired appears as the small difference between two large thiosulfate consumptions.   These two titrations may sometimes lead to different results; if they do, this indicates that the reaction between periodic acid and the organic compound is not complete.   The intermediate (mentioned above) may oxidize iodide ion in acid solution while not oxidizing arsenite in bicarbonate solution.[7]

The main advantage of periodic acid and periodates in organic analysis is their selectivity and their assistance in structural determinations.

Potassium permanganate.   As a quantitative reagent for organic compounds, potassium permanganate is best used in strongly alkaline solution according to the procedures of Stamm.[12, 13]   The concentration of sodium or potassium hydroxide is 1 to 2 N, the permanganate is in at least twofold excess, and the time of reaction is 20 minutes or less, usually 5 to 10 minutes, at 15°–25°C, or not more than 5 minutes at 40°C.   Under these conditions the only reduction step is from MnO_4^- to $MnO_4^=$, and the disproportionation of $MnO_4^=$ to MnO_4^- and MnO_2, which is autocatalytic and therefore introduces uncontrolled errors, is prevented.

To be attacked by permanganate under these conditions the

---

[11] C. C. Price and H. Kroll, *J. Am. Chem. Soc.*, **60**, 2726 (1938).

[12] H. Stamm in W. Böttger (ed.), *Newer Methods in Volumetric Analysis*, New York, Van Nostrand, 1938.

[13] H. Stamm, *Z. angew. Chem.*, **47**, 191 (1934); **48**, 150, 710 (1935).

organic compound must contain aliphatic C = C, alcoholic or phenolic OH, NH$_2$, or an aldehyde or keto group. The compound is broken down either to carbonate directly or to a mixture containing oxalate, which is further oxidized to carbon dioxide when the mixture is acidified. There are, therefore, two methods for back-titrating the unreacted permanganate. The first method is to titrate the excess of permanganate in alkaline solution with standard sodium formate solution, adding a drop of nickel nitrate solution as a catalyst and an excess of barium chloride to precipitate the dark green manganate ion as BaMnO$_4$ and so leave a colorless solution at the end point. In the second method the solution is acidified with sulfuric acid and quickly heated to 50°C; a measured excess of oxalic acid is added, sufficient to react with all the manganate and permanganate present, and the excess oxalic acid is titrated with standard permanganate.

The first method of back-titration is difficult in that the dark green barium manganate obscures the end point even though it is insoluble, because it is finely divided and does not settle easily. Moreover, the method is applicable to relatively few substances. The disadvantage of the second method is that it requires two standard solutions and three volume measurements, and the desired quantity is the difference between two much larger quantities; the reduction product, MnO$_4^=$, oxidizes four-fifths as much oxalate as the original MnO$_4^-$. Nevertheless, an accuracy of 0.5% to 1% is claimed for this method.

Examples of oxidations by alkaline permanganate are the following:

(a) MnO$_4^-$ back-titrated in *alkaline* solution.

$$CH_3OH + 8OH^- \rightarrow CO_3^= + 6H_2O + 6e$$

$$H \cdot COOH + 4OH^- \rightarrow CO_3^= + 3H_2O + 2e$$

$$H \cdot CHO + 6OH^- \rightarrow CO_3^= + 4H_2O + 4e$$

$$\begin{matrix} CH_2 \cdot COOH \\ | \\ C(OH) \cdot COOH + 30OH^- \rightarrow 6CO_3^= + 19H_2O + 18e \\ | \\ CH_2 \cdot COOH \end{matrix}$$

(b) MnO_4^- back-titrated in *acid* solution.

$$\begin{array}{l} CH_2OH \\ | \\ CH_2OH + 2H_2O \end{array} \qquad \rightarrow 2CO_2 + 10H^+ + 10e$$

$$\begin{array}{l} CH_2OH \\ | \\ CHOH + 3H_2O \\ | \\ CH_2OH \end{array} \qquad \rightarrow 3CO_2 + 14H^+ + 14e$$

$$+ 11H_2O \quad \rightarrow 7CO_2 + 28H^+ + 28e$$

Glycollic, tartaric, and malic acids can be determined by method (a), sugars and polyhydric alcohols by method (b).

Potassium ferricyanide; iodine. These are weaker oxidizing agents than those just discussed, and because they are weaker, they are more selective.

Potassium ferricyanide in alkaline (sodium carbonate) solution is used to determine reducing sugars.[14] An excess is added, the solution is heated to 80°C for one minute, then cooled, acidified, and back-titrated with ceric sulfate, using ferroin indicator. One mole of glucose or fructose uses 5 equivalents of ferricyanide. The method is faster than the gravimetric method of Munson and Walker, in which cuprous oxide is precipitated, but it is somewhat less selective. In plant products, citrates and other substances are oxidized to some extent and the results may be a few per cent high.

Iodine is used to titrate ascorbic acid (vitamin C) in acid solution.[15] It is generally harder to oxidize organic compounds in acid solution than in alkaline solution, because protons are usually withdrawn from the compounds along with the electrons. In acid solution, therefore, oxidation is more selective, and only the strongest reducing agents, of which ascorbic acid is one, are oxidized. Iodine is not quite as selective for ascorbic acid as 2,6-dichlorophenol indophenol,

[14] R. B. Whitmoyer, *Ind. Eng. Chem., Anal. Ed.,* **6,** 268 (1934); W. Z. Hassid, *Ind. Eng. Chem., Anal. Ed.,* **8,** 138 (1936), **9,** 228 (1937).

[15] R. Ballentine, *Ind. Eng. Chem., Anal. Ed.,* **13,** 89 (1941).

but it is satisfactory for citrus juices. A similar example of selective oxidation by iodine in acid solution is the quantitative oxidation of resorcinol at pH 5.0 in one minute at room temperature; monohydric phenols are not affected under these conditions.[16]

Another use for iodine is to determine aldehydes by the Ripper method.[17] The aldehyde is treated with excess of sodium bisulfite, forming the addition compound $R \cdot CH(OH) \cdot SO_3Na$, and the unreacted bisulfite is titrated with iodine. The iodine number of fats and oils, measuring unsaturation, is another familiar example of the use of iodine in quantitative organic analysis.

Reduction Methods

Titanous and chromous salts. Quantitative reduction methods in organic analysis have been less exploited than oxidation methods, probably because of the need for excluding air when using strong reducing agents. Titanous chloride was used by Green[18] for determining the constitution of aniline black, since it reduced quinonoid

—N=⟨ ⟩=N— groups quantitatively to —NH—⟨ ⟩—NH—.

Many dyestuffs containing a quinonoid grouping can be titrated directly with titanous salts in the cold, examples being rosaniline, malachite green, indigo carmine. More usually, reductions with titanous salts are slow. One therefore adds an excess of reagent in acid solution, heats to boiling (in the absence of air) for five minutes, cools, and back-titrates with standard ferric sulfate.[19, 20] Compounds which can be determined in this way are nitro and nitroso compounds (reduced to amines), azo and hydrazo compounds (also reduced to amines, with rupture of the N-N link), α-diketones, and quinones. An accuracy of 2% or better is obtained.

[16] H. H. Willard and A. L. Wooten, *Anal. Chem.*, **22**, 585 (1950).

[17] M. Ripper, *Monatshefte*, **21**, 1079 (1900); A. Parkinson and E. Wagner, *Ind. Eng. Chem., Anal. Ed.*, **6**, 433 (1934).

[18] A. G. Green and A. E. Woodhead, *J. Chem. Soc.*, **97**, 2388 (1910); **101**, 1117 (1912).

[19] E. Knecht and E. Hibbert, *New Reduction Methods in Volumetric Analysis*, London, Longmans, Green, 1918.

[20] S. Siggia, *Quantitative Organic Analysis via Functional Groups*, New York, Wiley, 1949, Chap. 12.

A drawback to this technique is that at high temperatures the reduction of water by the titanous salt becomes appreciable:

$$2Ti^{+++} + 2H_2O \rightarrow 2TiO^{++} + H_2 + 2H^+.$$

It is better, in some cases, to work at room temperature and facilitate the reduction by raising the pH. For example, dinitrotoluene is reduced quantitatively in 15 seconds in an acetate or citrate buffer:[21]

$$C_7H_6(NO_2)_2 + 12Ti^{+++} + 8H_2O \rightarrow C_7H_6(NH_2)_2 + 12TiO^{++} + 12H^+.$$

Reduction of aromatic nitro groups is also facilitated by first sulfonating the compound.[19]

An interesting use of titanous salts is the determination of reducing sugars.[19] The osazones are reduced as follows:

$$\begin{array}{l} CH{=}N{-}NHC_6H_5 \\ | \qquad\qquad\qquad\qquad + H_2O + 6H^+ + 6e \\ C\ \ {=}N{-}NHC_6H_5 \\ | \end{array}$$

$$\rightarrow \begin{array}{l} CHO \\ | \qquad\quad + NH_3 + 2C_6H_5NH_2. \\ CHNH_2 \\ | \end{array}$$

Chromous salts have not been as much used for quantitative organic analysis as titanous salts, yet with the recently improved techniques for handling them, there seems no reason why their use should not be extended. They are faster and cleaner in their action than titanous salts. Chromous chloride has been used to titrate quinone, azobenzene, *m*- and *p*-nitroaniline directly, using neutral red as indicator.[22]

Lithium aluminum hydride, LiAlH₄. This reagent is now much used in preparative organic chemistry to reduce carbonyl groups in such compounds as aldehydes, ketones, carboxylic acids, and the esters, anhydrides, and chlorides of carboxylic acids.[23,24] It is selective in its action and generally does not reduce carbon-carbon double

[21] P. G. Butts, W. J. Meikle, J. Shovers, D. L. Kouba, and W. W. Becker, *Anal. Chem.*, **20**, 947 (1948); see also I. M. Kolthoff and C. Robinson, *Rec. trav. chim.*, **46**, 169 (1926).

[22] A. P. Terent'ev and G. S. Gorjachewa, *Chem. Abstracts*, **30**, 8073 (1936).

[23] A. E. Finholt, A. C. Bond, and H. I. Schlesinger, *J. Am. Chem. Soc.*, **69**, 1199 (1947).

[24] R. F. Nystrom and W. G. Brown, *J. Am. Chem. Soc.*, **69**, 1197, 2548 (1947).

bonds. Reactions are carried out in ether solution, giving products such as the following:

$$4R_2CO + LiAlH_4 \longrightarrow LiAl(OCHR_2)_4$$

$$2R \cdot COOR' + LiAlH_4 \longrightarrow LiAl(OR')_2(OCH_2R)_2$$

$$4R \cdot COOH + LiAlH_4 \longrightarrow LiAl(OCH_2R)_4 + 2LiAlO_2 + 4H_2.$$

The products of these reactions are decomposed by water, or, better, dilute sulfuric acid, to give alcohols:

$$LiAl(OCH_2R)_4 + 4H_2O \longrightarrow LiOH + Al(OH)_3 + 4R \cdot CH_2OH.$$

With hydroxylic and amino compounds, lithium aluminum hydride liberates hydrogen:

$$4R \cdot OH + LiAlH_4 \longrightarrow LiAl(OR)_4 + 4H_2.$$

$$4R \cdot NH_2 + LiAlH_4 \longrightarrow LiAl(NHR)_4 + 4H_2.$$

These reactions suggest themselves for quantitative determination of active hydrogen in hydroxyl, amino, and carboxyl groups by measuring the volume of hydrogen gas formed with excess of the reagent, a method analogous to the Zerewitinoff method [25] which uses a Grignard reagent such as CH_3MgI and measures the volume of methane. Lithium aluminum hydride has been tested for this purpose and found to give faster and more reliable results.[26] If desired, the total amount of reagent combining with the compound can be found by decomposing the unreacted lithium aluminum hydride with an alcohol and measuring the volume of hydrogen given off in the process.[27] In this way ketones and esters can be determined, even though they produce no hydrogen themselves.

Lithium aluminum hydride reacts completely with water, and one might expect that water could be determined from the volume of hydrogen liberated from excess of hydride. However, this is not so; the reaction is not stoichiometric unless water itself is in excess.[28]

Measurement of the volume of a gas is a volumetric method in the strict sense of the term, but it is not a titrimetric method. A titrimetric technique with lithium aluminum hydride has, however, been

[25] R. Berg, *Das o-Oxychinolin*, Stuttgart, Enke, 1936.
[26] H. E. Zaugg and B. W. Horrom, *Anal. Chem.*, **20**, 1026 (1948).
[27] F. A. Hochstein, *J. Am. Chem. Soc.*, **71**, 305 (1949).
[28] B. B. Baker and W. M. MacNevin, *Anal. Chem.*, **22**, 364 (1950).

worked out.[29]   A measured excess of lithium aluminum hydride dissolved in tetrahydrofuran is added to the substance dissolved in the same solvent; some thirty minutes are allowed for reaction, and the excess of reagent is back-titrated with a standard solution of ethanol or n-propanol in benzene.   The titration is followed potentiometrically.   The reference electrode is silver or platinum, which, in the presence of excess lithium aluminum hydride, assumes a strongly negative potential (about 1 volt) compared to a reference electrode of silver in a solution of lithium bromide in tetrahydrofuran.   At the end point of the titration the electromotive force of the cell drops very sharply.   Substances titrated in this way include alcohols (primary, secondary, and tertiary), phenols, primary and secondary amines, ketones, aldehydes, and esters.

The Karl Fischer Reagent

Fundamental Reactions.   The Karl Fischer reagent[30, 31] is used for titrating water.   It is included in this chapter because the titration reaction is one of oxidation and reduction in which water plays a part.   The constituents of the reagent are iodine, sulfur dioxide, pyridine, and methanol.   Their reaction with water[32] may be represented as follows:

(a) $I_2 + SO_2 + H_2O \rightarrow 2HI + SO_3$.

(b) $SO_3 + C_5H_5N \rightarrow C_5H_5N \cdot SO_3$.

(b′) $C_5H_5N \cdot SO_3 + CH_3OH \rightarrow C_5H_5NH^+ \cdot CH_3SO_4^-$.

(c) $2HI + 2C_5H_5N \rightarrow 2C_5H_5NH^+ \cdot I^-$.

The intermediate $C_5H_5N \cdot SO_3$ can be isolated if the methanol is omitted.   It is a coordination compound analogous to that formed between dioxane and SO_3.

[29] T. Higuchi, C. J. Lintner, and R. H. Schleif, *Science*, **111**, 63 (1950); C. J. Lintner, R. H. Schleif, and T. Higuchi, *Anal. Chem.*, **22**, 534 (1950).

[30] K. Fischer, *Angew. Chem.*, **48**, 394 (1935).

[31] J. Mitchell and D. M. Smith, *Aquametry*, New York, Interscience, 1948; J. Mitchell, *Anal. Chem.*, **23**, 1069 (1951).

[32] D. M. Smith, W. M. D. Bryant, and J. Mitchell, *J. Am. Chem. Soc.*, **61**, 2407 (1939).

For every mole of iodine in the reagent there must be at least one mole of sulfur dioxide and three moles of pyridine; otherwise the iodine color will not be destroyed when water is added. This follows from the equations written above, and it is confirmed by experiment. The following directions are given by Smith, Bryant, and Mitchell for preparing the reagent:

84.7 grams (0.33 mole) of resublimed iodine are dissolved in 269 ml. (3.3 moles) of dry pyridine plus 667 ml. of pure synthetic methanol. The solution is cooled in ice and 64 grams (1 mole) of sulfur dioxide are gradually added, either as liquid or as gas.

The amount of water consumed per mole of iodine is always less than the equations above indicate, and the reagent deteriorates on standing, usually losing half its strength within a month. The reason is that side reactions take place with the methanol after the reagent is mixed; for example,

$$I_2 + SO_2 + 3C_5H_5N + 2CH_3OH$$
$$\rightarrow C_5H_5NCH_3^+ \cdot CH_3SO_4^- + 2C_5H_5NH^+I^-.$$

It is common practice, therefore, to prepare and store the reagent as two solutions, with the iodine in one and the sulfur dioxide in the other. Individually, these are stable indefinitely. They are mixed and allowed to stand overnight before using; the mixed solution is standardized every day against a reference solution of water in methanol. Another procedure is to add the sample to a solution of sulfur dioxide in pyridine and methanol, then titrate with iodine. The side reactions then do not interfere, provided excess iodine is avoided, or that, if excess has to be added, the temperature is kept below $-10°C$ and back-titration is done within three minutes.[33]

An excellent water standard for the Karl Fischer reagent is the dihydrate of sodium tartrate (Neuss et al., Anal. Chem., **23**, 1332, 1951).

General titration procedures. Methanol is the best solvent for Karl Fischer titrations, because it dissolves the amine salts formed in the reactions and is easily dried, although for some purposes ethylene glycol is used. It is most important to have everything dry, to exclude moist air during the titrations, and to run a blank on the solvents used. Water has a low equivalent weight, and even the

[33] W. Seaman, W. H. McComas, and G. A. Allen, *Anal. Chem.*, **21**, 510 (1949).

invisible film of moisture adsorbed on glassware may cause significant error in a Karl Fischer titration.

There are two ways to detect the end point. The easiest is the visual method; excess of iodine turns the solution a brown color which is quite distinct from the lemon yellow, resembling potassium chromate, which is the color of the solution before the end point is reached. In a dark-colored solution, of course, this method is not applicable. One then uses the electrical dead-stop method (see Chapter 12); an electromotive force of about 10 to 20 millivolts is impressed upon two platinum wires dipping into the solution. Current flows freely between them if iodine is in excess, because iodine depolarizes the cathode. But when water is in excess, little or no current can pass. The titration is best done by adding an excess of Karl Fischer reagent, then back-titrating with standard water in methanol. The current indicated by the galvanometer drops sharply to zero at the end point.[34] Direct titration with the reagent is also possible.[35]

Water determination. The Karl Fischer reagent is selective for water and has a very high affinity for it; consequently, it may be used to determine water in a great variety of substances, including petroleum, sugars, foods, most salt hydrates, liquid sulfur dioxide, hydrofluoric acid, and even such powerful adsorbents as silica gel and activated alumina. Insoluble solids should be finely ground and suspended in methanol. The chief interfering substances are the following:

(a) *Basic oxides and hydroxides.* These react in a similar way to water, e.g.,

$$MgO + I_2 + SO_2 + CH_3OH \rightarrow MgI_2 + CH_3HSO_4.$$

In many cases, e.g., Ag_2O, MgO, CaO, ZnO, HgO, the reaction is stoichiometric,[36] so that a correction may be applied in the titration, provided the proportion of water to oxide is not too small. Al_2O_3 does not react at all.

(b) *Certain decomposable salts of weak acids,* e.g., Na_2CO_3, $NaHCO_3$,

[34] G. Wernimont and F. J. Hopkinson, *Ind. Eng. Chem., Anal. Ed.,* **15,** 272 (1943).

[35] R. J. Carter and L. Williamson, *Analyst,* **70,** 369 (1945).

[36] J. Mitchell, D. M. Smith, E. C. Ashby, and W. M. D. Bryant, *J. Am. Chem. Soc.,* **63,** 2927 (1941).

Na_2SO_3.[36] These act in the same way as basic oxides, CO_2 and SO_2 being formed in the examples given.

(c) *Oxidizing and reducing substances.* Again the reaction may be stoichiometric; for example, with MnO_2, which oxidizes the iodide ion besides acting as a basic oxide according to (a). Organic compounds containing ethylenic double bonds, which might be expected to combine with iodine, do not seem to do so.[32]

(d) *Aldehydes, ketones, and formic acid.* These react slowly with methanol to form acetals and water. To avoid interference, one may either use a special reagent with more pyridine and much less methanol than usual, or one may inactivate the carbonyl group with hydrocyanic acid.

One can often separate the water from interfering substances by distilling it out with a liquid, such as benzene or toluene, which forms a minimum boiling azeotropic mixture.

Indirect determination of organic functional groups. The Karl Fischer reagent may be used to determine any substance which produces water in a suitable reaction or consumes it. By such indirect means it is possible to determine several classes of organic compounds, as follows:

(a) *Alcohols.* Primary, secondary, and tertiary alcohols can be determined by the water which is formed when they are esterified with glacial acetic acid:

$$R \cdot OH + CH_3 \cdot COOH \rightarrow CH_3 \cdot COOR + H_2O.$$

This reaction is catalyzed by boron trifluoride,[37] which is added as a solution in glacial acetic acid; esterification is complete in two hours at 65°C. Phenols react incompletely, and their reaction may be prevented almost entirely by using less catalyst. Before titrating with the Karl Fischer reagent, the boron trifluoride must be inactivated by adding pyridine, which forms a very stable addition compound with it; otherwise it would cause esterification of the excess acetic acid with the methanol of the reagent.[38]

(b) *Aliphatic carboxylic acids.* These are determined by esterification with excess of methanol, using boron trifluoride catalyst and

---

[37] H. D. Hinton and J. A. Nieuwland, *J. Am. Chem. Soc.*, **54**, 2017 (1932).
[38] W. M. D. Bryant, J. Mitchell, and D. M. Smith, *J. Am. Chem. Soc.*, **62**, 1 (1940).

inactivating the latter with pyridine before titration, just as in the determination of alcohols. Aromatic carboxylic acids cannot be determined, as they esterify much too slowly.[39, 40]

(c) *Acid anhydrides.* These are made to react with a small excess of water, and the unreacted water is back-titrated with Karl Fischer reagent. The reaction of the anhydride with water may be catalyzed either with boron trifluoride in acetic acid,[41] or better, with sodium iodide in pyridine;[42] 1–2 hours are allowed at 60°C. Boron trifluoride is inactivated by adding pyridine before the titration. By keeping the excess of water to a minimum, hydrolysis of esters is avoided.

(d) *Amines.* Primary and secondary amines are determined by reacting them with excess benzaldehyde for thirty minutes at 60°C:

$$R \cdot NH_2 + C_6H_5 \cdot CHO \rightarrow C_6H_5 \cdot CH{=}NR + H_2O.$$

The benzaldehyde remaining is next inactivated by adding sodium cyanide plus hydrocyanic acid dissolved in pyridine; otherwise it would react with the methanol in the reagent. After 45 minutes, the water which has been formed is titrated.[43]

(e) *Aldehydes and ketones.* The reaction used here is:

$$R_2CO + H_2N \cdot OH \rightarrow R_2C{=}N \cdot OH + H_2O.$$

The reagent is hydroxylamine hydrochloride in methanol plus a little pyridine (to liberate free hydroxylamine), the temperature 60°C, the time two hours. Before titration, the excess of hydroxylamine must be destroyed by adding sulfur dioxide in pyridine:

$$SO_2 + C_5H_5N + H_2N \cdot OH \rightarrow C_5H_5NH^+ \cdot SO_2ONH_2^-.$$

Pyridine sulfamate is formed.[44]

[39] J. Mitchell, D. M. Smith, and W. M. D. Bryant, *J. Am. Chem. Soc.*, **62**, 4 (1940).

[40] J. Mitchell and W. Hawkins, *J. Am. Chem. Soc.*, **66**, 1797 (1944).

[41] D. M. Smith, W. M. D. Bryant, and J. Mitchell, *J. Am. Chem. Soc.*, **62**, 608 (1940).

[42] D. M. Smith, W. M. D. Bryant, and J. Mitchell, *J. Am. Chem. Soc.*, **63**, 1700 (1941).

[43] S. Siggia, *Quantitative Organic Analysis via Functional Groups*, New York, Wiley, 1949, pp. 67–68. See also Mitchell *et al.*, *J. Am. Chem. Soc.*, **66**, 782, 1662 (1944).

[44] J. M. Mitchell, D. M. Smith, and W. M. D. Bryant, *J. Am. Chem. Soc.*, **63**, 573 (1941).

(f) *Nitriles*.   These are hydrolyzed to amides, the reagent being a solution of boron trifluoride in acetic acid containing water:

$$R \cdot CN + H_2O \rightarrow R \cdot CONH_2.$$

Reaction is for two hours at 80°C.   Pyridine is then added and the remaining water titrated.[45]

PROBLEMS

1. Write an equation for the oxidation of glycollic aldehyde, $CHO \cdot CH_2OH$, by ceric perchlorate.   Compare the numbers of equivalents of the three oxidants, ceric perchlorate, periodic acid, and potassium permanganate, consumed by this compound.

2. Suggest a method for determining glyoxalic acid $CHO \cdot COOH$.

3. What *ketones* could best be determined by the Ripper method (page 319)?

4. Sketch the pH titration curve for H_5IO_6 with NaOH, from the data on page 315.

5. Write a comprehensive account of the determination of reducing sugars.

6. You have a quantity of Karl Fischer reagent which will not give an end point with methanol-water mixture, but gives only a brown solution.   What is wrong with the reagent?

7. Suggest a good method for determining small quantities of water in acetone.

[45] J. Mitchell and W. Hawkins, *J. Am. Chem. Soc.*, **67**, 777 (1945).

17

Oxidation-reduction indicators

COMPARED TO THE GREAT NUMBERS of acid-base indicators, indicators for oxidation-reduction processes are few. The reason is that organic molecules usually suffer more radical changes in oxidation and reduction than they do when they merely accept or lose a proton, and such changes are not reversible. A requirement for an indicator is that the change from one colored form to the other shall be very rapid and reversible, so that it may be repeated many times. Side reactions which destroy the indicator must be absent, yet these are hard to avoid in strongly oxidizing media.

Along with the difficulty in finding suitable organic compounds for oxidation-reduction indicators, the stimulus to look for them has been lacking until rather recently. Primarily it is the increasing use of tetrapositive cerium as a volumetric oxidant which has led chemists to seek more indicators. A surprisingly large number of analyses can be done with permanganate, which needs no indicator except in very dilute solutions, or iodine, for which a specific indicator, starch, is available. For titrations involving ferric iron, for example its reduction by titanous chloride, another specific indicator, the thiocyanate ion, can be used. A common practice when none of these methods was available was to use an external indicator; for example, in titrating iron with potassium dichromate, one can locate the end point by removing drops of the solution at intervals and testing them on a white spot plate with potassium ferricyanide; when the end point is passed, no more blue precipitate is formed, but only a brown solution. Such methods are, of course, tedious and need careful standardization.

One of the first internal oxidation-reduction indicators to come into general use was diphenylamine, which is useful in potassium dichromate titrations. In 1929, studies of certain triphenylmethane derivatives were published, and in 1931 the first paper appeared describing the use of phenanthroline complexes as oxidation-reduction indicators. The phenanthroline indicators are undoubtedly the most important general oxidation-reduction indicators in use today. Very recently the peculiar characteristics of substituted chrysoidins have become known. Indicators having oxidation-reduction potentials in the neighborhood of that of hydrogen have been known for some time and have been used to study oxidation and reduction in biochemical systems. One of these indicators, methylene blue, is used in titrations with titanous chloride.

Potential requirements. To be acceptable in a titration, an oxidation-reduction indicator must not begin to change color until the substrate, or substance being titrated, has virtually all reacted, and its color change must be completed before any appreciable excess of the titrant appears in the solution. The graph of oxidation-reduction potential versus volume of oxidant for a mixture of substrate and indicator must look like the solid curve in Figure 2, not like any of the three broken curves. (In an actual titration, of course, the volume of oxidant used in oxidizing the indicator will be negligibly small compared to that used in oxidizing the substrate.) Suppose we allow the indicator to start changing color when all but 1 part in 1000 of the substrate has been oxidized, and suppose that the color change is perceptible when one-eleventh of the indicator has reacted; suppose further, that both the indicator and the substrate undergo one-electron changes in reduction and oxidation. Then at the point at which the color change is perceptible,

$$E = (E°) \text{ substrate} + 0.059 \log 1000$$
$$= (E°) \text{ indicator} + 0.059 \log 1/10,$$

whence $(E°)$ indicator $- (E°)$ substrate $= $ *0.236 volt.*

There should be the same interval between the standard potentials of the oxidant and the indicator. Titration is possible when the difference in the potentials is less than this, but it should not be much less.

Potential and **pH.** Many organic oxidations involve loss of protons as well as loss of electrons. When this happens, the potential of half change, at which the concentrations of oxidized and reduced forms are equal, depends on the hydrogen ion concentration.

The system quinone-hydroquinone is a case in point. Up to pH 8 or slightly above, the equilibrium can be represented by

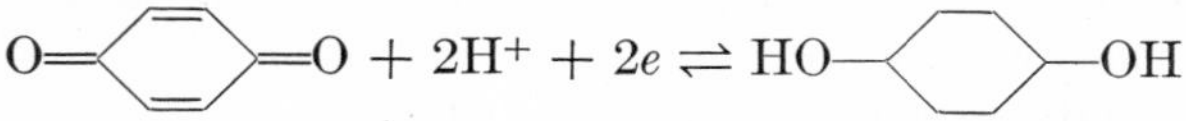

$$O=\!\!\left\langle\rule{0pt}{1.4em}\right\rangle\!\!=O + 2H^+ + 2e \rightleftharpoons HO\!\!-\!\!\left\langle\rule{0pt}{1.4em}\right\rangle\!\!-OH$$

and the potential is given accurately by the equation

$$E = E^\circ + \frac{RT}{2\mathfrak{F}} \ln \frac{[\text{quinone}]}{[\text{hydroquinone}]} + \frac{RT}{2\mathfrak{F}} \ln [H^+]^2$$

or the potential of half change, $E_{\frac{1}{2}} = E^\circ - 0.059$ pH at 25°C (see Chapter 11). Hydroquinone starts to ionize above pH 8, however. Its two acid ionization constants are close together and in the neighborhood of 10^{-9} to 10^{-10}. The equilibrium is represented intermediately by

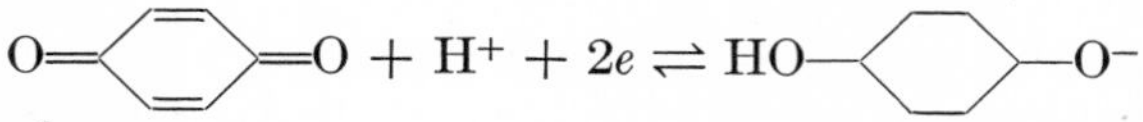

$$O=\!\!\left\langle\rule{0pt}{1.4em}\right\rangle\!\!=O + H^+ + 2e \rightleftharpoons HO\!\!-\!\!\left\langle\rule{0pt}{1.4em}\right\rangle\!\!-O^-$$

and finally by

$$O=\!\!\left\langle\rule{0pt}{1.4em}\right\rangle\!\!=O + 2e \rightleftharpoons {}^-O\!\!-\!\!\left\langle\rule{0pt}{1.4em}\right\rangle\!\!-O^-.$$

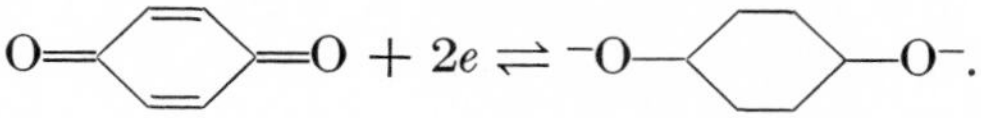

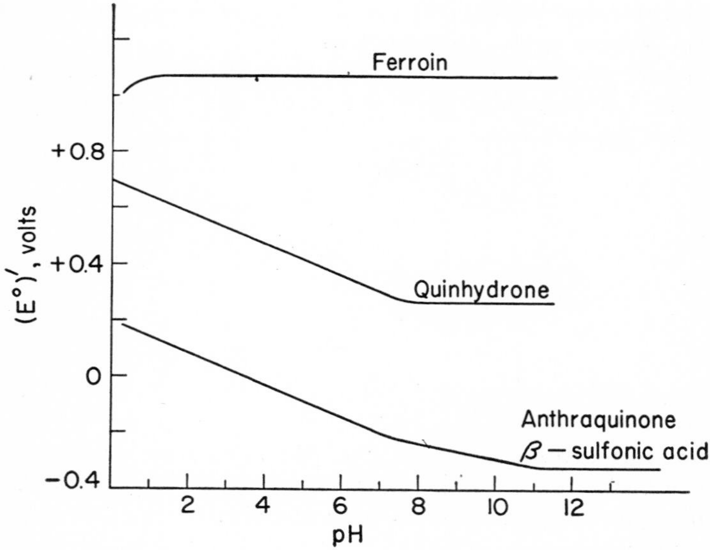

Fig. 17-1. Formal potential of oxidation-reduction indicators as a function of pH.

Above pH 10 the potential of half change becomes independent of pH (see Figure 1). With *anthraquinone sulfonic acid* the two ionization constants of the hydroquinone hydroxyls are sufficiently far apart so that two breaks in the $E_{\frac{1}{2}}$ — pH curve are obtained, with an intermediate straight line region in which $E_{\frac{1}{2}} = E° - 0.059$ pH$/2$ (Figure 1).

These types of behavior are found in a number of oxidation-reduction indicators, such as methylene blue (see below). Interionic attractions further complicate matters, since the charge on the colored ions is usually high; salt effects, in other words, are quite considerable (see Chapter 14).

An indicator in whose oxidation or reduction no hydrogen ions take part, for example, the orthophenanthroline ferrous complex, should have a half-change potential which is independent of pH. However, at very high acidities the acid concentration may have an effect. This may be due to a number of things, such as interionic attraction with high ionic charges at high ionic strengths, or to the appreciable substitution of the acid for the solvent water. Also it may in part be spurious, since the measured potential includes the junction potential between the solution and a reference half-cell, and this can be quite large in acid solutions.

1he **1,10-*phenanthrolines*.**[1] The parent substance of these indicators is 1,10-phenanthroline, also known as *orthophenanthroline*, which has the structure:

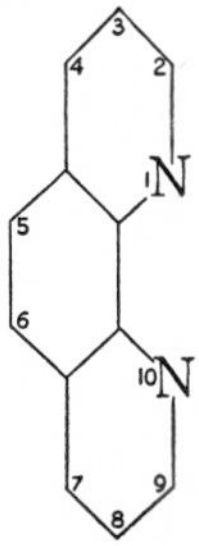

The two nitrogen atoms each have a pair of unshared electrons, and can coordinate with a number of metallic ions, forming chelate rings. The most important of these coordination compounds is formed with the ferrous ion:

[1] G. F. Smith and F. P. Richter, *Phenanthroline and Substituted Phenanthroline Indicators*, Columbus, G. Frederick Smith Chemical Co., 1944.

or $(Phen)_3Fe^{++}$.

This complex has an intense blood-red color and is extremely stable. A similar complex is formed by 2,2′-bipyridyl, and both serve for colorimetric determination of ferrous iron.   The ferric ion forms a phenanthroline complex too.   This is a light color and is less stable than the ferrous complex.   In presence of orthophenanthroline, therefore, the oxidation of ferrous iron to ferric is accompanied by a marked color change,[2] and it occurs at a higher potential than with ferrous ion alone:[2, 3]

$$(Phen)_3Fe^{+++} + e \rightarrow (Phen)_3Fe^{++}; \quad E° = +1.06 \text{ volts.}$$
light blue   dark red

The complex salt solution made by mixing equivalent quantities of orthophenanthroline and ferrous sulfate is called *ferroin*.   It is close to being the ideal indicator.   The red color is very intense, so that only 1 drop of 0.025 M indicator is needed for 50 ml. of solution, and titrations may be done in extremely dilute solution, which is useful in microtitrations with ceric sulfate or potassium permanganate.   The change is sharp and virtually instantaneous; the color is practically unaffected by acids, in spite of the basic nature of the complexing agent, and the ferric complex, called *ferriin*, is stable almost indefinitely in the presence of excess ceric sulfate, provided the solution is not heated above room temperature.   At 50°C, however, ceric sulfate destroys the indicator rapidly.

This indicator behaves so well because the oxidation-reduction process does not change the organic part of the molecule, but only the inorganic ion which is the nucleus of the complex.   However, in a molecular model of the complex, the ferrous ion is completely hidden

[2] G. H. Walden, L. P. Hammett, and R. P. Chapman, *J. Am. Chem. Soc.*, **53,** 3908 (1931); **55,** 2652 (1933).

[3] D. N. Hume and I. M. Kolthoff, *J. Am. Chem. Soc.*, **65,** 1895 (1943).

by the carbon atoms of the three phenanthroline molecules; a ceric ion could not possibly penetrate the complex to come into direct contact with the central ion.   The exchange of iron between the complex and radioactive Fe^{++} is slow, and so is the rate of dissociation of the complex.[4,5]   It seems, therefore, that the exchange of electrons must proceed through the aromatic rings.

Ferroin is ideal for titrating ferrous salts with ceric sulfate because the potential at its color change coincides almost exactly with the equivalence potential in the titration.   The value of $E°$ for $Fe^{+++} + e \rightarrow Fe^{++}$ is $+0.78$ volt; the formal potential (see Chapter 11) in presence of $1\ M$ sulfate or chloride ions is significantly less, about 0.68 volt.   The formal potential for $Ce^{++++} + e \rightarrow Ce^{+++}$ in $1\ M$ H_2SO_4 is 1.44 volts.   Since the electron transfer is symmetrical—the ferrous ion loses one electron, the ceric ion gains one electron—the potential at equivalence in $1\ M$ sulfuric acid is the arithmetic mean of 0.68 and 1.44; namely, 1.06 volts.   This is exactly the standard potential for the ferroin-ferriin system.   In $0.1\ M$ acid, the equivalence potential is a few centivolts higher.   Actually, the observed color change comes at a somewhat higher potential than 1.06 volts, because the dark red color of ferroin is so much more intense than the light blue of ferriin that the change is obscured only when about nine-tenths of the indicator has been oxidized, at about 1.11 volts.

We can modify the oxidation-reduction potential of the ferroin-ferriin system by introducing substituents into the phenanthroline rings.   Many substituted 1,10-phenanthrolines have been investigated[1]; two which are of importance are 5-nitro– and 5-methyl–1,10-phenanthroline.   Their ferrous complexes are called *nitroferroin* and *methylferroin*, and their standard oxidation-reduction potentials are 1.25 and 1.02 volts, respectively.   Nitroferroin is well suited to titrations with ceric perchlorate, for not only is its oxidation-reduction potential high, but the organic ring structure is sufficiently stable to withstand excess ceric perchlorate in cold $4\ N$ perchloric acid.   Its perchlorate is only slightly soluble, however.   It is more of a purple-red than ferroin, and its oxidized (ferric) form is a stronger blue than ferriin.   This makes the color change somewhat less striking, yet the

[4] S. Ruben, M. D. Kamen, M. B. Allen, and P. Nahinsky, *J. Am. Chem. Soc.*, **64**, 2297 (1942).

[5] T. S. Lee, I. M. Kolthoff, and D. L. Leussing, *J. Am. Chem. Soc.*, **70**, 3596 (1948).

indicator is possibly even more sensitive, and is excellent for titrating very small amounts of oxalate, arsenite, and ferrous salt with ceric perchlorate.[6]

Most of the possible methyl-substituted ferroins have been prepared, and their oxidation-reduction potentials and optical properties reported.[7] Some of the dimethyl- and trimethylferroins are suitable for use in titrating ferrous ions with dichromate, notably 4,7-dimethylferroin, the ferrous complex of 4,7-dimethyl–1,10-phenanthroline, which has a standard potential of 0.92 volt in 0.5 M sulfuric acid.[8]

The standard potentials of the ferrous-phenanthroline indicators are affected by acid concentration, in spite of the fact that the equa-

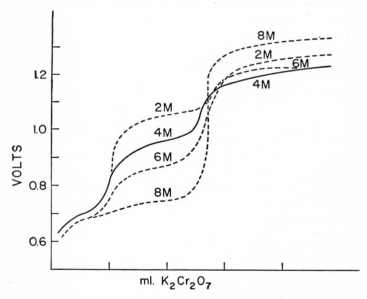

Fig. 17-2.   Titration of mixtures of ferrous sulfate and the sulfate of ferrous 5-methyl-1,10-phenanthroline, in sulfuric acid of the molarity shown, using $K_2Cr_2O_7$ as the oxidant.   (Smith and Richter, ref. 1).

[6] G. F. Smith and J. S. Fritz, *Anal. Chem.*, **20**, 874 (1948).

[7] W. W. Brandt and G. F. Smith, *Anal. Chem.*, **21**, 1313 (1949); G. F. Smith and W. W. Brandt, *Anal. Chem.*, **21**, 948 (1949).

[8] G. F. Smith, *Anal. Chem.*, **23**, 925 (1951).

tion for the oxidation-reduction process does not include hydrogen ions. The effect is most apparent at acid concentrations above 1–2 M; possible explanations were discussed above, p. 331. The ferrous-ferric potential, on the other hand, is independent of sulfuric acid concentration from 0.5 M to 4 M.[9] The effect, while not great, is sufficient to make it impossible to use methylferroin for titrating ferrous ions with dichromate in 2 M or 6 M sulfuric acid,[1,10] although the titration is satisfactory in 4 M acid (see Figure 2). Ferroin itself can be used for the iron—dichromate titration if the acidity is sufficient and *if the ferrous salt is added to the dichromate, but not vice versa*,[11] a fact which emphasizes the irreversible behavior of this reaction (see Chapter 12, page 217).

Table I gives the formal potentials of several phenanthroline indicators and of two related indicators derived from 2,2′-bipyridyl.

TABLE I

FORMAL POTENTIALS OF PHENANTHROLINE AND BIPYRIDYL INDICATORS

System	Formal potentials in H_2SO_4 of concentration:			
	0.5 M	1 M	4 M	8 M
Ferroin	1.06	1.06	0.96	.76
5-Methylferroin	. . .	1.02	0.93	0.70
4,7-Dimethylferroin	0.87	. . .	. . .	. . .
5,6-Dimethylferroin	0.97	0.97	. . .	. . .
3,5,7-Trimethylferroin	0.89	. . .	. . .	. . .
3,4,6,7-Tetramethylferroin	0.80	. . .	. . .	. . .
5-Nitroferroin	1.26	1.25	1.17	1.01
Ruthenium 1,10-phenanthroline	1.29	. . .	. . .	. . .
Chromium 1,10-phenanthroline*	. . .	0.77	. . .	. . .
Iron 2, 2′-bipyridyl	. . .	0.97	0.92	. . .
Ruthenium 2,2′-bipyridyl	1.25	. . .	1.16	0.98

* Of no use as an indicator as colors not intense.

Notes: 1. In every case the equilibrium is $M^{+++} + e \rightleftharpoons M^{++}$, and three organic molecules are coordinated around each metal ion. 2. Most of these data are from W. W. Brandt and G. F. Smith, *Anal. Chem.*, **23**, 925 (1951).

[9] G. F. Smith and C. A. Getz, *Ind. Eng. Chem.*, *Anal. Ed.*, **10**, 191 (1938).
[10] G. F. Smith and F. P. Richter, *Ind. Eng. Chem.*, *Anal. Ed.*, **16**, 580 (1944).
[11] E. Brennecke in W. Böttger (ed.), *Newer Methods of Volumetric Analysis*, New York, Van Nostrand, 1938.

The potential of the chromous-chromic-orthophenanthroline system is included to show the very great effect of the complexing agent on the stability of dipositive chromium, although the color change in this case is not enough to serve as an indicator.

Triphenylmethane indicators. A number of triphenylmethane dyes were investigated by Knop,[12] who wanted to find an indicator for titrating ferrocyanide with permanganate. Here the dark yellow or brownish color of the ferricyanide masks the natural purple color of the excess permanganate. He found twelve such dyestuffs which served satisfactorily, and measured the potential of their visible color change in 1 N sulfuric acid.[13] Table II lists four of these, with their colors in acid solution. These dyes are all acid-base indicators, and have different colors in neutral or alkaline solutions.

TABLE II

TRIPHENYLMETHANE INDICATORS

Indicator	Reduced color	Oxidized color	Potential of color change
Erioglaucin A (Alphazurine FG)	Yellow-green	Bluish-red	0.98 volt
Eriogreen B (Alkali Fast Green A)	Yellow	Orange	0.99 volt
Setoglaucin O.................	Yellow-green	Orange	0.99 volt
Xylene Cyanol FF.............	Yellow	Reddish-orange	0.98 volt

Notes: 1. Potentials and colors observed in 1 N H_2SO_4. 2. Potentials referred to standard hydrogen electrode.

The oxidized colors are all very intense, much more intense than the color of permanganate, and they permit ferrocyanide and ferrous ions to be titrated with great precision, even in very dilute solutions. The indicator end point coincides exactly with the potentiometric end point in titrating ferrous ions with permanganate or with ceric sulfate.[14] A drawback to these indicators, however, is the fact that the color change is not perfectly reversible. Back titration is not feasible, and since some destruction of the indicators takes place even before the end point in titrating with oxidizing agent is reached,

---

[12] J. Knop, *Z. anal. Chem.*, **77**, 111, 125 (1929).
[13] J. Knop, *Z. anal. Chem.*, **85**, 253, 401 (1929).
[14] N. H. Furman and J. H. Wallace, *J. Am. Chem. Soc.*, **52**, 2347 (1930).

the indicators should be added shortly before the end point for the best results.[11] The oxidized forms can be reduced, but the products do not have the same colors as the original indicators. The mechanism of the color change is unknown.

The formula of Erioglaucin A will serve to show the type of structure of these compounds:

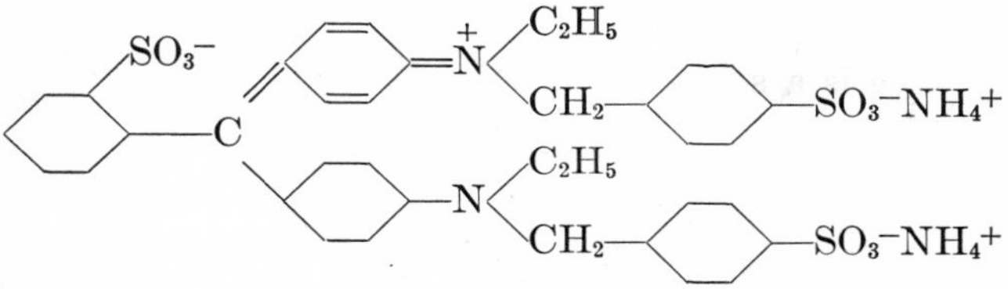

These indicators have largely been displaced by the more stable phenanthroline indicators. Ferrocyanide gives a satisfactorily sharp end point with ferroin indicator when titrated with ceric sulfate or potassium permanganate. However, xylene cyanol FF has recently been recommended as an indicator in titrating arsenite, ferrous ion, or ferrocyanide with ceric sulfate,[15] and it is of interest because it is commonly available in the laboratory. It is a constituent of "modified methyl orange," a popular acid-base indicator (see Chapter 14). The reduced color is yellow in 1 N H_2SO_4, yellowish-green in 0.5 N H_2SO4; the color change on oxidation is particularly sharp in 0.5 N acid, and it is satisfactorily reversible.

Diphenylamine and diphenylamine derivatives. Diphenylamine was first introduced as an indicator for dichromate titrations by Knop.[16] It is used as a 0.1–1.0% solution in concentrated sulfuric acid. It is oxidized in acid solution to diphenylbenzidine violet, a deep blue violet compound, colorless diphenylbenzidine being an intermediate:

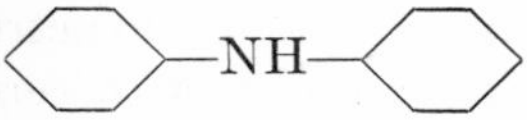

diphenylamine, colorless

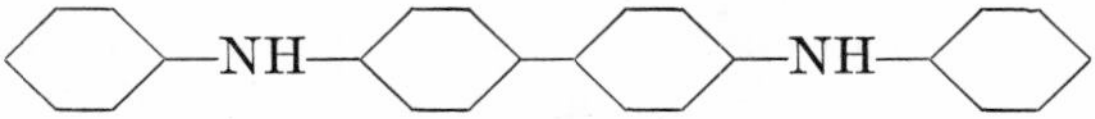

diphenylbenzidine, colorless

[15] H. M. Tomlinson, O. T. Aepli, and H. M. Ebert, *Anal. Chem.*, **23**, 286 (1951).
[16] J. Knop, *J. Am. Chem. Soc.*, **46**, 263 (1924).

diphenylbenzidine

diphenylbenzidine,
violet

This mechanism was demonstrated by Kolthoff and Sarver.[17] Their potentiometric titrations also showed that in the presence of iron a semiquinone, presumably

is formed from diphenylbenzidine by the loss of only one electron. (A semiquinone is a stabilized free radical; the right-hand nitrogen in this formula would have only seven valence electrons around it.) In the semiquinone stage the solution is a deep green, which is natural, for intense color is a characteristic property of free radicals.

The formal potential for the last oxidation stage is 0.76 volt in 1 N sulfuric acid, and it is practically independent of the acid concentration. This is rather too low for the titration of ferrous iron with dichromate, for the formal potential for $Fe^{+++} + e \rightarrow Fe^{++}$ in 1 M HCl or H_2SO_4 is 0.68 volt. By adding phosphoric acid, however, this can be lowered. In 1 M H_2SO_4 plus 0.5 M H_3PO_4 it is 0.61 volt, and the more phosphoric acid is added, the lower the potential becomes. In titrating ferrous iron with diphenylamine indicator, therefore, one always adds phosphoric acid or another complex former such as fluoride. The end point is then sharp, reversible, and precise, both with dichromate as oxidant and with ceric sulfate. It is not, however, accurate, for an appreciable amount of oxidant is used up by the indicator. Diphenylamine must be completely oxidized to diphenylbenzidine before any colored substance can be formed. Experimentally, Kolthoff [18] found that 0.21 ml. of 0.01 N $K_2Cr_2O_7$ was needed to react with 0.20 ml. of 0.17% (0.01 M) diphenylamine solution; in the average titration, the amount of diphenylamine taken is this or slightly more. The observed consumption agrees closely with the theoretical. Similar data for a range of concentrations and volumes are quoted by Kolthoff.

[17] I. M. Kolthoff and L. A. Sarver, *J. Am. Chem. Soc.*, **52**, 4179 (1930).
[18] I. M. Kolthoff and L. A. Sarver, *J. Am. Chem. Soc.*, **53**, 2906 (1931).

The indicator correction could be considerably reduced by using *diphenylbenzidine* as the indicator rather than diphenylamine. Its disadvantage is that it is extremely insoluble in water, much more so than diphenylamine. When added as an indicator solution, it immediately precipitates and reacts with excess oxidant extremely slowly. This does not happen when it is formed from diphenylamine, for then it is formed evenly throughout the solution and remains colloidal during the titration. Diphenylbenzidine, of course, has the same potential of color change as diphenylamine.[17]

Diphenylamine has the disadvantage that it is relatively insoluble in water and must be dissolved in concentrated sulfuric acid. Another drawback in steel analysis is that its blue oxidation product forms a very insoluble tungstate. In presence of tungstate a dark blue precipitate forms as soon as any oxidant is added, and stays there, making the indicator quite useless. Still another disadvantage is that mercuric salts slow down the reaction between the indicator and dichromate very considerably. Ferrous salts accelerate this reaction, but when ferrous and mercuric salts are present together, the accelerating effect of the former only partly offsets the inhibiting effect of the latter. It will be remembered that, in the Zimmerman-Reinhardt method for titrating iron, mercuric chloride is added to remove the excess of the stannous chloride used as reductant.

Diphenylamine sulfonic acid has none of these disadvantages. It is customarily used as an aqueous $0.1–1.0\%$ solution of its barium or sodium salt. Tungstate does not interfere with its action, nor does mercuric chloride. The color change is extremely sharp, more so even than with diphenylamine, from colorless through the green of the semiquinone to a deep reddish violet. The color change occurs at a potential of 0.83–0.84 volt in dilute sulfuric acid, the potential again being independent of acid concentration.[18]

Diphenylamine sulfonic acid reacts very rapidly with permanganate, vanadic acid, and ceric sulfate, but very slowly with dichromate. However, the reaction with dichromate is accelerated enormously by a trace of iron, and the indicator is very suitable for titrating ferrous iron with dichromate; in fact, it is the indicator usually chosen for this titration. Phosphoric acid is added, as with diphenylamine, but, in view of the higher oxidation-reduction potential of this indicator, no great error would be caused by omitting the phosphoric acid. The indicator correction is slightly larger than with diphenylamine.[18]

The diphenylamine indicators are only moderately stable to excess of strong oxidants; however, they can be used in back-titrating dichromate, and in the zinc-ferrocyanide titration (see Chapter 18, p. 364), diphenylbenzidine violet is not destroyed by the excess of ferricyanide which is present.

The chrysoidin indicators. These are azo dyes derived from chrysoidin. The one most studied is *p*-ethoxychrysoidin,

$$C_2H_5O-\langle\ \rangle-N{=}N-\langle\ \rangle-NH_2$$
(with NH₂ substituent shown on the ring)

This substance may be called an all-purpose indicator, for it is an acid-base indicator, an adsorption indicator (see Chapter 18, p. 359), and an oxidation-reduction indicator, besides being a reversible indicator for bromine titrations. The oxidation step is the addition of an oxygen atom to the acid, cationic form to give an azoxy compound:

$$H_2O + -N{=}N- \rightleftharpoons -N{=}N- + 2H^+ + 2e$$
$$\downarrow$$
$$O$$

azo, red   azoxy, pale yellow

The value of $E°$ for *p*-ethoxychrysoidin is about $+0.76$ volt, according to a brief statement by the discoverers of these indicators.[19] This is too low for the indicator to be used in titrating ferrous ion unless phosphoric acid is added, but the indicator is very satisfactory for titrating ferrocyanide with permanganate or ceric sulfate. Over thirty of these azo dyes have been prepared and tested as oxidation-reduction indicators,[20, 21] yet very little systematic study of them has been made. Different substituents will modify the oxidation-reduction potential in characteristic ways, and a considerable range of oxidation-reduction potentials should be available.

The behavior of chrysoidin indicators toward bromine is particularly interesting. When, for example, a warm solution of sodium arsenite, containing potassium bromide and made about 1 N in hydrochloric acid, is titrated with potassium bromate with *p*-ethoxychrysoidin added as indicator, the first color change observed is from

[19] E. Schulek and P. Rosza, *Z. anal. Chem.*, **115**, 185 (1939).
[20] E. Schulek and Z. Somogyi, *Z. anal. Chem.*, **128**, 398 (1948).
[21] I. M. Kolthoff, *Anal. Chem.*, **22**, 65 (1950).

an orange-red to a more intense, somewhat purplish red. This happens with a few drops of bromate and is due to an irreversible bromination of the chrysoidin:

orange-red

full red, with purplish tinge

At the titration end point, the color changes sharply to light lemon yellow, with formation of an azoxy compound. This change is to some extent reversible, for one may overtitrate a little with bromate, and then back-titrate with arsenite, whereupon the purple-red color returns, though less intense than it was originally. The end point may be passed and repassed several times in this way before all the indicator is destroyed. In the chrysoidin compounds, therefore, we have a group of indicators which changes color *reversibly* with bromine —in contrast to methyl red, for example, which is irreversibly bleached by a small excess of bromine. With methyl red as indicator in a bromate titration, there is always the possibility that the end point may come too soon, because of premature destruction of the indicator by local excesses of bromine; with p-ethoxychrysoidin this uncertainty is avoided. Caution, however, is necessary because the oxidation of brominated p-ethoxychrysoidin and the reduction of the corresponding azoxy compound are rather slow. One must approach the end point by adding bromate slowly, one drop every 2–3 seconds, and one must back-titrate with arsenite very slowly, waiting up to 10 seconds between drops.

Belcher[22] has compared three reversible indicators for bromate titrations in acid solutions: p-ethoxychrysoidin, α-naphthoflavone, and fuchsin. He considers α-naphthoflavone to be the best, and for titrating 8-hydroxyquinoline the only good indicator. Schulek,[23]

[22] R. Belcher, *Anal. Chim. Acta*, **3**, 578 (1949).
[23] E. Schulek, *Z. anal. Chem.*, **102**, 111 (1935); E. Schulek and P. Rosza, *Z. anal. Chem.*, **115**, 185 (1939).

in fact, mixed α-naphthoflavone with p-ethoxychrysoidin for bromate titrations. There is no doubt that much remains to be done to follow up Schulek's pioneer work before the potentialities of the chrysoidins as oxidation-reduction indicators are properly realized.

Indicators with low oxidation-reduction potentials. It is much easier to find organic oxidation-reduction indicators with low standard potentials than with high, because at lower potentials the molecules suffer less oxidative destruction. A great many dyestuffs are converted by strong reducing agents to colorless "leuco" compounds. Some of these are important in vat dyeing, for the leuco compounds are water-soluble where the colored, oxidized forms are not. *Indigo* is such a compound. *Indigo sulfonic acids* are water-soluble in their blue forms as well as in their reduced leuco forms, and they are useful as oxidation-reduction indicators, since the oxidation and reduction are easily reversible:

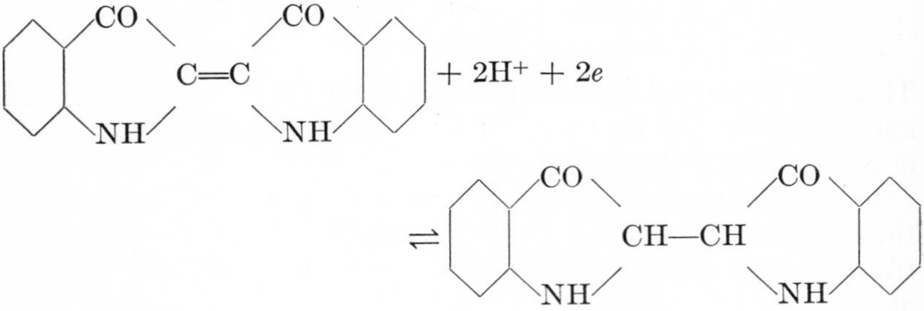

A similar example is *methylene blue:*

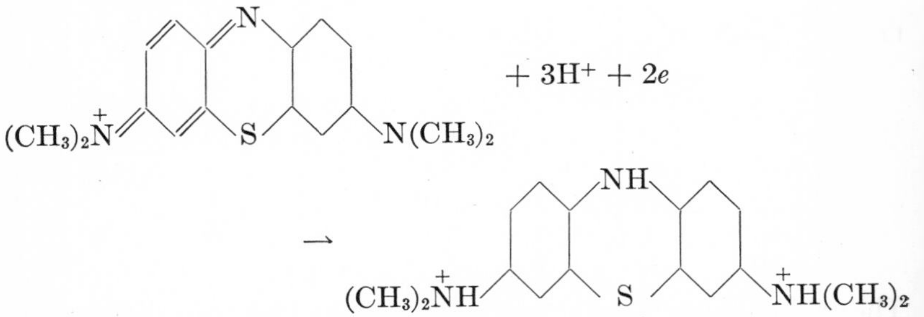

This equation represents the reaction at pH < 5; at pH > 5, the two protons of the cationic reduced form are lost, and the reaction should now be written:

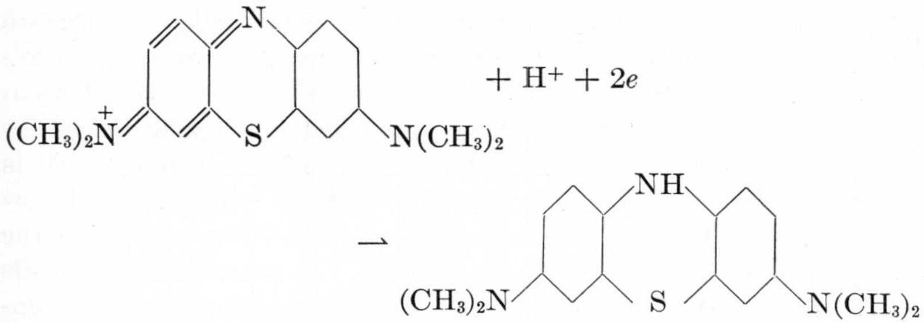

$$+ H^+ + 2e$$

$$\longrightarrow$$

At pH < 5, the oxidation-reduction potential of the methylene blue system at 25°C is expressed by an equation:

$$E = E° + \frac{0.059}{2} \log \frac{[\text{blue form}]}{[\text{leuco form}]} - \frac{0.059 \times 3}{2} \cdot \text{pH},$$

while at pH > 5,

$$E = (E°') + \frac{0.059}{2} \log \frac{[\text{blue form}]}{[\text{leuco form}]} - \frac{0.059}{2} \cdot \text{pH}.$$

There is, of course, an intermediate region where neither equation applies exactly (see Figure 1). Such behavior is typical of the effect of pH on oxidation-reduction indicators.

Indigo sulfonic acids and methylene blue are used as indicators in titanous chloride titrations. Another substance of interest in titrimetry, both as an indicator and as a titrant, is 2,6-dichlorophenol-indophenol:

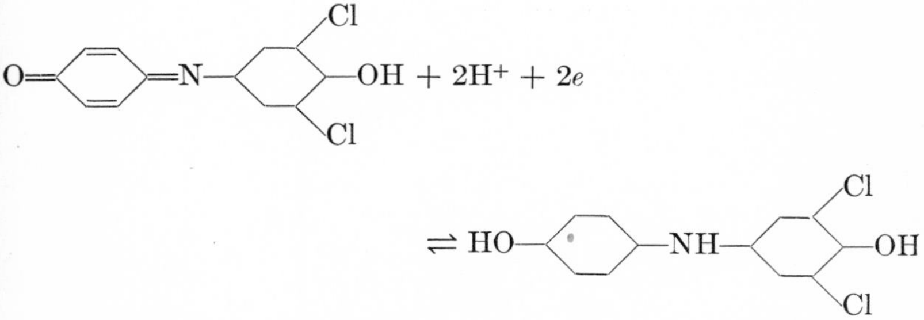

The oxidized form is used to titrate ascorbic acid, for which it is somewhat more specific than iodine (see Chapter 16).

The oxidation-reduction potentials of many classes of compounds, including indophenols, sulfonated indigos, oxazines, and thiazines, have been measured over a wide pH range by W. Mansfield Clark,[24] Michaelis,[25] and others.[26]   They were interested particularly in using these indicators to measure colorimetrically the oxidation-reduction potential of various solutions of biochemical interest, such as the potential of suspensions of enzymes and bacteria and even the protoplasm inside a living cell.   The principle is exactly the same as that of pH measurement by acid-base indicators.   In interpreting the results of optical measurements with oxidation-reduction indicators, one must take account, not only of the pH, but also of the ionic strength of the solution.   The effect of ionic strength is apt to be quite large because of the high charges of the colored ions (see Chapter 14).

Formal potentials of a few representative indicators of these classes are listed in Table III.   Many of these indicators may have applications in volumetric analysis which have not yet been exploited.

TABLE III

OXIDATION-REDUCTION INDICATORS FOR LOW POTENTIAL RANGE

Indicator	Formal potential at $[H^+] = 1$
m-Bromophenol indophenol	+0.248 volt
2,6-Dichlorophenol indophenol	+0.217 volt
2,6-Dichlorophenol indo-o-cresol	+0.181 volt
Methylene blue	+0.011 volt
Indigo tetrasulfonate	−0.046 volt
Indigo trisulfonate	−0.081 volt
Indigo disulfonate	−0.125 volt
Phenosaframine	−0.252 volt
Neutral red	−0.325 volt
Methyl viologen	−0.445 volt

Taken from S. Glasstone, *Textbook of Electrochemistry*, New York, Van Nostrand, 1942, p. 289.

[24] W. M. Clark, *U. S. Public Health Reports*, **38**, 443 (1923) and following years. For a summary, see I. M. Kolthoff and V. A. Stenger, *Volumetric Analysis*, New York, Interscience, 1948, Vol. I, Chap. 5.

[25] L. Michaelis, *Oxydations-Reductions Potentiale*, 2d ed., Berlin, Hirschwald, 1933.

[26] S. Glasstone, *Ann. Rep. on Progress Chem.*, **31**, 305 (1934).

PROBLEMS

1. A solution containing 1 gram of diphenylamine in 100 ml. concentrated sulfuric acid is used as an indicator in titrating ferrous iron with dichromate in presence of phosphoric acid. Assuming that the blue color appears exactly at the equivalence potential, what is the per cent error due to consumption of oxidant by the indicator if 0.5 ml. indicator is used with 100 ml. of 0.02 N Fe^{++}, and one-quarter of the indicator must be oxidized to the blue form for the color change at the end point to be apparent?

2. Calculate the potential of half change of indigo disulfonic acid in 1 M HCl from the data of Table III. Also calculate the potential at which the color change occurs, assuming that the change is seen when 90% of the blue compound has been reduced.

3. How would you expect the oxidation-reduction potential of chrysoidin indicators to change with pH? (As an acid-base indicator, p-ethoxychrysoidin changes color at pH 4.5.)

4. Discuss the uses of (a) starch, (b) iodine monochloride, as oxidation-reduction indicators.

18

Precipitation titrations

A REACTION WHICH YIELDS A PRECIPITATE can be made the basis for titration, provided that the reaction is fast and quantitative, and provided there is a way of telling when the equivalence point is reached. In practice these conditions seriously limit the number of precipitation reactions which can be used in volumetric analysis. Many precipitations are slow at low concentrations, for an orderly crystal lattice has to be built; hence, supersaturation is very common. This is not very important in gravimetric analysis, for one can always add an excess of reagent and digest for a time before filtering, but in volumetric analysis one cannot wait half an hour after adding each drop of reagent; the reaction must be rapid even when only a slight excess of reagent is present. In gravimetric analysis the solubility of the precipitate may be depressed, if necessary, by adding a large excess of the precipitant; in volumetric analysis the solubility product must be low enough so that precipitation is quantitative within experimental error when only a drop of excess reagent is added (unless electric conductivity is used to detect the end point: see Chapter 20). Side reactions must of course be absent. Coprecipitation, which causes errors in gravimetric analysis, will cause the same errors in volumetric work.

The greatest limitation on the number of precipitation reactions which may be used for titrations is, however, the choice of indicators which is available. We shall not consider conductometric and potentiometric methods here, but only those methods in which a visible change marks the end point. Since this is such an important restriction, it will be appropriate to classify precipitation titrations according to the means used to locate the end point.

Titration by turbidity; no indicator used. One of the earliest volumetric methods, and probably the most accurate of all, is the Gay-Lussac method for titrating silver. It is used today for the routine analysis of silver bullion in mints.[1] To the silver salt solution is added a standard solution of sodium chloride in slightly less than the equivalent amount, and the suspension is shaken until the silver chloride coagulates. The speed of coagulation is an indication of the nearness of the equivalence point, for the less the concentration of silver ions remaining, the smaller the positive charge on the particles of the precipitate. The precipitate is allowed to settle, then a small volume of diluted sodium chloride solution, one-tenth the concentration of the original standard, is added to the clear supernatant solution. Any silver ions remaining will give a cloudiness. If this is faint, its intensity is used as a measure of the silver remaining; if it is dense, the suspension is shaken again until coagulated, and the process repeated until a faint turbidity or none at all results. A precision of one part in two thousand is obtained in this way.

In this procedure somewhat more sodium chloride is added than is actually equivalent to the silver. At exact equivalence the silver and chloride ion concentrations in the solution are the same, and are equal to the square root of the solubility product of silver chloride; $[Ag^+] = [Cl^-] = \sqrt{1.6 \times 10^{-10}} = 1.25 \times 10^{-5}$ at 25°C. In 100 ml. of solution there remains 0.14 mg. of silver, equivalent to 0.125 ml. of 0.0100 M chloride. Most of this silver will precipitate, in accordance with the solubility product principle, when more chloride is added. Sodium chloride solution, added to a saturated solution of silver chloride, produces a slight but quite noticeable opalescence. In the researches of Richards and Wells[2] on the atomic weight of silver, even this small amount was significant, so they invented an instrument, the nephelometer, to measure the intensity of the opalescence and so determine the quantity of silver present in silver chloride solutions.

Aside from the Gay-Lussac method there are very few practical procedures in which the end point is located by the disappearance

[1] N. H. Furman (ed.), *Scott's Standard Methods of Chemical Analysis*, 5th ed., New York, Van Nostrand, 1939, Vol. I, p. 826.

[2] T. W. Richards and R. C. Wells, *J. Am. Chem. Soc.*, **27**, 484 (1905); R. C. Wells, *Am. Chem. J.*, **35**, 99 (1906); T. W. Richards, *Am. Chem. J.*, **35**, 510 (1906).

of turbidity. One such procedure is that of Krause[3] for titrating various metallic ions with a solution of diammonium phosphate, $(NH_4)_2HPO_4$. The metallic salt solution is brought to the appropriate pH, usually about 8, and phosphate is added until no fresh precipitate is seen to form in the supernatant liquid. The precipitates are crystalline, or become so after brief shaking, and settle quickly. Among the metals which can be titrated in this way are Zn, Mn, Co, Ca, Sr, Ba, Cd, and Pb, all of which form $MHPO_4$ or MNH_4PO_4, and Cr and Al, which give MPO_4. In certain cases the precipitate forms too slowly for direct titration, so a measured excess of phosphate is added and the excess back-titrated with standard zinc sulfate. Magnesium cannot be titrated in this way as its phosphate is too soluble.

This method is of limited value in titrating metals because it is unselective, but it may be useful for titrating phosphate. Coprecipitation may lead to significant errors.

Formation of a colored substance in the solution. The most familiar titration in which excess reagent produces a colored substance in the solution is the titration of a silver salt with thiocyanate using a ferric salt as indicator. During the titration, insoluble silver thiocyanate is formed. At the end point, the excess thiocyanate ions combine with ferric ions to form a deep blood-red colored complex:

$$Fe^{+++} + CNS^- \rightarrow FeCNS^{++}.$$

The amount of thiocyanate which will give a visible color is extremely small. Experimentally, if 2 ml. of saturated ferric ammonium alum are used as indicator in 100 ml. of solution, 10^{-6} mole of thiocyanate suffices to give a color. The end-point error is therefore negligibly small. One precaution only is necessary. Near the end point the precipitate and solution must be shaken violently between additions of thiocyanate, or the end point may come a little early. This is because silver ions are adsorbed on the precipitate at first and are desorbed only slowly.[4]

The Volhard Method. The chief practical application of the silver-thiocyanate titration is in the determination of chloride ions by the Volhard method. This method is popular because it permits chloride to be titrated in acid solution. Indeed, the solution *must* be

[3] H. Krause, *Z. anal. Chem.*, **126**, 404 (1944); **128**, 18, 99, 241 (1947).
[4] I. M. Kolthoff, *Z. anal. Chem.*, **56**, 568 (1917).

acid, or the ferric salt used as indicator will hydrolyze. A measured excess of silver nitrate is added to the chloride solution, followed by ferric alum indicator, and the uncombined silver ions are then back-titrated with standard thiocyanate to the appearance of a permanent brown-red color.

The Volhard method has a source of error which is potentially very serious. Silver thiocyanate is much less soluble than silver chloride; thiocyanate ions therefore can react with solid silver chloride:

$$AgCl + CNS^- \longrightarrow AgCNS + Cl^-.$$

If this happens, too much thiocyanate will be used in back-titrating, and the chloride content of the sample will appear to be lower than it really is. The error thus introduced may amount to 2% and more.[5] This error may be avoided by filtering off the silver chloride precipitate before back-titrating the excess silver, but this is a tedious process. Alternatively, a little nitrobenzene is added and shaken with the precipitate before back-titrating. The nitrobenzene adheres to the silver chloride curd and covers it, protecting it from reaction with the thiocyanate.[6] This is faster than filtering and gives very satisfactory results. However, the nitrobenzene merely slows down the reaction between silver chloride and excess thiocyanate; it does not prevent it altogether. A new way of eliminating this error has been proposed by Swift.[7] Before describing this, we shall evaluate the error theoretically from the equilibrium constants involved.

At 25°C, we have the following constants:

$$[Ag^+][Cl^-] = 1.6 \times 10^{-10}$$
$$[Ag^+][CNS^-] = 1.2 \times 10^{-12}$$
$$\frac{[Fe^{+++}][CNS^-]}{[FeCNS^{++}]} = 7.25 \times 10^{-3} \text{ (at ionic strength 0.5)}[8]$$

In the ordinary procedure 2 ml. of saturated ferric alum are added. If the volume at the end point is 100 ml., it is found experimentally

[5] M. A. Rosanoff and A. E. Hill, *J. Am. Chem. Soc.*, **29,** 269 (1907).

[6] J. R. Caldwell and H. V. Moyer, *Ind. Eng. Chem.*, *Anal. Ed.*, **7,** 38 (1935).

[7] E. H. Swift, G. M. Arcand, R. Lutwack, and D. J. Meier, *Anal. Chem.*, **22,** 306 (1950).

[8] H. S. Frank and R. L. Oswalt, *J. Am. Chem. Soc.*, **69,** 1321 (1947). The calculation of the Volhard titration error given by I. M. Kolthoff and V. A. Stenger in *Volumetric Analysis*, 2d ed. (New York, Interscience, 1947, Vol. II, p. 259), ignores this equilibrium, as do those in other texts written before 1947, but they lead to results of the same order of magnitude.

that 10^{-6} mole of thiocyanate must be added to give a color; that is,

total thiocyanate conc. $= [CNS^-] + [FeCNS^{++}]$

$$= 1.0 \times 10^{-5} \text{ mole per liter.}$$

The ferric iron concentration is about 0.015 mole per liter. From the instability constant of $FeCNS^{++}$ we now calculate that $[FeCNS^{++}]$ $= 6.9 \times 10^{-6}$ and $[CNS^-] = 3.1 \times 10^{-6}$. Now since chloride ions and thiocyanate ions are both in equilibrium with silver ions and their corresponding solid silver salts,

$$\frac{[Cl^-]}{[CNS^-]} = \frac{K_{sp} \text{ for AgCl}}{K_{sp} \text{ for AgCNS}} = \frac{1.6 \times 10^{-10}}{1.2 \times 10^{-12}} = 130,$$

and $[Cl^-] = 130 \times 3.1 \times 10^{-6} = 4.0 \times 10^{-4}.$

Therefore, $[Ag^+] = \dfrac{1.6 \times 10^{-10}}{4.0 \times 10^{-4}} = 4.0 \times 10^{-7}.$

Now if the silver nitrate added were exactly equivalent to the sum of the chloride and thiocyanate, which would be the case if there were no end point error, one could write

$$[Ag^+] = [Cl^-] + [CNS^-].$$

The amounts of these ions are equivalent in the solid, so they must be equivalent in the solution at the end of the titration too. Any discrepancy represents an error in the titration. From the figures quoted above,

$$[Ag^+] = 4.0 \times 10^{-7}.$$
$$[Cl^-] + [CNS^-] = 4.0 \times 10^{-4} + 3.1 \times 10^{-6} = 4.03 \times 10^{-4}.$$

The chloride and thiocyanate concentrations together exceed the silver ion concentration by *4.03 × 10⁻⁴ mole per liter*, or *0.0403 millimole in 100 ml*. If the sample contained 2.5 millimoles of chloride, the percentage error would be $4.03/2.5 = 1.6\%$, or about what Rosanoff and Hill found experimentally.

This error would be less if the free thiocyanate concentration at the end point were less. We can make this concentration less, and at the same time have enough of the red $FeCNS^{++}$ complex to be visible, by making the ferric ion concentration larger. Swift *et al.*[7] calculated that if the total ferric ion concentration at the end point is made 0.2 M, the end point error is reduced to 0.1%. They propose a procedure in which ferric nitrate and a small, measured amount of thiocyanate are added to the chloride solution at the start, together with an appropriate amount of nitric acid, and the solution is titrated with silver nitrate until the red color disappears. The mixture is shaken vigorously to ensure equilibrium. (In the author's laboratory this method has given excellent results in student hands.)

The Volhard method can, of course, be used for determining bromide and iodide. Here no precautions need be taken against reaction of thiocyanate with the precipitate, for silver bromide has about the same solubility product as silver thiocyanate, and silver iodide has a considerably smaller one.

Formation of a new, colored precipitate. The Mohr method of titrating halides with silver nitrate uses sodium chromate as the indicator. At the end point the excess of silver ions precipitates brick-red silver chromate, Ag_2CrO_4. The solution must be neutral or slightly alkaline. If it is too alkaline, silver hydroxide precipitates or coprecipitates, while if it is too acid (pH less than 5), the end point arrives late and is very indefinite, the red color appearing gradually. The reason is the lowering of the chromate concentration through the reaction

$$H^+ + CrO_4^= \rightarrow HCrO_4^-.$$

Under proper conditions, the Mohr method is accurate, convenient, and applicable to low chloride concentrations; 0.001 M chloride can be titrated with a precision of about 1%. To obtain the full accuracy of the method, a certain correction is necessary which will now be discussed.

The solubility product of silver chromate at 25°C is 1.1×10^{-12}. Ordinarily about 2 ml. of 5% potassium chromate are used as indicator in 100 ml. of solution; this gives $[CrO_4^=] = 5 \times 10^{-3}$ M, and in presence of solid silver chromate, $[Ag^+] = 1.5 \times 10^{-5}$. This is very close to the theoretical silver ion concentration at the equivalence point, which is $\sqrt{K_{sp}} = 1.25 \times 10^{-5}$. Silver chromate starts to precipitate so soon after the equivalence point that the end-point error would be negligible if the silver chromate could be seen as soon as it started to precipitate. However, about 0.5 milligram of silver chromate must be formed before the red color is visible, and 0.03 ml. of 0.1 M silver nitrate is consumed in producing this. This correction must be subtracted from the volume of silver nitrate used. The correction is best determined experimentally. It increases somewhat with the amount of silver chloride precipitated, as this hides the silver chromate, and more of the latter must be produced to give a visible color.

In titrations of this type, the colored indicating precipitate must be more soluble than the main precipitate formed during the titration, or it will come down before the equivalence point is reached; on the other hand, it must not be too soluble, or an appreciable excess of titrant will be needed to precipitate it, and the end-point error will again be large. It is seldom that an indicating precipitate can be found which has the right solubility and at the same time has a distinctive color. Perhaps with sufficient searching, organic reagents will be found which are suitable indicators for precipitation titrations, but the only organic precipitants now regularly used for this purpose are sodium rhodizonate and the sodium salt of tetrahydroxyquinone:

sodium
rhodizonate

sodium salt of
tetrahydroxyquinone

Both are used in titrating sulfate solutions with barium chloride, the end point being marked by the precipitation of red barium salts. Tetrahydroxyquinone is used in routine water analysis.[9] The solution is adjusted to pH 8 and an equal volume of isopropyl alcohol added. The temperature must be kept below 25°C, or the red barium salt is too soluble. A precision of 1–2% can be obtained by an experienced operator. Coprecipitation, of course, limits the accuracy of the method, just as it limits the accuracy of the gravimetric method for sulfate, and in addition the color change at the end point is not very sharp. It should be viewed in a good white or bluish-white light.

[9] W. C. Schroeder, *Ind. Eng. Chem., Anal. Ed.,* **5,** 403 (1933); R. T. Sheen and H. L. Kahler, *Ind. Eng. Chem., Anal. Ed.,* **8,** 127 (1936); **10,** 206 (1938).

Control of pH is necessary in this titration for the same reason as in the Mohr method, namely, to give a sufficient concentration of indicator anions without precipitating unwanted substances, in this case calcium or barium carbonate. An end point of sorts can be obtained at pH 4, and if phosphate is present this pH is used.

Lake-forming organic reagents are used as indicators in certain titrations, the most familiar being the titration of fluoride with thorium nitrate solution using sodium alizarin sulfonate as indicator.[10] Thorium fluoride, ThF_4, precipitates during the titration. At the end point a red lake appears which is formed by union of the alizarin sulfonate ions with colloidal thorium nitrate formed by hydrolysis of the excess thorium nitrate. The pH must be between 2.9 and 3.4; if it is too low, the precipitate is too soluble, while if it is too high, the indicator, which is yellow at pH 3.4, turns pink or red owing to the loss of a second proton, and then there is not enough contrast between the color of the dissolved indicator and that of the precipitated lake. Moreover, thorium hydroxide will form if the pH is too high. Where the amount of fluoride is relatively large, 20 to 50 mg. or more, the pH adjustment can be guided by the color of the indicator; the solution is brought just to the acid side of the change point. For small amounts of fluoride it is best to use a monochloracetic acid buffer to control the pH, and the earlier workers claimed that it was best to use aqueous alcohol as the solvent. From 0.1 to 1 mg. of fluoride can be titrated in this manner.

Willard and Horton[11] studied some sixty different indicators for this titration, and showed that the best indicators were purpurin sulfonate, sodium alizarin sulfonate, eriochromecyanin R, quercitin, and morin. The most precise results were obtained with quercitin, locating the end point, not by the change in color, but by the marked increase in fluorescence produced by excess thorium nitrate. (A simple technique for titrating with fluorescent indicators is described on page 273.)

Use of adsorption indicators. When silver nitrate is added to a neutral chloride solution containing a little fluorescein, the equivalence point in the titration is marked by a color change from light

[10] H. H. Willard and O. B. Winter, *Ind. Eng. Chem., Anal. Ed.*, **5,** 7 (1933); W. D. Armstrong, *Ind. Eng. Chem., Anal. Ed.*, **8,** 384 (1936); R. J. Rowley and H. V. Churchill, *Ind. Eng. Chem., Anal. Ed.*, **9,** 551 (1937).

[11] H. H. Willard and C. A. Horton, *Anal. Chem.*, **22,** 1190, 1194 (1950).

yellow to rose pink. As the mixture settles, it is seen that the precipitate is uniformly pink while the solution is colorless or nearly so. The fluorescein has been removed from the solution and adsorbed on the precipitate, with an accompanying change of color.

The silver salt of fluorescein is sparingly soluble, and it might be thought that fluorescein acts as an indicator in the same way as potassium chromate. That this is not so may be shown by adding silver nitrate to a solution containing no chloride, but a few milligrams of the sodium salt of fluorescein per liter. No precipitate appears, and no color change is seen, until 1 ml. or more of 0.1 M silver nitrate has been added, and when the precipitate does form, its color is not as intense as if silver chloride were present. Moreover, the color of a chloride precipitate formed in presence of fluorescein is uniform; there is no tendency towards segregation, as there would be if the color were due to a second solid phase.

It is well known that the color of a substance is greatly modified by adsorption on a surface, and usually it is intensified. The adsorption of basic dyestuffs on clays is a striking example, and so is the spreading of chlorophyll on water; even a unimolecular film of chlorophyll on water has a distinct green color, and the extinction coefficient of the chlorophyll in the film is about a million times that of chlorophyll in an alcoholic solution. It is no wonder, then, that fluorescein adsorbed on a silver halide has such an intense color.

This property of fluorescein and substituted fluoresceins was discovered by Fajans,[12,13] who showed that they were typical of a great many adsorption indicators which become adsorbed on a precipitate at the equivalence point and so can be used as indicators in precipitation titrations. Fajans explained the action of these indicators in the following way. They are all salts, fluorescein itself being a weak acid which in neutral solution gives an anion, $C_{20}H_{11}O_5^-$, or Fl^- for short. So long as chloride ions are in excess during the titration of chloride with silver nitrate, the silver chloride particles are charged negatively, because an ionic precipitate adsorbs its own lattice ions in preference to others, and Cl^- is the lattice ion which is in excess. At the equivalence point the precipitate is uncharged, while just

[12] K. Fajans and O. Hassel, *Z. Elektrochem.*, **29**, 495 (1923).

[13] K. Fajans, Chapter VII of W. Böttger (ed.), *Newer Methods of Volumetric Analysis*, New York, Van Nostrand, 1938.

beyond, it becomes charged positively due to adsorption of Ag^+. As soon as it is positively charged it attracts and adsorbs the fluorescein anion. The process can be represented as follows:

Excess Cl^-: $(AgCl)Cl^- + Fl^-$, no action.

Excess Ag^+: $(AgCl)Ag^+ + Fl^- \rightarrow (AgCl)AgFl$, adsorption.

After the dye has become adsorbed, it can be desorbed again by adding excess chloride, provided the precipitate has not coagulated in the meantime. The precipitate does coagulate rapidly, however, unless a protective colloid such as dextrin or gelatin is added, and fluorescein is not a suitable indicator for the reverse operation of titrating a silver salt with a chloride unless it is added just before the end point *and* a protective colloid is used. For titrating in this direction we may use methyl violet, however, which is the chloride of an organic base (see page 255). The cation of methyl violet is adsorbed by silver chloride when chloride ions are in excess, but not when silver ions are in excess:

Excess Cl^-: $(AgCl)Cl^- + (M.V.)^+ \rightarrow (AgCl)Cl^-(M.V.)^+$, adsorption.

Excess Ag^+: $(AgCl)Ag^+ + (M.V.)^+$, no action.

This kind of indicator is called a *cationic* indicator, in contrast to the *anionic* type of adsorption indicator exemplified by fluorescein.

Adsorption balance. Electric attraction between ions is not the only cause of adsorption. We know that activated carbon, for example, adsorbs organic molecules of all description without regard for their ionic charge. The larger and more polarizable they are, the more strongly they are adsorbed. So it is with the adsorption of these indicators. An indicator anion may be adsorbed on a completely neutral precipitate, and it may even be adsorbed on a precipitate which is negatively charged, displacing some of the negative ions which were adsorbed originally. Thus the anion of eosin (tetrabromofluorescein) displaces adsorbed chloride ions from a silver chloride precipitate. We have the possibility of different adsorption isotherms, as shown in Figure 1.

Ideally, the graph of per cent adsorption against excess reagent should look like curve 1. Adsorption should start just before the equivalence point is reached, so as to be apparent to the eye at the equivalence point itself, the adsorption increasing fastest at the equivalence point. If adsorption does not start until an excess of silver ions has been added (curve 2) the end point will arrive late, and if it starts while there is still a substantial excess of halide ions, as in curve 3, the end point arrives early and is indistinct.

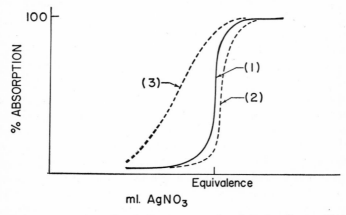

Fig. 18-1. Adsorption indicators, good and bad. Curve (1) is that for an ideal indicator; in (2), the end point comes too late, and in (3), too soon.

We can modify the adsorbability of fluorescein anions by substitution. Introduction of halogen atoms makes them more polarizable and therefore more strongly adsorbed, as the following examples show:

fluorescein
(I)

dichlorofluorescein
(II)

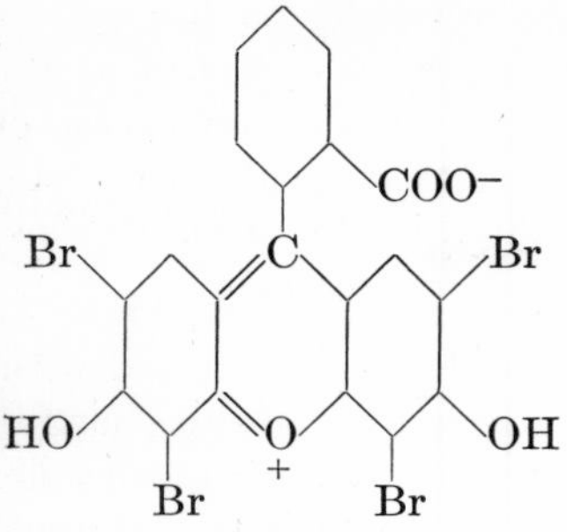

eosin
(III)

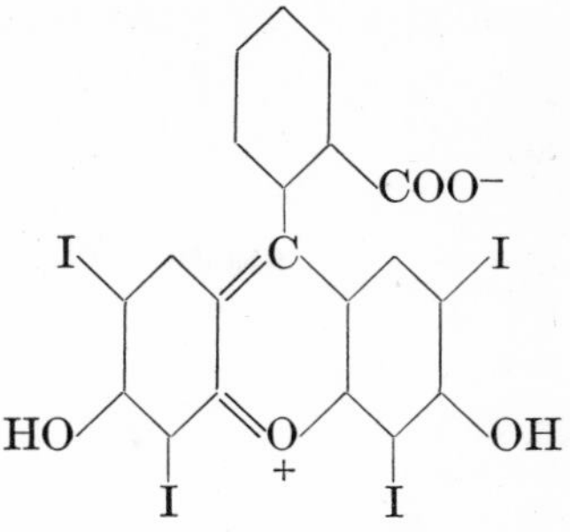

erythrosin
(IV)

A range of adsorptive powers is needed in titrating the different halide ions with silver nitrate. The adsorbability of the halide ions themselves increases in the order $Cl^- < Br^- < I^-$, that is, the order of the lyotropic series; CNS^- falls between Br^- and I^-. In titrating chloride with silver nitrate, I and II give adsorption curves of type 1, while III and IV, which are more strongly adsorbed, give curves of type 3 and are unsuitable as indicators. In titrating bromide and iodide, however, III gives a type 1 curve; Br^- and I^- are sufficiently strongly adsorbed to prevent the eosin anion from being adsorbed prematurely. Erythrosin, however, is even more strongly adsorbed on silver iodide than the iodide ion. It gives a type 3 curve and is useless as an indicator.

The strength of adsorption of the fluoresceins is greater, the less the solubility of their silver salts, and Fajans stresses this factor, rather than the polarizabilities, in explaining the different strengths of adsorption.

Because of the differences in adsorption between indicators, it has been proposed to titrate a mixture of iodide and chloride ions by using selective adsorption indicators. One portion of the mixture is titrated with silver nitrate using fluorescein or dichlorofluorescein; this gives the sum of iodide and chloride. Another portion is then titrated with eosin as indicator; this gives the iodide alone. Actually, eosin will not displace chloride ions from silver chloride unless the concentration of chloride ions is low, so the eosin end point arrives late and is indistinct. Under favorable circumstances the error in titrating iodide in presence of chloride may be only 1%,[12] and even better accuracy is possible if Rose Bengal (dichlorotetraiodofluorescein, with the chlorine atoms substituted in the phthalic acid ring) is used as the indicator.[14]

Certain adsorption indicators work even though they remain adsorbed during the whole course of the titration; the adsorbed dye shows a color change at the equivalence point. Phenosafranine is such an indicator. This is blue with excess silver ions and red with excess halide. Nitrate ions seem to be necessary for the change, whose mechanism is still somewhat obscure.[13,14] Another example is p-ethoxychrysoidin; the mode of action here is somewhat different from that of the indicators we have been discussing, and it will be described below.

Acid Strength of Fluorescein Derivatives. All adsorption indicators are ionic or are capable of ionizing. Anionic indicators are the anions of weak acids, cationic indicators the cations of weak bases. Acid-base equilibria, therefore, must always be considered along with adsorption equilibria. The pH must be such that the appropriate *ion* is present, not the neutral molecule. Fluorescein has an ionization constant of about 10^{-7}; below pH 7, therefore, the undissociated acid predominates and the substance is of little or no use as an indicator. In any case the undissociated acid of fluorescein is insoluble in water. Dichlorofluorescein (II above) is a stronger acid, of dissociation constant about 10^{-4}; moreover, its anion is more strongly adsorbed than that of fluorescein, which makes it applicable in lower concentrations. Eosin (III) is a stronger acid still. The limits of usefulness of these indicators are summarized in Table I. The upper pH limit of 10 is set by the precipitation of silver hydroxide.

TABLE I

FLUORESCEIN DERIVATIVES AS ADSORPTION INDICATORS

Indicator	Ions titrated	pH range	Lowest titratable halide concentration
Fluorescein..................	Cl^- (Br^-, I^-)	7–10	0.005 N
Dichlorofluorescein............	Cl^- (Br^-, I^-)	4–10	0.0005 N
Eosin (Tetrabromofluorescein)..	Br^-, I^-, CNS^-	2–10	0.0005 N

[14] A. J. Berry, *Analyst*, **61**, 315 (1936).

If halides must be titrated in strongly acid solution and an adsorption indicator is desired, one may add excess silver nitrate and back-titrate with standard chloride solution, using a cationic indicator such as methyl violet or Rhodamine 6G.[15]

Acid-base indicators as adsorption indicators. All acid-base indicators exist as positive or negative ions in at least one of their forms, and are therefore potential adsorption indicators. Whether they are serviceable or not depends on the strength of adsorption and the intensity of the accompanying color change. Several of the sulfonephthalein indicators have been used for this purpose, including bromphenol blue, bromthymol blue, bromcresol green, bromcresol purple and chlorphenol red; of these the best seems to be bromphenol blue. It is used in the yellow range (pH less than 4), in which the molecule has a net charge of -1 (see Chapter 14); the color change on adsorption is from yellow to a green or lilac color. It has been used in titrating chloride, bromide, iodide, and thiocyanate ions against silver,[16,17] mercurous,[18] and thallous ions.[19] An advantage of this indicator is that it can be used in acid solutions.

Acid-base indicators which show fluorescence in one of their forms can of course be used as adsorption indicators; adsorption is accompanied by a loss of fluorescence.[20]

Chrysoidin derivatives: a new type of indicator. The azo dyes derived from chrysoidin are indicators of a special class, and are the only really new indicators to have been developed in the last twenty years. Not only are they acid-base indicators and adsorption indicators, but at the same time they are oxidation-reduction indicators and the only indicators to give a reversible color change with bromine. The properties of 30 substituted chrysoidins have been studied by Schulek and collaborators[21] and reviewed by Kolthoff.[22] The one which has been the most studied is *p*-ethoxychrysoidin

[15] K. Fajans and H. Wolff, *Z. anorg. Chem.*, **137**, 221 (1924).

[16] R. C. Mehrotra, *Anal. Chim. Acta*, **4**, 38 (1950).

[17] K. Sisido and H. Yagi, *Anal. Chem.*, **20**, 677 (1948).

[18] I. M. Kolthoff and W. D. Larson, *J. Am. Chem. Soc.*, **56**, 1881 (1934).

[19] R. C. Mehrotra, *Anal. Chim. Acta*, **3**, 69, 73, 78 (1948).

[20] E. A. Koesis, J. F. Kallos, G. Zador, and L. Molnar, *Z. anal. Chem.*, **126**, 452 (1944).

[21] E. Schulek and P. Rosza, *Z. anal. Chem.*, **115**, 185 (1939); E. Schulek and Z. Somogyi, *Z. anal. Chem.*, **128**, 398 (1948).

[22] I. M. Kolthoff, *Anal. Chem.*, **22**, 65 (1950).

$$\text{C}_2\text{H}_5\text{O}-\left\langle\bigcirc\right\rangle-\text{N}=\text{N}-\left\langle\bigcirc\right\rangle-\text{NH}_2.$$
$$\overset{\text{H}_2\text{N}}{\diagdown}$$

This compound is red in acid solutions and yellow in alkali. In the acid form it is a cation, in the base form a neutral molecule:

$$\text{MH}^+ + \text{H}_2\text{O} \rightleftharpoons \text{H}_3\text{O}^+ + \text{M};$$

pK for the acid MH^+ is 4.5.

As an adsorption indicator, this compound is used in titrating iodide ions against silver ions. The titration may be made in either direction, for the dye is adsorbed on the precipitate throughout. A typical procedure is the following:[23] To a 0.001 N silver salt solution a few drops of 0.5% indicator are added, then acid or base until the indicator is orange-red (pH 4 to 5). Then 0.01 N potassium iodide is added. As silver iodide precipitates it adsorbs the dye, the color becoming intense yellow. At equivalence the yellow changes sharply to raspberry red.

The color changes are accompanied by slight changes in the pH of the solution, which are consistent with the following mechanism.[23] In presence of excess silver, the precipitate is positively charged and adsorbs preferentially the neutral form of the indicator:

$$(\text{AgI})\text{Ag}^+ + \text{MH}^+ \rightharpoonup (\text{AgI})\text{Ag}^+ \cdot \text{M} + \text{H}^+.$$
$$\text{yellow}$$

At equivalence, iodide ions become adsorbed, and with them the cationic form of the indicator:

$$(\text{AgI})\text{M} + \text{I}^- + \text{H}^+ \rightharpoonup (\text{AgI})\text{I}^- \cdot \text{MH}^+.$$
$$\text{red}$$

Adsorption changes the ionization constant of the indicator, so that MH^+ ionizes more on the positively charged precipitate, and less on the negatively charged precipitate, than in water. The shift in ionization constant from excess Ag^+ to excess I^- is a factor of about 10^4. It is important to note that the adsorption of positive MH^+ on the positively charged precipitate is not prevented entirely, nor is that of neutral M on the negatively charged precipitate; hence, to

[23] E. Schulek and E. Pungor, *Anal. Chim. Acta,* **4,** 213 (1950).

prevent the concentration of either of these in solution from predominating unduly, the pH must be held between 4 and 7.

Though I^- is the only anion which is sufficiently strongly adsorbed to affect the ionization of the indicator significantly, other anions, such as Cl^-, Br^-, and CNS^-, can be titrated by adding excess silver nitrate, coagulating the precipitate with ammonium nitrate (this is very important), then back-titrating slowly with dilute potassium iodide.[24]

Congo red is another acid-base indicator which can be used as an adsorption indicator, and it seems to act in a similar way to the chrysoidins.[25]

Adsorption indicators: summary. The chief advantage of adsorption indicators, if they are properly chosen, is their very small or imperceptible end-point error. This advantage is specially significant in the silver-iodide titration, for iodide ions are adsorbed very strongly by silver iodide, and unless an adsorption indicator is present to displace them, the end point will appear while there is still a deficiency of silver. Thus the Mohr method is not suited to the titration of iodide, quite apart from the fact that if the pH were too low, iodide would be oxidized by the chromate indicator. Furthermore, color changes with adsorption indicators are usually very sharp.

Adsorption being a surface effect, these indicators are best suited to precipitates having a large surface area, such as the curdy precipitates of silver halides and the silky precipitates of certain mercurous salts. Adsorption indicators lose their effectiveness if these precipitates are coagulated, hence it is difficult or impossible to use adsorption indicators if highly charged ions, such as Al or citrate, are present, and back titrations are difficult since at equivalence the precipitates coagulate very easily. Coagulation may be hindered by adding a protective colloid, such as dextrin, and this is often done as a matter of routine to sharpen the color change.

We have seen that many adsorption indicators have limitations of pH or of concentration of precipitant which are necessary to give that balance between adsorption and desorption upon which the action of these indicators depends.

Table II lists the chief adsorption indicators and their applications.

[24] E. Schulek and E. Pungor, *Anal. Chim. Acta*, **4**, 109 (1950).
[25] R. C. Mehrotra, *Anal. Chim. Acta*, **2**, 36 (1948).

TABLE II

ADSORPTION INDICATORS AND THEIR APPLICATIONS

Indicator	Titrant	Ion titrated	pH	Color change
Anionic type:				
Fluorescein........	Ag^+	Cl^-, $(Br^-$, $CNS^-)$ $Fe(CN)_6^{----}$	7–8	Yellow to red
Dichlorofluorescein	Ag^+ Pb^{++}	$Fe(CN)_6^{----}$ $C_2O_4^=$	5–8	Yellow to red
Eosin.............	Ag^+ $SO_4^=$	Br^-, I^-, CNS^- Pb^{++}	3–8	Pink to deep red
Rose bengale......	Ag^+	I^- (in pres. Cl^-)	Neutral	Carmine to blue-red
Tartrazine.........	Ag^+ Cl^-, Br^-	I^-, CNS^- Ag^+	Acid Acid	Yellow to green
Tetrahydroxy-anthraquinone...	Ag^+	Cl^-	Acid	Orange to red
Sodium alizarin sulfonate........	Pb^{++} $Fe(CN)_6^{\equiv}$	$Fe(CN)_6^{\equiv}$ Pb^{++}	4.5 4.5	Yellow to red
Bromphenol blue...	Ag^+ Tl^+ Cl^-, Br^-	Cl^-, CNS^- I^- Hg_2^{++}	2–3 4–8 Acid	Yellow to blue Yellow to green Lilac to yellow
Bromcresol green...	Ag^+	CNS^-	4–5	Yellow to blue
Amphiprotic type:				
Congo red.........	Ag^+ Br^-	Cl^-, Br^-, I^- Ag^+	3–5 3–5	Blue to pink Pink to green
Cationic type:				
Diphenylamine blue	Cl^-	Ag^+	Acid	Violet to green
Methyl violet, crystal violet....	Cl^-, I^-	Ag^+	Acid	Red to violet
Rhodamine 6G....	Br^-	Ag^+	Acid	Orange to violet
Phenosafranine....	Br^- Ag^+	Ag^+ Cl^-, Br^-, I^-, CNS^-	Acid Acid	Blue to red
p-Ethoxychrysoidin	Ag^+ I^-	I^-, CNS^- Ag^+	5	Red to orange

Hydrolytic titrations. Hydrolytic titrations are those in which the end point is marked by hydrolysis of the excess reagent, which in turn causes a color change in an acid-base indicator. This can happen if the reagent is the salt of a weak acid or a weak base, and such reagents are common. Thus barium ions could be titrated with sodium carbonate. As long as barium carbonate is precipitating, the addition of sodium carbonate will not raise the pH significantly, but as soon as excess carbonate is present it hydrolyzes and raises the pH sharply. Phenolphthalein could be used as the indicator in such a titration. In the same way barium and other metallic ions could be titrated with trisodium phosphate.[26] These titrations do not give good results, either because the rise in pH at the end point is not sharp enough, or because the precipitate is impure or of indefinite composition.

The hydrolytic titration which has had the widest use is the Blacher method for measuring the total hardness of water, that is, the equivalent concentration of those cations which will precipitate soap.[27] The reagent is a solution of pure potassium palmitate in 50% n-propanol, and it precipitates the very insoluble palmitates of calcium and magnesium. Before titration the water is freed from carbonate and bicarbonate by acidifying and boiling, then adjusted to pH 8.0 after adding phenolphthalein. The end point is marked by the development of a full red color. It arrives 0.1 to 0.2 ml. too late, so an end-point correction must be made (see p. 177). Good precision is possible, but experience is necessary as the indicator turns slightly pink before equivalence is reached, owing to the slight but appreciable solubility of the precipitated palmitate. This effect is more marked with magnesium than with calcium. Other divalent metals can be titrated in the same way. It is evident that buffering substances must be absent; thus bicarbonate ions must be removed, and the method is useless if phosphate ions are present. In this respect the Schwarzenbach titration is superior (p. 377).

Another valuable hydrolytic titration is that of aluminum with sodium hydroxide in the presence of excess chloride. Free hydrochloric acid is first neutralized by adding base to the bromphenol

[26] K. Jellinek and J. Czerwinski, *Z. anorg. Chem.*, **130**, 253 (1923); K. Jellinek and P. Krebs, *Z. anorg. Chem.*, **130**, 263 (1923).

[27] C. Blacher, P. Grünberg, and M. Kissa, *Chem.-Z.*, **37**, 56 (1913); M. Suter, *J. Am. Water Works Assoc.*, **29**, 1001 (1937).

blue end point; the solution is then heated to 80°C and the titration continued. Colloidal $Al_2(OH)_5Cl$ is formed, and a sharp rise in pH occurs when 5 moles of base have been added to 2 moles of aluminum. This rise, like that corresponding to the neutralization of free hydrochloric acid, can be detected by an indicator, but it is better to do the whole titration potentiometrically using an antimony electrode.[28]

Use of an oxidation-reduction indicator. Just as the excess of reagent can change the pH, so, if the reagent happens to be an oxidizing or reducing agent, the excess can change the oxidation-reduction potential of the solution. In such cases an oxidation-reduction indicator can be used to mark the end point of a precipitation titration. The only familiar example is the titration of zinc with potassium ferrocyanide.[29] The reaction is:

$$2Fe(CN)_6^{\equiv} + 3Zn^{++} + 2K^+ \rightharpoonup K_2Zn_3[Fe(CN)_6]_2$$

The indicator is diphenylamine used in conjunction with a little potassium ferricyanide. The ferricyanide does not enter the precipitate, but exchanges electrons with the ferrocyanide ions:

$$Fe(CN)_6^{\equiv} + e \rightleftharpoons Fe(CN)_6^{\overline{\equiv}}.$$

The standard potential for this reaction is 0.36 volt; that for the reduction of diphenylamine blue is 0.76 volt. If the ferrocyanide and ferricyanide concentrations are about equal, the indicator is colorless, but if ferricyanide is present in great excess the indicator is oxidized to the blue form. This is the case before equivalence is reached in titrating zinc with ferrocyanide, for the ferrocyanide ion concentration is extremely low, and the oxidation-reduction potential correspondingly high. At equivalence there is a sudden drop in potential as ferrocyanide ions accumulate, and the indicator changes from blue to colorless.

The titration is best done at 60°C. It is not easy, and it is empirical. A small end-point correction must be added, and this depends on concentration, temperature, salt content, and other factors; however, reproducible results can be obtained with a little practice. If the zinc concentration is below 0.01 M it is best to add excess ferrocyanide, then add the indicator and back-titrate with standard zinc solution.

[28] *Magnesium Laboratory Methods*, Midland, Dow Chemical Co.
[29] I. M. Kolthoff and E. A. Pearson, *Ind. Eng. Chem., Anal. Ed.*, 4, 147 (1932).

Cadmium, calcium, and indium can be titrated with ferrocyanide in a manner similar to the titration of zinc. It is claimed that in these titrations, as well as the titration of zinc, 3,3'-dimethylnaphthidine is a better indicator than diphenylamine.[30]

Other examples of precipitation titrations in which the end point is marked by a shift in oxidation-reduction potential are known. In a recent procedure, fluoride is titrated with lead nitrate in a solution containing ferrous and ferric chlorides and saturated with sodium chloride. Lead chlorofluoride, PbClF, is precipitated. As long as fluoride ions are in excess, the small amount of ferric ions present is complexed, and the oxidation-reduction potential is low, but when the fluoride is all precipitated the potential rises sharply. An indicator could obviously be used to detect this change. The method is satisfactory for 40 to 120 mg. of fluoride.[31]

PROBLEMS

1. Recommend a volumetric method for determining chloride in each of the following materials, explaining in each case the principle of the method and giving reasons for your choice:

(a) A natural water containing some 25 ppm of Cl^-.

(b) A solution of $AlCl_3$, acidified with HCl.

(c) A solution of a long-chain quaternary ammonium chloride, such as $C_{12}H_{25}NH_3Cl$.

(d) A solid mixture of AgCl, AgBr, and AgI.

(e) A red-colored solution, such as one of the cobalt complexes, which is also acidic.

(f) Aqua regia.

(g) A mixture containing NaCl and NaI.

(*Note:* Do not restrict yourself necessarily to the methods discussed in this chapter.)

2. A solution contains Cl^- and Br^-. By the Volhard titration, 100 ml. of solution is equivalent to 28.14 ml. of 0.1226 N silver nitrate. Another 100 ml. of solution, treated with excess silver nitrate, gave 0.5482 gram of silver halide precipitate. Calculate the molar concentrations of Cl^- and Br^-, and also the error that would be caused in the chloride determination by an error of 0.4 milligram in the weight of silver halide.

[30] R. Belcher, A. J. Nutten, and W. I. Stephen, paper presented at the XIIth International Congress of Pure and Applied Chemistry, New York, September 9, 1951.

[31] F. R. Cropper, *Analyst*, **76**, 370 (1951).

3. Under what circumstances would phenosafranin and p-ethoxychrysoidin be preferable to the fluorescein derivatives for titrating halides?

4. How would you titrate the iodide in a solid mixture containing sodium iodide and sodium chromate?

5. How would you determine the bromide content of sea water?

6. Sulfate interferes in titrating fluoride with thorium nitrate, making the fluoride content appear too large. Why? What other substances might interfere in this titration?

7. An accurate method for determining fluoride is based on the precipitation of the salt PbClF, followed by titration of the chloride in the precipitate. Suggest a procedure, and note any possible complications which might affect the result.

8. What divalent ions form sparingly soluble double-ammonium phosphates of definite composition near pH 7, and are hence suitable for titration by the Krause method? Calcium does *not* give accurate results with this method. What calcium compounds can be precipitated from phosphate solutions?

19

Complex-forming titrations

THE REACTIONS in this class of titrations are those which yield complex ions or undissociated neutral molecules in solution. Reactions of this kind are extremely common, yet few of them can be used for titrations. Most complexes are too unstable to permit a titration, and most complex-forming reactions yield more than one product. The ions Fe^{+++} and F^-, for example, form not only the saturated complex ion $FeF_6^{\equiv}$, but lower complexes such as $FeF_5^=$ and even FeF^+ (see Chapter 7). Such reactions are not clear-cut, and would not yield a sharp end point except under carefully controlled conditions. Furthermore, indicators for complex-forming reactions are hard to find.

The reactions to be discussed in this chapter are all stoichiometric, or nearly so, under the conditions used. They are: reactions of mercuric ions with chloride, bromide, iodide, and thiocyanate; reaction of silver ions with cyanide; reaction of aluminum ions with fluoride; and the reactions of the organic chelating agents called complexones with metal ions in general.

Titrations with Mercuric Nitrate

Mercury is unique among the metals of the periodic table for the number of covalent compounds which it forms. It is said that more organometallic compounds of mercury are known than of all the other metals combined. Among the inorganic compounds of mercury, compounds such as the chloride, which one would expect to be highly ionized in aqueous solution, are hardly ionized at all. The

only simple salts which are ionized to any considerable extent are
the perchlorate, nitrate, and fluoride. The sulfate is less strongly
ionized. We are speaking here of dipositive mercury; the mercurous
salts, derived from Hg_2^{++}, are more highly ionized, as one would
expect from the covalency rules.

Titration of chloride. Mercuric chloride, $HgCl_2$, is less than
1% ionized in 0.1 N solution. One may titrate chloride ions
with mercuric nitrate provided an indicator is available which will
show a visible reaction with small (but not too small) concentrations of mercuric ions. Such an indicator is sodium nitroprusside,
$Na_2[Fe(CN)_5NO]$. One milliliter of a 10% solution of this salt is
added per 100 ml. of solution at the end point. Excess of mercuric
nitrate produces a white turbidity due to precipitated mercuric
nitroprusside, whose solubility product is about 2×10^{-9}.[1] The turbidity is faint, but increases on standing, so the titration should
be made slowly near the end point. The end point is perfectly
sharp and definite (unless, of course, the original solution was turbid,
in which case this indicator cannot be used).

The titration may be done in presence of quite high nitric acid
concentrations (1 N and more) and is applicable to very low chloride
concentrations (0.0005 N and less). It is a useful alternative to the
Volhard method and deserves to be more popular than it is. For
the best results, however, certain corrections have to be applied.
There are two sources of error inherent in the method. First, the
ionization of $HgCl_2$ tends to make the end point early, and second, the
association $HgCl_2 + Hg^{++} \rightleftharpoons 2HgCl^+$ tends to make it arrive too
late. The former predominates in dilute, the latter in concentrated
solution. Because the concentration of Hg^{++} needed to give a precipitate with nitroprusside is relatively large, the amount of mercuric
nitrate is always slightly in excess of the stoichiometric amount.
With 100 ml. of solution and 0.1 gram of sodium nitroprusside, the
excess ranges from 0.08 ml. of 0.1 N $Hg(NO_3)_2$ when no chloride is
present to 0.20 ml. with 2.5 milliequivalents of chloride.[2] The correction depends on temperature and acidity, and for accurate work
it should be determined experimentally.

[1] O. Tomicek and O. Procke, *Collection Czechoslov. Chem. Commun.*, **3,** 116
(1931).
[2] I. M. Kolthoff and V. A. Stenger, *Volumetric Analysis*, 2d ed., New York,
Interscience, 1947, Vol. II, p. 333.

Instead of sodium nitroprusside, diphenylcarbazide and diphenyl-carbazone can be used as indicators. These form intense violet-colored complexes with mercuric ions, and give a striking and spectacular end point. The complexes are decomposed by acid, of course, since the reagents are weak bases, and this is an advantage; the association of the complex must be properly controlled, and this may be done by controlling the pH. If the complex is too stable, it will form before all the chloride ion has been titrated, whereas if it is too unstable, an appreciable excess of mercuric nitrate will be needed to produce it. With diphenylcarbazide, the optimum pH, which gives optimum stability of the complex, is 1.5 to 2.0;[3] with diphenyl-carbazone, it is 3.2 to 3.3.[4] In the method of Clarke, bromophenol blue is used as indicator for the pH adjustment; the greenish-yellow color of bromophenol blue at pH 3.3 is complementary to the violet of the mercuric diphenylcarbazone complex, and masks the slight color which otherwise would appear in advance of the end point. About 1 mg. of diphenylcarbazone and 0.1 mg. of bromophenol blue are used per 100 ml., but these amounts are not critical. A feature of the method is the very wide range of chloride concentrations to which it is applicable—10^{-4} N to 0.05 N.

Certain sources of interference in mercurimetric titrations will be evident. Any metal which precipitates nitroprusside (e.g., Cu, Ni) or forms a complex with diphenylcarbazone will interfere. So will any anion which forms a complex with the mercuric ion, and in practice this may be an important limitation. Few data are available, but Clarke[4] reported that nitrate, sulfate, and phosphate in concentrations of 1000 ppm were without effect on the chloride titration, and the author, in unpublished work, found that the solution could be 0.1 M in fluoride without interference. Chromate and ferric ions must be absent.[4]

Bromide and thiocyanate. These ions may be titrated in exactly the same way as chloride, though the end-point corrections will be different. Mercuric thiocyanate is somewhat sparingly soluble, so that one cannot use nitroprusside indicator unless the concentration is low. Instead, one uses ferric sulfate or nitrate. The reverse titration, of mercuric nitrate with standard thiocyanate, is used to

[3] I. Roberts, *Ind. Eng. Chem., Anal. Ed.,* **8,** 365 (1936).
[4] F. E. Clarke, *Anal. Chem.,* **22,** 553 (1950); J. V. Dubsky and J. Trtilek, *Mikrochemie,* **12,** 315 (1933); **15,** 302 (1934).

determine mercury. Corrections are necessary, and these must be determined empirically; since several complex ions—$Hg(CNS)^+$, $Hg(CNS)_3^-$, and $Hg(CNS)_4^=$—may be present at the end point in significant amounts.[5] In dilute solutions below 18°C, however, these corrections are very small.

Cyanide. Mercuric cyanide, $Hg(CN)_2$, is so slightly dissociated that it gives practically none of the reactions of mercuric ions. Cyanide can, therefore, be determined by adding a measured excess of mercuric nitrate and back-titrating with thiocyanate.

Iodide. In accordance with the covalency rules, the Hg—I bond is even less ionic than the bond Hg—Cl. Not only this, but HgI_2 combines with two iodide ions to form a complex, $HgI_4^=$. Further, HgI_2 is insoluble in water and is bright red. Hence, when mercuric nitrate solution is added to a solution of an iodide, the first reaction is:

$$Hg^{++} + 4I^- \rightarrow HgI_4^=.$$

This is followed by

$$Hg^{++} + HgI_4^= \rightarrow 2HgI_2 \text{ (red ppt.)}.$$

The red precipitate should appear when one mole of mercuric nitrate has been added for every four moles of iodide. Actually it appears earlier, when less mercuric nitrate has been added, because of the dissociation of the $HgI_4^=$ complex. If mercuric chloride is substituted for mercuric nitrate, the mercuric ion concentration is less, and the end-point error is also less, but the volume of mercuric solution is still too small. The error is of the order of 1 ml. 0.05 M $HgCl_2$, and therefore the method cannot be recommended except in special applications where conditions can be carefully standardized.[6]

The Silver-Cyanide Titration

Silver forms only one complex cyanide ion, $Ag(CN)_2^-$, and this is extremely stable. Conditions are therefore favorable for titrating cyanide ions with silver ions. Originally this titration was done by observing the precipitation of silver cyanide at the end point:

[5] L. M. Kolthoff and V. A. Stenger, *Volumetric Analysis*, 2d ed., New York, Interscience, 1947, Vol. II, p. 337.

[6] A. C. Titus and J. S. Olsen, *Ind. Eng. Chem., Anal. Ed.*, **12**, 133 (1940).

$$Ag^+ + Ag(CN)_2^- \rightarrow 2AgCN \text{ (or } Ag[Ag(CN)_2]),$$

but this was unsatisfactory as traces of silver cyanide precipitate are not easily seen. The original method of Liebig was modified by Deniges, who introduced potassium iodide as indicator, together with ammonia. Silver iodide is bulky, opaque, and easily seen. Its solubility product is less than that of silver cyanide, so it precipitates in place of silver cyanide at the end point. Because of its low solubility product, however, it tends to precipitate before the equivalence point is reached. Ammonia is added to counteract this tendency by forming the complex ion $Ag(NH_3)_2^+$, and so reducing the activity of free silver ions.

The end-point error in this titration is small, and can be calculated as follows. The necessary constants are:

$$[Ag^+][I^-] = 1.5 \times 10^{-16} \qquad \frac{[Ag^+][CN^-]^2}{[Ag(CN)_2^-]} = 10^{-21}$$

$$\frac{[Ag^+][NH_3]^2}{[Ag(NH_3)_2^+]} = 1.0 \times 10^{-7} \qquad [Ag^+][Ag(CN)_2^-] = 2.2 \times 10^{-12}.$$

Suppose that we are titrating $0.1 \ M$ cyanide with $0.05 \ M$ silver nitrate, and that in accordance with usual practice[7] we have added enough ammonia and potassium iodide so that at the end point, $[NH_3] = 0.5$ and $[I^-] = 0.02$. When silver iodide starts to precipitate,

$$[Ag^+] = \frac{1.5 \times 10^{-16}}{[I^-]} = 7.5 \times 10^{-15};$$

$$[Ag(NH_3)_2^+] = \frac{7.5 \times 10^{-15} \times 0.5^2}{1.0 \times 10^{-7}} = 1.9 \times 10^{-8}.$$

Since $[Ag^+]$ and $[Ag(NH_3)_2^+]$ are both extremely small, we can write, to a very close approximation,

$$[Ag(CN)_2^-] = \text{total Ag conc.} = 0.025.$$

$$[CN^-]^2 = \frac{0.025 \times 10^{-21}}{7.5 \times 10^{-15}} = 3.33 \times 10^{-9},$$

and $$[CN^-] = 5.8 \times 10^{-5}.$$

At exact equivalence, the total number of moles of silver per liter is half the total number of moles of cyanide per liter. The end-point

[7] E. H. Swift, *A System of Chemical Analysis*, New York, Prentice-Hall, 1939, p. 229.

error is the excess of silver, in addition to this amount, which is needed to reach the end point. If we stop the titration at the instant the first trace of AgI forms, end-point error = (total Ag) − $\frac{1}{2}$(total CN)

$$= [Ag^+] + [Ag(NH_3)_2{}^+] + [Ag(CN)_2{}^-] - \tfrac{1}{2}[CN^-] - [Ag(CN)_2{}^-]$$

$$= 7.5 \times 10^{-15} + 1.9 \times 10^{-8} - 2.9 \times 10^{-5}$$

$$= -2.9 \times 10^{-5} = -0.12\% \text{ of the amount at equivalence.}$$

That is, the end point arrives somewhat too soon.

In reality, however, we must form a certain amount of solid AgI before we can see it. This takes enough silver nitrate to cancel out this calculated error, so that the end point and equivalence point in this titration virtually coincide.

Parenthetically, we note that the solubility product of Ag[Ag(CN)₂] is not exceeded at the end point.

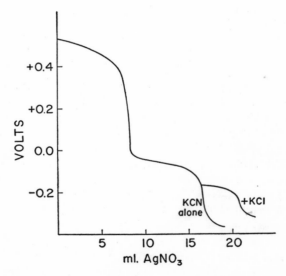

Fig. 19-1. Potentiometric titration of cyanide-chloride mixtures with AgNO₃.

The potentiometric titration of cyanide with silver nitrate is discussed in Chapter 12. Figure 4, Chapter 12 shows the form of the electromotive force-titration curve. Cyanide and chloride can be titrated successively with silver nitrate by potentiometric means, which is useful in the analysis of silver plating solutions.[8]   A typical curve is shown in Figure 1.

The titration of cyanide with silver nitrate can be used to determine the silver in a silver halide precipitate.   The precipitate is dissolved in an excess of standard potassium or sodium cyanide solution, and the unreacted excess of CN^- is back-titrated with silver nitrate.   If the unknown contained silver iodide, it may be unnecessary to add any iodide as indicator in the Deniges method, but if the amount of iodide present is large, one must compensate by adding more ammonia than usual.

Titration of Fluoride

Fluoride being the complex-former which it is, attempts have been made to titrate it by a complex-forming reaction.   The best for this purpose is

$$Al^{+++} + 6F^- \rightarrow AlF_6^{\equiv},$$

aluminum chloride being used as titrant.   The end point can be detected in various ways, such as the formation of a red lake by a dye, Eriochromecyanine R, with excess of aluminum at pH 8, the titration being done at 90°C in a solution saturated with sodium chloride,[9] or by the hydrolysis of the excess aluminum ions with accompanying color change of an acid-base indicator.   Geyer,[10] in a comprehensive comparison of methods for determining fluoride, considers this the best of the volumetric methods.   He neutralizes the boiling solution to phenolphthalein, saturates with sodium chloride, adds methyl red, and titrates with aluminum chloride until the indicator changes from yellow to orange-red.   It is also possible to locate the end point conductometrically[11] (see Chapter 20).   In all these methods fluosilicate reacts in the same way as fluoride.

A potentiometric titration of fluoride with ferric chloride has been

[8] J. N. Gregory and R. R. Hughan, *Ind. Eng. Chem., Anal. Ed.*, **17**, 109 (1945).
[9] J. H. Saylor and M. E. Larkin, *Anal. Chem.*, **20**, 194 (1948).
[10] R. Geyer, *Z. anorg. Chem.*, **252**, 42 (1943).
[11] J. Harms and G. Jander, *Z. Elektrochem.*, **42**, 315 (1936).

described;[12] this titration can also be performed with thiocyanate indicator. Aluminum has been titrated amperometrically with sodium fluoride, using a small amount of ferric salt as indicator. So long as the ferric ion remains uncomplexed, it can be reduced at the dropping mercury cathode, and a current passes through the cell; excess fluoride complexes the ferric ion and stops the current.[13]

Titrations with Chelating Agents

Reference was made in Chapter 7 to the power of certain tertiary amino acids, called the complexones or Versenes, to form soluble chelated complexes with many metal ions. Chelation makes these complexes very stable, and furthermore the complex is formed in a single reaction step and not in several consecutive stages. Titration of metal ions with complexones therefore gives sharp, useful end points. The chief use of these compounds in analytical chemistry is the titration of calcium and magnesium ions, where the procedures are so simple and accurate that they will probably replace the Blacher palmitate titration and other older methods for determining the hardness of water. Methods for other metallic cations have also been developed.

The two complexones which have been used in volumetric analysis are nitrilotriacetic acid (H_3X) and ethylene diamine tetraacetic acid (H_4Y):

$$
\begin{array}{cc}
\begin{array}{l}
\diagup CH_2COOH \\
N{-}CH_2COOH \\
\diagdown CH_2COOH
\end{array}
&
\begin{array}{l}
HOOC \cdot CH_2 \diagdown \qquad\qquad \diagup CH_2 \cdot COOH \\
\qquad\qquad N{-}CH_2{-}CH_2{-}N \\
HOOC \cdot CH_2 \diagup \qquad\qquad \diagdown CH_2 \cdot COOH
\end{array}
\end{array}
$$

nitrilotriacetic acid, H_3X ethylene diamine tetraacetic acid, H_4Y

Of these the second is the more important. They form weak complexes with univalent ions, such as $LiY^=$, and much more stable complexes with divalent ions, such as CaX^- and $CaY^=$. Ions of the type of $CaHY^-$ also exist, but are relatively unstable; $CaHY^-$ is a

[12] S. T. Talipov and J. L. Teodorovich, *Zavodskaya Lab.*, **15**, 529 (1949); *Chem. Abstracts*, **43**, 6942 (1949).

[13] A. Ringbom and B. Wilkman, *Acta Chem. Scand.*, **3**, 22 (1949).

stronger acid than $H_2Y^=$, as will be seen from the titration curves in Figure 2, and it is entirely dissociated above pH 7.

From Figure 2 it will be evident that a solution of $Y^{\equiv}$ or $HY^=$ is much more alkaline, due to hydrolysis, than a solution of $CaY^=$. Therefore one may titrate a calcium salt solution with a solution Na_4Y or Na_3HY, and use the sudden rise in pH to detect the equivalence point in the reaction. This is one way of finding the equiva-

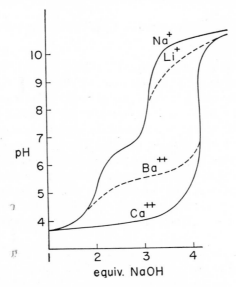

Fig. 19-2. Titration of ethylene diamine tetraacetic acid in presence of excess of different metallic cations. (Acc. Schwarzenbach).

lence point in these titrations. Another way is to use as an indicator a colored complex between a metal and another substance, choosing this complex so that it breaks down at the equivalence point by the formation of a stronger complex between the metal and the excess of titrating agent. Both methods are used, and we shall discuss them in turn.

End point by hydrolysis. In their last stage of ionization, the complexones are very weak acids. Their ionization constant exponents in 0.1 N KCl at 20°C are:[14,15]

[14] H. Ackermann and G. Schwarzenbach, *Helv. Chim. Acta*, **32**, 1543 (1949).
[15] G. Schwarzenbach and H. Ackermann, *Helv. Chim. Acta*, **30**, 1798 (1947).

H_3X: $pK_1 = 3.03$, $pK_2 = 3.07$, $pK_3 = 10.70$

H_4Y: $pK_1 = 1.99$, $pK_2 = 2.67$, $pK_3 = 6.16$, $pK_4 = 10.26$.

A 0.01 M solution of K_3X or K_4Y has, therefore, a pH of more than 11. When a neutral or weakly acid solution of a metal salt is titrated with K_3X, the pH rises sharply at the end point, the sharpness of the rise depending on the stability of the metal complex. Figure 3 shows pH titration curves for metal salts with K_3X, calculated by Schwarzenbach for different values of $\dfrac{[Me^{++}]\,[X^=]}{[MeX^-]}$, the dissociation constant of the metal complex.[16] In practice, different pH ranges were found for the "jump" at the end point with different metals, as follows:

Ca, pH 8.5 − 9.6

Pb, pH 5.0 − 8.0

Cd, pH 5.0 − 7.0

Co, pH 6.0 − 8.7

La, pH 8.5 − 10.1

Phenolphthalein would thus be a suitable indicator for titrating calcium, bromthymol blue for lead, and so on. The K_3X solution must be free from carbonate, and so must the solution being titrated, for carbonate would buffer the solution in these pH ranges and so obscure the end points. Another point to note is that K_3X is somewhat preferable to Na_3X as a titrant, because the hydrolysis of Na_3X is checked quite appreciably

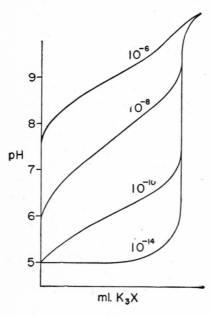

Fig. 19-3. Titration of metal salts with the potassium salt of nitrilotriacetic acid. The figures give the dissociation constant of the MeX complex. The initial pH is taken as 5 in each case. (Curves calculated by Schwarzenbach and Biedermann.)

[16] G. Schwarzenbach and W. Biedermann, *Helv. Chim. Acta*, **31**, 331 (1948).

by the formation of the complex ion $NaX^=$. The complex $KX^=$ is considerably less stable (which accords with the covalency rules). Schwarzenbach prepared carbonate-free potassium hydroxide from silver oxide and potassium chloride; an easier way would be the ion exchange method of Davies (see Chapter 8).

The titration of metal salts with Na_4Y or K_4Y was worked out independently by Hahn[17] and Schwarzenbach.[15,18] Hahn used a reagent consisting of one part of Na_3HY to ten parts of Na_4Y, since it is difficult and tedious to neutralize H_4Y with exactly four equivalents of base. The calcium solution is freed from carbonate and adjusted to pH 7.5–8.5; on adding the reagent, the pH first drops on account of the reaction

$$HY^= + Ca^{++} \rightarrow CaY^= + H^+,$$

then rises sharply from 7 to 8 at the end point. Phenol red and bromthymol blue are suitable indicators. Schwarzenbach obtained similar curves, and showed that the sharpest end point is obtained if a reagent of the exact composition K_4Y is used.

An alternative procedure is to use a reagent K_2HX, K_2H_2Y, or K_3HY, and titrate the liberated acid with standard base.[16,18,19]

End point by colored metal complex indicator. The procedures which use pH changes to mark the end point have the practical drawback that the solutions must be carbonate-free. Furthermore, solutions of K_3X and K_4Y are highly alkaline and soon lose their strength if kept in glass bottles. A simpler procedure for routine analysis is that which uses as the indicator the magnesium complex of a hydroxylated azo dye, Eriochrome Black T. This is made by coupling nitro-1-amino-2-naphthol-4-sulfonic acid with α-naphthol. It is a tribasic acid, which we shall represent as H_3Z; it has different colors in different stages of ionization:

$$H_2Z^- \quad \rightleftharpoons \quad HZ^= \quad \rightleftharpoons \quad Z^{\equiv}$$

	pH		pH	
purple-red	6.3	blue	11.5	orange

With magnesium ions it forms a complex, MgZ^-, which is a purple-red or plum color, very like that of H_2Z. This complex is less stable

[17] F. L. Hahn, *Anal. Chim. Acta*, **4**, 583 (1950).
[18] G. Schwarzenbach and W. Biedermann, *Helv. Chim. Acta*, **31**, 459 (1948).
[19] G. Schwarzenbach, W. Biedermann, and F. Bangerter, *Helv. Chim. Acta*, **29**, 811 (1946).

than the magnesium complex of ethylene diamine tetraacetic acid, $MgY^=$, so an excess of $H_2Y^=$ breaks down the purple MgZ^-, leaving sky-blue $HZ^=$.

For the routine determination of total hardness (Ca^{++} plus Mg^{++}) in water[20,21] one uses as the reagent a solution of NaH_2Y to which one-third of an equivalent of magnesium chloride has been added. This is to take care of the eventuality that the solution titrated contains little or no magnesium; in such a case, calcium ions from the solution will react with $MgY^=$, which is a less stable complex than $CaY^=$, and furnish enough magnesium ions to give the purple indicator complex. If $MgY^=$ is not added to the reagent, it must be added to the buffer. The indicator solution is 0.5% Eriochrome Black T plus 4.5% hydroxylammonium chloride in methanol, the hydroxylamine being added to protect the azo dye from oxidation. The water to be titrated is buffered to pH 10 with an ammonia-ammonium chloride solution, indicator is added (4 drops to 50 ml. water), and the solution titrated until the last reddish tinge disappears, leaving a pure blue color.

The color change is very sharp and the method is applicable down to a combined Ca^{++} and Mg^{++} content of 0.2 milliequivalent per liter (10 ppm hardness, as $CaCO_3$). In this case a 100 ml. sample is taken. The reagent is usually 0.02 N, and is standardized against a known calcium chloride solution. Lower concentrations may be determined if a measured volume of standard calcium chloride is added before titration.

There is one important complication. Certain heavy metal ions form more stable complexes with the indicator than they do with the complexone reagent. If these are present in the water being analyzed, they will tie up the indicator so that it does not change color at the end point. The chief offender is copper. Even the traces of copper—0.3 ppm or less—which may be picked up from copper piping, or added to a reservoir to control algae, are sufficient to destroy the end point altogether. If this condition is recognized, the cure is simple; a few drops of sodium sulfide or diethyldithiocarbamate solution, added after the buffer and before the indicator, will eliminate the interference. Cobalt and nickel give the same interference, and

[20] W. Biedermann and G. Schwarzenbach, *Chimia*, **2,** 56 (1948).
[21] H. Diehl, C. A. Goetz, and C. C. Hach, *J. Am. Water Works Assoc.*, **42,** 40 (1950).

must be complexed by potassium cyanide. Up to 15 ppm of iron and 2 ppm of manganese can be present if sulfide is added.

To determine magnesium or calcium separately, one either precipitates the calcium as oxalate and filters it out before titrating the magnesium, or precipitates magnesium hydroxide by buffering to pH 12 and titrates the calcium without filtering.[19] In this case a different indicator is used, such as ammonium purpureate, which forms a red-violet complex with calcium. This color turns to blue, tinged with violet, at the end point.

In addition to calcium and magnesium, the following metal ions can be titrated with "complexones": Li^+, Sr^{++}, Ba^{++}, Zn^{++}, Cd^{++}, Hg^{++}, Cu^{++}, Fe^{++}, Co^{++}, Ni^{++}, Mn^{++}, Ce^{+++}, La^{+++}, Al^{+++}, Cr^{+++}.

PROBLEMS

1. What titration procedure would you use to determine (a) calcium, (b) magnesium, in solutions containing phosphate, and why?

2. In one of Schwarzenbach's experiments an unbuffered, dilute solution of calcium chloride was brought to pH 5.0 by adding hydrochloric acid, and then titrated with a relatively concentrated solution of K_3X (the potassium salt of nitrilotriacetic acid). Halfway to the equivalence point, when 0.5 mole of K_3X had been added per mole of Ca^{++}, the pH was 7.0, and the total calcium concentration 0.001 mole per liter. Using the ionization constants for H_3X given on page 376, calculate the complexity constant,

$$\frac{[Ca^{++}][X^{\equiv}]}{[CaX^-]}$$

How sharp will the end point be in such a titration?

3. How might a potassium cyanide solution be used to titrate zinc or cadmium?

4. (a) Ten milliliters of 0.100 M $AgNO_3$ are added to 10.00 ml. of 0.200 M KCN plus 90 ml. water. Calculate $[CN^-]$ and $[Ag^+]$, assuming no precipitate to be formed. Is this assumption correct?

(b) If this solution also contains NH_3 in 0.1 M concentration, what are $[Ag^+]$ and $[Ag(NH_3)_2]^+$? What volume of 0.1 M $AgNO_3$ must be added, in addition to the 10.00 ml. added already, before a precipitate appears? (*Note:* here, $[Ag(CN)_2^-] \gg [Ag(NH_3)_2^+] \gg [Ag^+]$.)

Dissociation constants:

$$Ag(CN)_2^-, \quad 1 \times 10^{-21}; \qquad Ag(NH_3)_2^+, \quad 7 \times 10^{-8}.$$

Solubility product:

$$Ag[Ag(CN)_2], \quad 2 \times 10^{-12}.$$

5. Given the equilibrium constant

$$\frac{[HgI_2][I^-]^2}{[HgI_4^-]} = 10^{-7},$$

calculate the percentage error in titrating 0.2 M iodide with 0.2 M mercuric nitrate, the end point being that at which a precipitate of HgI_2 appears.   In what circumstances would this method of titrating iodide be useful?

20

Conductometric titrations

CONDUCTOMETRIC TITRATIONS are those in which the end point is located by changes in the electric conductivity of the solution. Since all ionic solutions conduct, titrations of every kind can be done conductometrically provided ionic substances are involved. Whether the end point so obtained will be good or bad depends on the contrast between the conductivity of the reagent and the conductivity of the products of the titration.

The conductometric method is very versatile, and can be applied in many cases where indicators are not available and potentiometric methods are inapplicable. Its very versatility, however, is a limitation, for conductivity is not a selective property. All the ions which are present in a solution contribute to its conductivity, and the changes occurring in the titration may be quite minor in comparison with the conductivity which is due to nonreacting species. Another limitation is that the equipment and technique are fairly cumbersome. Conductometric titrations are not nearly as common or important as potentiometric titrations, but they are useful nevertheless.

Laws of electric conductivity of solutions. The conductivity of a highly ionized salt AB is due to its ions A^+ and B^-. The more concentrated the solution, the more ions are present in a unit volume, and the better the solution conducts. *Specific conductance* is defined as the current flowing across a centimeter cube of the solution, between parallel electrodes one square centimeter in area, when a potential difference of one volt is applied. Specific conductance is greater, the greater the concentration. To express the ability of individual ions to conduct, a function is needed which takes account of the number of ions present or, still better, of the number of ionic *charges* present; for, other things being equal, a doubly charged ion should conduct electricity twice as well as a singly charged ion. This function is the *equivalent conductance*, defined as

$$\Lambda = \frac{\text{conductance in ohm}^{-1}\,\text{cm}^{-1}}{\text{concentration in gram-equivalents} \cdot \text{cm}^{-3}}.$$

The equivalent conductance falls with rising concentration. This is caused by the electrostatic attraction of unlike charge. In an electric field, the positive and negative ions move in opposite directions, and by their mutual attraction, exert a drag on one another. This drag is greater, the closer the ions are together. Conversely, as the electrolyte is diluted, the ions move farther and farther apart, their interactions become less and less, until in the limit of infinite dilution the interionic attraction is zero and the equivalent conductance reaches a maximum. This maximum value is easily found by extrapolating the equivalent conductance against the square root of the concentration, and is called Λ_0, the equivalent conductance at infinite dilution.

The equivalent conductance of a binary electrolyte AB is the sum of the contributions of A^+ and B^-, and at infinite dilution, these con-

TABLE I

EQUIVALENT IONIC CONDUCTANCES AT INFINITE DILUTION (25°C)

Cation		Anion	
H^+	349.8	OH^-	198.0
Li^+	38.7	Cl^-	76.3
Na^+	50.1	Br^-	78.4
K^+	73.5	I^-	76.8
NH_4^+	73.4	NO_3^-	71.4
Ag^+	61.9	CH_3COO^-	40.9
Mg^{++}	53.1	ClO_4^-	68.0
Ca^{++}	59.5	$SO_4^=$	79.8
Sr^{++}	59.5	$Fe(CN)_6^{\equiv}$	111.0
Ba^{++}	63.6	$C_2O_4^=$	24.0
Cu^{++}	53.8		
Zn^{++}	53.0		
La^{+++}	69.6		

Note: Data taken from H. S. Harned and B. B. Owen, *The Physical Chemistry of Electrolytic Solutions*, New York, Reinhold, 1943.

tributions are characteristic of the individual ions and have definite values for a definite solvent and temperature. Algebraically,

$$\Lambda_{AB} = \lambda_{A^+} + \lambda_{B^-}$$

where λ_{A^+} and λ_{B^-} are the "equivalent ionic conductances" of the ions A^+ and B^-. This relation is known as Kohlrausch's law of independent mobilities. The equivalent ionic conductances of some common ions are shown in Table I. From these values, the equivalent conductance of different salts at infinite dilution can be found; for example, sodium bromide has $\Lambda_0 = 51 + 78 = 129$.

The conductivity of solutions increases rapidly with rising temperature for two main reasons. First, the viscosity of the solution falls with rising temperature, so that ions can move faster; second, those ions which are hydrated (or solvated) become less so as the temperature rises, which means that their effective radius diminishes. A secondary effect of temperature is that the dielectric constant of liquids falls with rising temperature, causing increased interionic attraction.

The conductivity also depends upon the solvents, because of the effects of solvation and viscosity. Large anions and cations are not solvated, so that, for a salt whose ions are large, Walden's rule applies:

$$\Lambda_0 \eta_0 = \text{constant}$$

where η_0 is the viscosity of the solvent. This holds good for changes of solvent and of temperature. At finite concentrations, of course, interionic attraction disturbs this simple relation.

Experimental measurement of conductivity. The conductivity of an electrolytic solution is measured by putting the solution between platinum plate electrodes in a cell of suitable design and measuring the resistance of this cell. An alternating current must be used, or the products of electrolysis would accumulate at the anode and cathode of the cell and set up an electromotive force opposing the flow of the current. In other words, a direct current would have to do work to bring about chemical decomposition as well as to overcome the resistance of the solution. A symmetrical alternating current is used, therefore, and to assist the recombination of anodic and cathodic decomposition products, the electrode surfaces are made absorptive and catalytic by coating them with platinum black.

The dimensions of the cell, in particular the area of the electrodes and their distances apart, depend on the order of magnitude of the specific conductances to be measured. A typical cell for conductometric titrations is shown in Figure 2; the electrodes are about 1 sq. cm. in area (one side) and 3 to 5 cm. apart. Such a cell filled with 0.1 N KCl would have a resistance of about 400 ohms. To obtain reproducible results, the electrodes must be well covered with solution. Where titrations are concerned, it is not necessary to know the dimensions of the cell or even the actual value of the resistance, so long as the relative *changes* in resistance are followed;

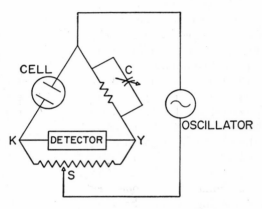

Fig. 20-1. Wheatstone bridge circuit for measuring conductance of electrolytes.

but to measure specific conductances, one must know the cell constant, the relation between the cell's conductance (in reciprocal ohms) and the specific conductance of the contents. This could be calculated if the dimensions of the cell were accurately known, but it is much easier to calibrate the cell with a standard potassium chloride solution. For conductometric titration such calibration is unnecessary.

The simplest electric circuit is that of the Wheatstone bridge shown in Figure 1. For rough work, the source of alternating current can be a small induction coil. A refined form of this uses a tuning fork for the circuit make and break. A better source of alternating current is an audio-frequency vacuum tube oscillator supplying 1000 to 2000 cycles per second. In some cases, 60-cycle alternating current from the city supply can be used, though this low frequency is likely to lead to polarization in the cell.

The ordinary types of galvanometer do not respond to alternating current, and therefore cannot be used to detect current flowing across the bridge. A pair of earphones may be used, but this is inconvenient and seldom used in titrations. A cathode ray oscilloscope is a much more convenient and sensitive null instrument and is the best choice where highest accuracy is desired. The "magic eye," used in many commercial instruments, is a simplified oscilloscope.

Figure 1 shows a small variable capacitor C placed across the arm of the bridge parallel to the conductivity cell. This is to compensate for the electrostatic capacity of the cell, so that the current will increase and decrease at the same rate on both sides of the bridge, to permit a sharp balance point.

Balancing a bridge takes time, and in conductometric titrations at least six readings and preferably eight or ten, are necessary. Several circuits have been devised [1,2,3] in which the Wheatstone bridge is set slightly off balance and the sliding contact S is kept at the same setting during the titration. In such a case the current passing across KY is proportional to the conductance of the cell. It is measured by rectifying it electronically, amplifying it if desired, and passing it through a microammeter. All one needs to do now is to plot the microammeter reading against the volume of titrant. Such instruments are very convenient and are available commercially.

Conductance can be measured very accurately and changes in conductance of the order of 0.01-0.02% can easily be detected with proper equipment. This means that conductometric titrations can often be done accurately even in the presence of large amounts of unreacting electrolytes. Conductometric titrations are also possible in extremely dilute solutions, where potentiometric methods would fail because of the slowness with which the electrodes reached equilibrium. In fact, in very dilute solutions, electrode potentials may not be determined by oxidation-reduction processes at all, but by ionic adsorption.

Titration procedure. A convenient type of cell for conductometric titration is shown in Figure 2. Solutions to be titrated are

[1] W. D. Treadwell, *Helv. Chim. Acta*, **8**, 89 (1925).
[2] R. L. Garman, *Ind. Eng. Chem., Anal. Ed.*, **8**, 146 (1936).
[3] L. J. Anderson and R. R. Revelle, *Anal. Chem.*, **19**, 264 (1947).

introduced through the small funnel and withdrawn after titration
through the siphon tube shown.   Mechanical stirring is provided.
The titrant is added from a microburet with a capillary connection,
and the cell is placed in a thermostat.

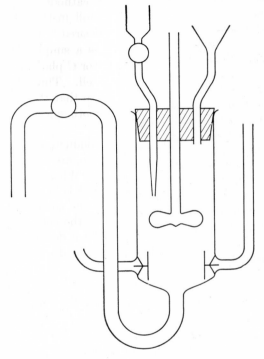

Fig. 20-2.   Cell for conductivity titrations.   The solution is introduced through the funnel on the right, and removed after titration
by the siphon on the left.   The cell can be immersed in a thermostat.

Conductivity is very dependent upon temperature as was explained
above.   One degree of temperature rise increases the conductance of
potassium chloride solutions by about 2%.   The temperature must
therefore be held constant during a titration.   One may dispense
with the thermostat if no great amount of heat is liberated in the
titration reaction and the titration is done quickly, but generally
the cell should at least be immersed in a large vessel of water during
the titration and allowed to come to thermal equilibrium before the

titration is begun. One worker has compensated for temperature fluctuations by using two conductivity cells placed side by side, but connected on opposite arms of the bridge; one contains the solution being titrated, the other a sample of the same original solution which is not touched during titration. Temperature fluctuations affect both cells equally and do not disturb the bridge balance.[3]

Conductivity also depends on the concentration of the solution, and not in a linear manner, since the more the solution is diluted, the better the individual ions conduct. If the solution is appreciably diluted during the titration, therefore, the graph of conductance against volume of titrant will not be linear, but curved. Now it is very important that this graph be straight, since otherwise the accurate interpolation to the end point (see next section) is difficult or impossible. To avoid unnecessary dilution, the titrant is added in a solution which is much more concentrated than the solution being titrated, preferably by at least a factor of ten. Hence the use of the microburet. This feature is particularly important in titrations made in the presence of much indifferent electrolyte, for the changes in conductance of this electrolyte with dilution may overshadow the small changes which are produced by the titration reaction. The dilution effect can be partially corrected by multiplying each conductance reading by the ratio of solution volume to initial solution volume.

The cell shown in Figure 2 has vertical plates. These do not become blocked with precipitates, air bubbles, or sediments as would horizontal plates.

Typical titration curves. The conductance of a solution is the sum of the conductances of the individual ions, so that as one ion is removed by the titrating agent and replaced by another, the conductance of the solution changes in the manner shown in Figure 3. This shows the conductivity change during the titration of hydrochloric acid with sodium hydroxide, for the ideal case in which the volume of the solution does not increase during titration. Initially, the conductance is represented by the ordinate OA, which is made up of two portions: OP, the contribution of the chloride ion, and PA, the contribution of the hydrogen (i.e., hydronium) ion. As sodium hydroxide is added, the hydrogen ion concentration is decreased and drops virtually to zero at the equivalence point. As the hydrogen ions disappear, they are replaced by an equal number of sodium ions, which contribute conductivity, represented at the equivalence point by the height BQ. Since the sodium ions do not move nearly as fast as the hydrogen ions, the total conductance drops, as represented by the line AB. Meanwhile, the conductance due to chloride ions re-

mains constant (neglecting the small amount of dilution caused by adding the sodium hydroxide solution); this is represented by the level line PQ.

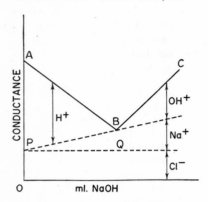

Fig. 20-3. Conductivity titration curve; HCl plus NaOH.

Beyond the equivalence point the conductance rises steeply, for now the fast moving hydroxyl ions are being added along with sodium ions. The rise follows the line BC.

Figure 4 shows another case, the titration of sodium chloride solution by silver nitrate. Before equivalence is reached, chloride ions are being removed from so-lution and replaced by the somewhat less mobile nitrate ions; the conductance therefore drops slightly. Beyond the equivalence point it rises steadily as the excess silver nitrate accumulates in the solution.

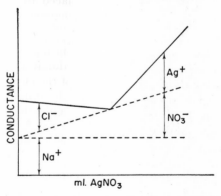

Fig. 20-4. Conductivity titration curve; NaCl plus AgNO₃.

In both these titrations (and indeed in every case where the titrant is an electrolyte), unreacting ions are necessarily added along with the reacting species. These inert ions contribute to the conductivity. The end points are sharper; that is, the angle ABC is less obtuse, if the inert ions are chosen to have the lowest possible conductivity. Thus where a strong base is needed, LiOH is a better choice than NaOH, for the specific ionic conductance of Li^+ is only 42, while that of Na^+ is 51. Likewise, where a metallic ion such as Ag^+ or Ba^{++} is needed for a titration, the acetate is a better choice than the nitrate or chloride (see the conductance data in Table I).

In Figures 3 and 4 the conductivity graph is represented as two straight lines intersecting at a point B. Actually the graphs are rounded in the immediate neighborhood of B, because the titration reactions are not completely irreversible; hydrogen and hydroxyl ions do coexist in the region of the equivalence point of an acid-base titration, and so do silver and chloride ions in the titration of a chloride with a silver salt. The graph obtained in titrating a chloride with silver nitrate is more truly represented by Figure 5, in which the rounded portion is clearly shown. We might obtain a curve like this when titrating very dilute solutions, where the solubility of silver chloride would be appreciable compared to the total solution concentration, or

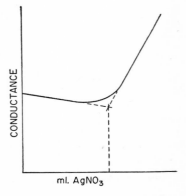

Fig. 20-5. Conductivity titration curve; end point detail. The dotted lines intersect at the equivalence point.

in a precipitation titration where the product was appreciably soluble —for example, lead iodide or lead sulfate. *It is important to note, however, that on either side of the curved portion the graph is straight;* the equivalence point can be located exactly, in spite of the incompleteness of the reaction, by prolonging the straight line portions and noting the point at which they intersect. This is one of the advantages of conductometric titration as compared to potentiometric or indicator methods; the end point does *not* necessarily have to be sharp for the titration to be feasible. The conductance readings taken close to the equivalence point have little significance. The important thing is to locate the straight-line branches

accurately, and this can be done by three or four readings taken before
the equivalence point and three or four taken after.

A special case of a reversible reaction used in titration is that of a
weak acid titrated with a strong base. Potentiometrically, such
titrations give sharp end points if the acid is not too weak (i.e., K_A is
about 10^{-5}), but if the acid is very weak ($K_A = 10^{-10}$ or so), a poor,

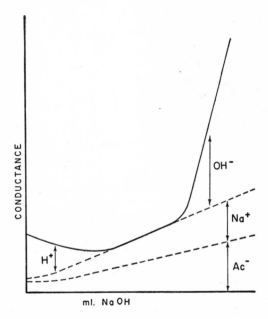

Fig. 20-6.   Conductivity titration curve; acetic acid plus NaOH.
If the acid were a little more dilute, the curve would be valueless for
titration.

indefinite end point is obtained.   Conductometrically, the reverse is
the case.   The reason is that, as an acid of the strength of acetic is
neutralized, the hydrogen ion concentration, which in pure dilute
acetic acid is quite significant, falls off very rapidly in the early part
of the titration and reaches a low value (insignificant as far as conductance is concerned) before the equivalence point is reached.   This
gives a curved graph, as shown in Figure 6, and the straight portion
to the left of the equivalence point is either nonexistent or too short

to be of much use for extrapolation. If the acid is very weak, however, its initial conductance is very small, and after the first drop or two of the titrant, the hydrogen ion conductance is quite negligible; adding base now increases the conductance in a linear manner as the anion of the weak acid is liberated. Beyond the equivalence point the conductance increases much faster as rapidly moving OH^- ions are added (see Figure 7).

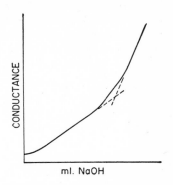

Fig. 20-7. Conductivity titration curve; very weak acid (e.g. boric) plus NaOH.

Oxidation-reduction reactions are generally not suited for conductometric titrations, as the products and the reactants have about the same conductance, but if hydrogen ions are produced or consumed in the reaction, the conductivity titration curve may show a sharp break. An example of such a titration is given below.

Specific applications. In this section we shall describe a few representative applications to illustrate the uses of the method.

(a) *Sulfate.* The titration of sulfate conductometrically with barium nitrate or barium acetate illustrates the use of this method where potentiometric methods cannot be used and indicators are unsatisfactory. Sulfate has been titrated thus in sea water[3] and in sulfuric acid solutions obtained by the oxidation of organic compounds.[4] Sharp end points are obtained, especially when supersaturation is avoided by seeding the solution with barium sulfate, but coprecipitation limits the accuracy here just as in gravimetric analysis. The sulfate in sea water was determined to ±0.3%.

(b) *Chloride* could be determined conductometrically in sea water to ±0.01%, which shows the great accuracy that this technique can give.[5] The sensitivity is shown by the titration of one microgram of chloride in 3–4 ml. of solution to an accuracy of 10%; 13 micrograms in 3–4 ml. were determined to ±2%.[6] In titrating at these very low

[4] G. A. Schöberl, *Z. anal. Chem.*, **128**, 210 (1948).
[5] L. J. Anderson, *Anal. Chem.*, **20**, 618 (1948).
[6] G. Jander and H. Immig, *Z. Elektrochem.*, **43**, 211 (1937).

concentrations, alcohol was added to reduce the solubility of silver chloride.

(c) *Fluoride* can be titrated with aluminum chloride solution with formation of the soluble complex ion $AlF_6^{\equiv}$. The end point may be detected by the hydrolysis of the excess reagent (see Chapter 19, page 373); it may also be detected conductometrically. Some 30% of alcohol is added to check the dissociation of the complex. An excess of sodium acetate or sodium perchlorate is also added, apparently for the same purpose. It is claimed that 12 micrograms of fluoride can be titrated to an accuracy of 0.6 micrograms, and 20 milligrams to 0.04 milligrams.[7] Nevertheless, the method does not seem to have displaced the thorium nitrate titration of fluoride.

(d) *Very weak acids and bases.* Vanillin, isovanillin, and other phenolic compounds have been titrated with good accuracy, using lithium hydroxide.[8] A very interesting example is the titration of the ammonium ion with sodium or barium hydroxide.[9] Here the titration graph is particularly good, because the conducting acid, NH_4^+, is converted to nonconducting NH_3, and is replaced by the more slowly moving Na^+ or Ba^{++}, so that the conductance drops

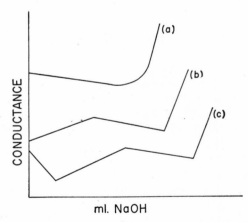

Fig. 20-8. Conductivity titration curves, (a), NH_4Cl; (b), $NH_4H_2PO_4$; (c), $NH_4H_2PO_4$, plus a little HCl. (Jander *et al.,* *Z. anal. Chem.,* **128,** 468 (1948).)

[7] J. Harms and G. Jander, *Z. Elektrochem.,* **42,** 315 (1936).
[8] O. Pfundt and C. Junge, *Ber.,* **62,** 515 (1929).
[9] G. Jander, C. Gensch, and H. Hecht, *Z. anal. Chem.,* **128,** 468 (1948).

before the equivalence point and rises afterwards (see Figure 8a). An analogous case is the titration of salts of weak acids, such as the soaps, with hydrochloric acid.[10]

(e) *Acid mixtures.* Conductance is a linear function of acid concentration, electrode potential a logarithmic function; conductance and electromotive force give entirely different kinds of titration curves, and one may give a sharp end point where the other does not.

Potentiometric titration does not give a sharp end point for an acid which is neutralized in the presence of a weaker acid, unless this second acid is very much weaker than the first (see Chapter 13). Thus hydrochloric acid cannot be titrated at all accurately in the presence of acetic acid by potentiometric means, although the *total* acid (hydrochloric plus acetic) can be determined very well. Conductometrically, hydrochloric acid can be titrated in presence of acetic acid very accurately, while the total acid concentration is not given accurately. Figure 9 shows the contrast between the conductometric and potentiometric titration curves for this mixture. Here conductometric and potentiometric methods

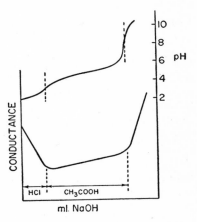

Fig. 20-9. Titration of a mixture of hydrochloric and acetic acids. Upper curve, potentiometric; lower curve, conductometric.

complement one another. Conductometric titration has been used to determine small amounts of hydrochloric acid in vinegar.[11] A similar application is the titration of free sulfuric acid in commercial aluminum sulfate,[12] a determination which is difficult to do potentiometrically, because of hydrolysis. The method has also been used to titrate free sulfurous acid in calcium bisulfite liquors in the paper industry. Analogously, free alkali can be titrated in soaps, using hydrochloric acid.[10]

Figure 8, curves *b* and *c*, show titration curves for the salt

[10] S. H. Maron, I. N. Ulevitch, and M. E. Elder, *Anal. Chem.*, **21**, 691 (1949).
[11] H. T. S. Britton, *Conductometric Analysis*, London, Chapman and Hall, 1934.
[12] I. G. Murgulescu and E. Laiu, *Z. anal. Chem.*, **128**, 142 (1948).

$NH_4H_2PO_4$ alone and $NH_4H_2PO_4$ to which a small amount of hydrochloric acid has been added.[9] The ion $H_2PO_4^-$ is an acid and so is $HPO_4^=$; the former is stronger than NH_4^+, the latter weaker; the graphs show the successive stages of neutralization. These titrations are potentially useful in fertilizer analysis.

(f) *Miscellaneous microdeterminations.* The combination of high sensitivity and high accuracy which conductometric titration often affords is shown by the titration of tripositive arsenic by iodine. This reaction produces hydrogen ions:

$$I_2 + HAsO_2 + 2H_2O \rightarrow 2I^- + H_2AsO_4^- + 3H^+,$$

and as a result the conductance rises rapidly until the equivalence point is reached, but very little after that. As little as 0.04 microgram of arsenic can be titrated in presence of a 500-fold excess of indifferent electrolyte.[13]

Another example of high sensitivity is the titration of metal ions in 10-microgram quantities by aqueous hydrogen sulfide.[14]

High-frequency Titrations

In alternating electric fields of very high frequency, of the order of tens of millions of cycles per second, ionic solutions transmit electric energy by a mechanism somewhat different from that at low frequencies or in a nonalternating field. The ions have, so to speak, no time to migrate through the solution in the ordinary way, but instead oscillate back and forth very rapidly about a mean position. This behavior is analogous to the back-and-forth twisting of dipolar molecules, which is going on at the same time in the solvent. In other words, the solutions behave in a high-frequency field very much like dielectrics. A conductivity cell containing a solution behaves more like a capacitor than a resistor.

In high-frequency titrations, the electrodes do not need to touch the solution. The vessel containing the solution is placed between the plates of a capacitor (which in one model of titrimeter are copper bands fused into the outside of the titration beaker), and this capac-

[13] G. Jander and J. Harms, *Angew. Chemie,* **48,** 267 (1935).
[14] H. Immig and G. Jander, *Z. Elektrochem.,* **43,** 207 (1937).

itor is combined with an inductance to form an oscillating circuit, as in Figure 10. A circuit of this kind, consisting of an inductance L and a capacitance C, oscillates freely with a frequency of $1/(2\pi\sqrt{LC})$ cycles per second. The energy for the oscillations is provided by a dry battery; the flow of electrons is converted into resonating pulsations by means of a triode tube. The principle used in titrations is that, as the titrant is added to the solution, the capacitance of the latter changes, and with it the frequency of resonance of the circuit. It is very hard to measure this frequency directly, for it is of the order of tens or hundreds of megacycles, and the changes are only of the order of kilocycles. The instrument, therefore, uses *two* oscillat-

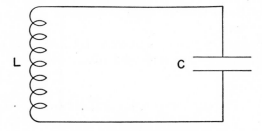

Fig. 20-10. Oscillating circuit.

ing circuits, one containing the titration vessel, the other a reference capacitance in the form of a variable tuning capacitor which can be adjusted to give any desired oscillation frequency in this second circuit. This circuit is tuned to give a frequency slightly different from that of the circuit containing the titration cell. A portion of the alternating current from each circuit is fed into a third oscillating circuit, where the two primary frequencies combine to give a *beat frequency*, which is the difference between the two. This is of the order of kilocycles and can be conveniently measured. In titration, this beat frequency is plotted against the volume of titrant. Curves are obtained which look somewhat like those obtained in conductometric titration (see Figure 11).

To understand the mechanism of these changes and, with them, the possibilities and limitations of this method, we go back to the analogy between the back-and-forth oscillation of ions in a high-frequency field and the oscillation of solvent dipoles. Unlike the solvent molecules, which merely turn around, the ions move from place to place. The higher the frequency, the less distance an ion travels before it has to turn around and go back, but is there any fundamental difference, other than the mere length of path, between the back-and-forth motions at 1000 cycles per second and those at 10^8 cycles per second? If the ions moved quite independently of each other, their period of motion would have little significance, but they do not move independently. Because of interionic attraction, each ion is surrounded by an atmosphere of ions in which those of

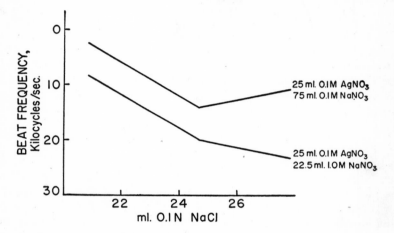

Fig. 20-11. High-frequency titration curves, showing effect of salt concentration. (Blaedel and Malmstadt, *Anal. Chem.*, **22**, 1413 (1950).)

charge opposite to its own predominate. Now it takes time for this atmosphere to form or to die away. As an ion moves steadily in an electric field, it builds up a new atmosphere ahead of itself as the old atmosphere behind it is dissipated. There is, however, a lag in the formation and disappearance of the atmosphere, which causes the atmosphere to be unsymmetrical, with its center of charge falling behind the moving central ion. This creates a drag upon the motion of the latter, which is one cause of the fall in equivalent conductance with rising concentration. If the ions move back and forth in an alternating field, and if the period of oscillation of the field is small compared to the time it takes for the atmosphere to form or die away, the dissymmetry and the resulting drag do not occur. This effect of frequency upon conductivity is the well-known Debye-Falkenhagen effect.[15]

High frequency, in the sense of this discussion, means a frequency such that the time of one oscillation is of the same order of magnitude as that required for the ionic atmosphere to form or die away. The rate of growth or decay of the atmosphere is characterized by a *relaxation time* τ defined by

$$-\frac{d\rho}{dt} = \frac{\rho}{\tau},$$

where ρ is the charge density at any point in the atmosphere and $-d\rho/dt$ the rate at which it would fall if the central ion were removed. The relaxation time depends upon the temperature, the frictional coefficients of the various ions in the solution, and the charges and concentrations of the latter. For a given electrolyte at a given temperature,

relaxation time $\times$ concentration = a constant.

In a high-frequency titrimeter, the aim is to use a frequency of oscillation whose reciprocal is of the same order of magnitude as the relaxation time of the solution. The capacity of the titration vessel, and with it the exact oscillation frequency of the circuit, then depend in a sensitive manner on the concentration and nature of the ions in the solution, as may be seen from the following considerations. Concentration influences the relaxation time—the smaller the concentration, the larger is the relaxation time. If the relaxation time is large compared to the period of oscillation of the circuit, the ionic atmospheres are not distorted as the alternating current passes, and the current passes relatively easily; the loading is light, the resonance frequency relatively high. If, however, the relaxation time is small compared to the period of oscillation, the ionic atmospheres do get distorted, and the alternating current passes with more difficulty; loading is heavy; that is, the polarization and effective dielectric constant are high. This makes the resonance frequency relatively low. Summarizing:

[15] H. Falkenhagen, *Electrolytes*, trans. R. P. Bell, New York, Oxford, 1934, Chap. 9.

Low Concentration	High Concentration
$\tau \gg 1/\nu$	$\tau \ll 1/\nu$
Small loading	Large loading
Small capacitance	Large capacitance
High resonance frequency	Low resonance frequency

Figure 12 shows the quantitative effects. The changes in frequency are not great percentagewise, but they may none the less amount to hundreds of kilocycles. *The major part of the change of frequency with concentration occurs within a tenfold concentration range.* This means that in high-frequency titrations the total electrolyte

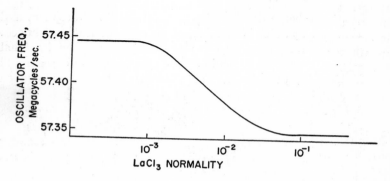

Fig. 20-12. Resonance frequency versus concentration, showing effect of relaxation time of ion atmosphere. (Forman and Crisp, *Trans. Faraday Soc.*, **52A**, 186 (1946).)

concentration must be held within certain limits, which depend upon the nature of the electrolyte, but more particularly upon the frequency range of the oscillator used. A 30-megacycle oscillator operates in the range 10^{-3} to 10^{-2} M; with a 350-megacycle oscillator, concentrations of 10^{-2} to 10^{-1} M, and up to 0.5 M with certain electrolytes, can be handled.[16,17]

The high-frequency technique is most sensitive in titrations where the total concentration of dissolved ions changes; for example, precipitation and complex-forming reactions. It is applicable also to cases where a fast-moving ion is replaced by a slow-moving ion, as in acid-base titrations; the faster the ions move, the smaller is the re-

[16] W. J. Blaedel and H. V. Malmstadt, *Anal. Chem.*, **22**, 734, 1410, 1412 (1950).
[17] K. Anderson, E. S. Bettis, and D. Revinson, *Anal. Chem.*, **22**, 743 (1950).

laxation time. Charge type influences relaxation time, too; high ionic charges lead to small relaxation times. The technique is therefore also applicable to oxidation-reduction titrations.

It is very sensitive, since very low concentrations can be handled by using relatively low frequencies. It is also highly accurate; an accuracy of 1 in 1000 is readily obtained.[16] The fact that the electrodes do not come into contact with the solution gives the technique certain advantages; for example, precipitates cannot clog up the electrodes, as sometimes happens in conductometric work. High-frequency titrimeters are relatively expensive and difficult to adjust, but once set up, they are very easy to maintain. Their great advantage seems to be their versatility and accuracy; their major disadvantage, the limitations on total electrolyte concentration which are imposed by the frequency used.

Amperometric Titrations

Amperometric titrations have been mentioned occasionally in this book, and therefore a brief description is in order, although a proper treatment would necessitate a chapter on the polarograph.

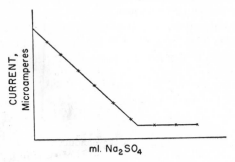

Fig. 20-13.   Amperometric titration curve; lead ions plus Na_2SO_4.

Amperometric titrations are performed with direct current in a polarograph cell.   In the usual form of this cell, the cathode is a tiny mercury drop.   The experimental conditions are such that the current passing through the cell depends upon the rate at which reducible ions (usually metallic cations) can diffuse up to this mercury drop;

the diffusion rate, in turn, depends upon the concentration of the reducible substance in the solution. The potential applied across the cell has to exceed the decomposition potential of the electrolyte, of course (see Chapter 5), or no current will pass at all.

Suppose, for example, a lead salt solution is to be titrated with sodium sulfate. The lead salt is placed in the cell and a potential is applied which is sufficient to reduce lead ions to lead amalgam, but not sufficient to reduce hydrogen ions or sodium ions (the high overvoltage of hydrogen on mercury helps prevent the discharge of hydrogen ions). A current passes and is recorded. The sodium sulfate solution is then added from a buret and the current is plotted against the volume of added reagent. It falls linearly to near zero, then remains constant at a very small value, the capacity current (see Figure 13). Half a dozen readings are sufficient to establish the end point of the titration. In exactly the same way, a sulfate solution could be titrated with a lead salt; the current would remain near zero until the equivalence point was reached, after which it would rise regularly with the volume of titrant.

The current flowing is of the order of microamperes, and the amount of metal removed from the solution is infinitesimal. In the usual form of cell, the metal is returned to the solution again as the mercury drops fall and become part of the anode pool. The practical advantages of the technique are its high sensitivity—very dilute solutions are used and a few micrograms of material can be titrated—and its wide range of applications. The accuracy is moderate, being 1–2% under favorable conditions.

PROBLEMS

1. Sketch as accurately as you can the conductivity-titration curves for the following titrations, and note probable sources of error in each case: (a) Ca^{++} with $Na_2C_2O_4$; (b) $SO_4^=$ with $Ba(CH_3COO)_2$; (c) K^+ with $LiClO_4$; (d) Pb^{++} with H_2S.

2. Suggest two oxidation-reduction titrations which could be performed conductometrically.

3. Give two examples each (other than those cited in Problem 2) of (a) titrations which give a good potentiometric end point but a poor conductometric end point, (b) titrations which give a good conductometric end point but a poor potentiometric end point.

4. How is a cathode ray oscilloscope used in conductance determinations?

5. Of the following titrations, which should give the best results in high-frequency titration, and which the poorest: (a) arsenic acid plus potassium iodide; (b) iodine in potassium iodide plus thiosulfate; (c) chloride plus mercuric nitrate?

6. Would high-frequency titrations in *ethyl alcohol* require higher or lower frequencies for a given concentration than in water?

APPENDIX I

Bibliography of selected texts

General

G. L. Clark, L. K. Nash and R. B. Fischer, *Quantitative Chemical Analysis*, Philadelphia, Saunders, 1949.

W. F. Hillebrand and G. E. F. Lundell, *Applied Inorganic Analysis*, New York, Wiley, 1929.

I. M. Kolthoff and E. B. Sandell, *Textbook of Quantitative Inorganic Analysis*, 3d ed., New York, Macmillan, 1952.

G. E. F. Lundell and J. I. Hoffman, *Outlines of Methods of Chemical Analysis*, New York, Wiley, 1938.

J. W. Mellor and H. V. Thompson *Treatise on Quantitative Inorganic Analysis*, 2d ed., London, Griffin, 1938.

W. Rieman III, J. D. Neuss and B. Naiman, *Quantitative Analysis, A Theoretical Approach*, 3d ed., New York, McGraw-Hill, 1951.

W. W. Scott, *Standard Methods of Chemical Analysis*, 5th ed., edited by N. H. Furman, New York, Van Nostrand, 1939.

T. B. Smith, *Analytical Processes, A Physico-Chemical Interpretation*, 2d ed., London, Arnold, 1940.

F. D. Snell and F. M. Biffen, *Commercial Methods of Analysis*, New York, McGraw-Hill, 1944.

E. H. Swift, *A System of Chemical Analysis*, New York, Prentice-Hall, 1939.

A. I. Vogel, *A Textbook of Quantitative Inorganic Analysis*, New York, Longmans, Green, 1939.

H. H. Willard and H. Diehl, *Advanced Quantitative Analysis*, New York, Van Nostrand, 1943.

Special Topics

A.S.T.M. Methods for Chemical Analysis of Metals, Philadelphia, American Society for Testing Materials, 1950.

W. Boettger, *Physikalische Methoden der analytischen Chemie*, 3 vols., Leipzig, Akademische Verlagsgesellschaft, 1939.

W. Boettger (ed.), R. A. Oesper (translator), *Newer Methods of Volumetric Analysis*, New York, Van Nostrand, 1938.

H. T. S. Britton, *Conductometric Analysis*, New York, Van Nostrand, 1934.

H. T. S. Britton, *Hydrogen Ions*, 2 vols., 3d ed., London, Chapman and Hall, 1942.

F. Feigl, *Chemistry of Specific, Selective and Sensitive Reactions*, New York, Academic Press, 1949.

J. F. Flagg, *Organic Reagents used in Gravimetric and Volumetric Analysis*, New York, Interscience, 1948.

I. M. Kolthoff and N. H. Furman, *Potentiometric Titrations*, New York, Wiley, 1926.

I. M. Kolthoff and H. A. Laitinen, *pH and Electrotitrations*, 2d ed., New York, Wiley, 1941.

I. M. Kolthoff and C. Rosenblum, *Acid-Base Indicators*, New York, Macmillan, 1937.

I. M. Kolthoff and V. A. Stenger, *Volumetric Analysis*, New York, Interscience, 1942, 1947, 1952.   Vol. I, *Theoretical Fundamentals;* Vol. II, *Titration Methods (Acid-Base, Precipitation and Complex-Forming Reactions)*; Vol. III, *Oxidation-Reduction Methods.*

J. Mitchell, Jr., and D. M. Smith, *Aquametry*, New York, Interscience, 1948.

J. B. Niederl and V. Niederl, *Micromethods of Quantitative Organic Elementary Analysis*, 2d ed., New York, Wiley, 1942.

C. J. Rodden (ed.), *Analytical Chemistry of the Manhattan Project*, New York, McGraw-Hill, 1950.

H. J. S. Sand, *Electrochemistry and Electrochemical Analysis*, 2 vols., Brooklyn, Chemical Publishing Co., 1940.

E. B. Sandell, *Colorimetric Determination of Traces of Metals*, 2d ed., New York, Interscience, 1950.

R. E. Burk (ed.), *Recent Advances in Analytical Chemistry*, New York, Interscience, 1949.

W. R. Schoeller and A. R. Powell, *The Analysis of Minerals and Ores of the Rarer Elements*, 2d ed., London, Griffin, 1940.

S. Siggia, *Quantitative Organic Analysis via Functional Groups*, New York, Wiley, 1949.

Pamphlets published by the G. Frederick Smith Chemical Co., Columbus, Ohio:

H. Diehl, *The Application of the Dioximes to Analytical Chemistry*, 1940.

H. Diehl, *Electrochemical Analysis with Graded Cathode Potential Control*, 1948.

G. F. Smith, *Cerate Oxidimetry*, 1942.

G. F. Smith, *Cupferron and Neocupferron*, 1938.

G. F. Smith, *Perchloric Acid*, 4th ed., 1940.

G. F. Smith, *Analytical Applications of Periodic Acid and Iodic Acid*, 5th ed., 1950.

G. F. Smith and F. P. Richter, *Phenanthroline and Substituted Phenanthroline Indicators*, 1944.

A. Steyermark, *Quantitative Organic Microanalysis*, New York, Blakiston, 1951.

H. S. Washington, *The Chemical Analysis of Rocks*, 4th ed., New York, Wiley, 1930.

F. J. Welcher, *Organic Analytical Reagents*, 4 vols., New York, Van Nostrand, 1948.

H. H. Willard, L. L. Merritt and J. A. Dean, *Instrumental Methods of Analysis*, 2d ed., New York, Van Nostrand, 1951.

J. H. Yoe and L. A. Sarver, *Organic Analytical Reagents*, New York, Wiley, 1941.

APPENDIX II

Selected methods for determination of the elements

Abbreviations: c., colorimetric; g., gravimetric; v., volumetric; det., determined; ppt., precipitated; sep., separated.

GROUP I

H:

In organic compounds, as H_2O, by combustion (g.), Chap. 9; Niederl and Niederl, *Micromethods*.

As H_2O; Karl Fischer reagent (v.), Chap. 16; Mitchell and Smith, *Aquametry*.

Titration of acids, Chaps. 12, 13, 14.

Alkali metals, general:

Flame photometer is fastest and best for traces.   Barnes et al., *Ind. Eng. Chem., Anal. Ed.*, **17**, 605 (1945), **18**, 19 (1946).

Li:

Sep. from Na and K as LiCl in pyridine or HCl-*n*-butanol, det. as Li_2SO_4 (g.), Chap. 9; Smith and Ross, *J. Am. Chem. Soc.*, **47**, 774 (1925); Kallmann, *Ind. Eng. Chem., Anal. Ed.*, **16**, 712 (1944).

Na:

By zinc uranyl acetate in acetic acid (g. or v.), Chap. 2; Barber and Kolthoff, *J. Am. Chem. Soc.*, **50**, 1625 (1928).

As NaCl (g.), Chap. 9; Smith and Ross, *J. Am. Chem. Soc.*, **47**, 774 (1925).

K:

As K_2PtCl_6 in alcohol (g.), Chap. 9; Fresenius, *Z. anal. Chem.*, **16**, 63 (1877); Smith and Shead, *J. Am. Chem. Soc.*, **54**, 1722 (1932).

As $KClO_4$ in *n*-butanol-ethyl acetate (g.), Chap. 9; Smith, *J. Am. Chem. Soc.*, **47**, 762 (1925).

Sep. as $K_2NaCo(NO_2)_6$ in acetic acid, titrated with $Ce(SO_4)_2$ (semi-micro); Brown et al., *Ind. Eng. Chem., Anal. Ed.*, **10**, 652 (1938); Twisley, *Analyst*, **73**, 86 (1948).

Rb, Cs:

As perchlorates (g.), see K; in mixtures, flame photometer.

Cu:

As metal, electrolytic (g.), Chap. 5.

By α-benzoin oxime in NH_3 (g., semi-micro), Chap. 6.

By thiosulfate (v.), Chap. 11.

By sodium diethyldithiocarbamate (c., micro), Chap. 6; Sandell, *Colorimetric Det. of Traces of Metals.*

Ag:

As AgCl (g. or v.), Chaps. 2, 18.

By KCNS (v.), Chap. 18.

In Ag halides, by KCN (v.), Chap. 19.

Au:

As metal (g.) by dry assay, fusing with PbO, Na_2CO_3, etc.; Scott, *Standard Methods.*

By thiophenol as $AuSC_6H_5$, dried below 150° (g.); Currah et al., *Ind. Eng. Chem., Anal. Ed.*, **18**, 120 (1946); Duval, *Anal. Chem.*, **23**, 1271 (1951).

GROUP II

Be:

Sep. from Fe, Al by ppt. these with oxine at pH 5; ppt. as $Be(OH)_2$ at pH 8; weighed as BeO (g.); Churchill et al., *Ind. Eng. Chem., Anal. Ed.*, **2**, 405 (1930); Stevens and Carron, *U. S. Geol. Survey Bull.*, **950**, p. 91 (1946); Dupuis, *Compt. Rend.*, **230**, 957 (1950).

Mg, Ca, Sr, Ba, general:

By ethylenediamine tetraacetic acid (v.), Chap. 19, 7; Diehl et al., *J. Am. Water Works Assoc.*, **42**, 40 (1950).

By K. palmitate (v.), Chap. 18; Suter, *J. Am. Water Works Assoc.*, **29**, 1001 (1937).

Mg:

As $MgNH_4PO_4$, ppt. at pH 9.5, weighed as $Mg_2P_2O_7$ (g.), Chaps. 2, 4.

By oxine (v., not g.), Chaps. 6, 4; Miller and McLennan, *J. Chem. Soc.*, 1940, p. 656.

By 8-hydroxyquinaldine (g.), Chaps. 6, 4; Merritt and Walker, *Ind. Eng. Chem., Anal. Ed.*, **16**, 387 (1944).

Ca, Sr, Ba, general:

Flame photometer most convenient for mixtures and traces; for reference see Alkali Metals above.

Ca:

Sep. from Ba and Sr as nitrate by butyl cellosolve or by 76% HNO_3, Chap. 9; Barber, *Ind. Eng. Chem., Anal. Ed.*, **13**, 572 (1941); Willard and Goodspeed, *ibid.*, **8**, 414 (1936).

As CaC_2O_4 (g. or v.), Chaps. 2, 3, 4.   Titrated best with $Ce(ClO_4)_4$, Chap. 15.

By picrolonic acid at pH 4 (g., v. or c.), Chap. 6; Flagg, *Organic Reagents;* Alten et al., *Biochem. Z.*, **265**, 85 (1933).

Sr:

Sep. from Ca and Ba, see Ca and Ba.   Det. as sulfate in 70% methanol (g.).

Ba:

Sep. from Sr and Ca by HCl in *n*-butanol; Kallmann, *Anal. Chem.*, **20**, 449 (1948); see also Willard and Goodspeed, *Ind. Eng. Chem., Anal. Ed.*, **8**, 414 (1936).

As $BaSO_4$ (g.), Chaps. 2, 3; in presence Ca, as $BaCrO_4$, (g.), Chap. 3.

By Na_2SO_4 (v.), Chap. 18; Sheen and Kahler, *Ind. Eng. Chem., Anal. Ed.*, **8**, 127 (1936), **10**, 206 (1938).

Zn:

As $ZnNH_4PO_4$, ppt. at pH 7, weighed as $Zn_2P_2O_7$ (g.); Kolthoff and Sandell, *Quantitative Inorganic Analysis.*

Sep. as ZnS, ppt. at pH 2.5; det. as ZnO or $ZnSO_4$ (g.), Chap. 2; Fales and Ware, *J. Am. Chem. Soc.*, **41**, 487 (1919).

By potassium ferrocyanide (v.), Chap. 18.

By dithizone (c., micro), Chap. 6; Bricker et al., *Ind. Eng. Chem., Anal. Ed.*, **17**, 661 (1945).

Cd:

Sep. as CdS, or electrolytically with potential control, Chap. 5; det. as $CdNH_4PO_4$, cf. Zn.

As $Cd(C_5H_5N)_2Cl_2$, drying above 270° (g.); Duval, *Anal. Chim. Acta*, **4**, 190 (1950).

By ferrocyanide (v.), 3,3′-dimethylnaphthidine indicator, Chap. 18.

In presence of Zn, is most conveniently det. polarographically.

Hg:

As HgS(g.); as metal (g.), Chaps. 5, 9; Scott, *Standard Methods.*

By thiocyanate (v.), Chap. 19; Kolthoff and Sandell, *Quantitative Inorganic Analysis.*

In presence halides, by acetone and alkali; Fernandez et al., *Anal. Chem.*, **23**, 899 (1951).

By dithizone (c.), Chap. 6.

GROUP III

B:

Sep. as CH_3BO_2, Chap. 9.

By alkali, as H_3BO_3—mannitol complex, Chaps. 7, 13; Blumenthal, *Anal. Chem.*, **23**, 992 (1951).

Al:

As Al_2O_3, ppt. at pH 6 (g.), Chaps. 3, 4.   By NaOH (v.), Chap. 18.

As basic benzoate at pH 4, sep. from Cu, Mn, etc.; weigh as Al_2O_3 (g.), Chap. 3; Kolthoff et al., *J. Am. Chem. Soc.*, **56**, 812 (1934); Smales, *Analyst*, **72**, 14 (1947).

By oxine (g., v., or c.), Chaps. 6, 4, 15.

Sc:

Sep. from Y, La, Zr, Th by extracting $Sc(CNS)_3$ from 1 N HCl with ether; Fischer and Bock, *Z. anorg. Chem.*, **249**, 146 (1942).

Det. as Sc_2O_3 by NH_3 above pH 7; Fischer, *loc. cit.*

Y, La, rare earths:

General: ppt. as oxalates in acid solution, weigh as R_2O_3 (g.).

Specific: x-ray emission spectra; certain elements by absorption spectra in aqueous solution.

Separations: by ion exchange, Chap. 8.   Sep. of La from others by ion exchange; Fitch and Russell, *Anal. Chem.*, **23**, 1469 (1951).

Ga:

Sep. by isopropyl ether extraction of $GaCl_3$, Chap. 9; Nachtrieb and Fryxell, *J. Am. Chem. Soc.*, **71**, 4035 (1949).

Sep. from Zn, Tl, etc. by ppt. with tannin in dil. acetic acid, weighing as Ga_2O_3 (g.), Chap. 6; Moser, *Monatshefte*, **50**, 181 (1928), **51**, 325 (1929).

By oxine (g. or v.); Nachtrieb, *loc. cit.*

In:

As In_2O_3 ppt. by NH_3 above pH 5 (g.), or as In_2S_3 ppt. at pH 2 (g.); Moser, *Monatshefte*, **55**, 14 (1930).

Tl:

As Tl_2CrO_4 (g.); Chretien and Longli, *Bull. Soc. Chim.*, **11**, 241 (1944).

Tl(I), by KI, adsorption indicator (v.), Chap. 18; Mehrotra, *Anal. Chim. Acta*, **3**, 73 (1949).

Tl(I), by Ce(SO₄)₂ (v.); Willard and Young, *J. Am. Chem. Soc.*, **55**, 3260 (1933).

GROUP IV

C:

As CO_2, absorbed by base (g.), Chap. 9; Niederl and Niederl, *Micromethods*.

CO: by reduction of I_2O_5 to I_2 and titration of latter (v.), Chap. 9; Aluise et al., *Anal. Chem.*, **19**, 347 (1947).

By ammonium molybdate and $PdSO_4$ on silica gel (c.); Shephard, *Anal. Chem.*, **19**, 77 (1947).

Si:

As SiO_2 (g.), evaporate silicate solution with HCl or, better, $HClO_4$; Willard and Cake, *J. Am. Chem. Soc.*, **42**, 2208 (1920). *In presence of F:* add boric acid; Schrenk and Ode, *Ind. Eng. Chem.*, *Anal. Ed.*, **1**, 201 (1929).

As oxine silicomolybdate (g. or v., semi-micro; can be used in presence of F), Chap. 7; Brabson et al., *Anal. Chem.*, **20**, 504 (1948).

As silicomolybdic acid (c., micro), Chap. 7; Scott, *Standard Methods;* Jewsbury, *Analyst*, **75**, 256 (1950).

Ti:

Sep. from Fe, by Hg cathode, Chap. 5.

By cupferron in 1 M H_2SO_4, weighing as TiO_2 (g.), Chap. 6; sep. from Al.

By H_2O_2, as yellow TiO_2^{++} (c.); Cunningham, *Ind. Eng. Chem.*, *Anal. Ed.*, **5**, 305 (1933); in presence V and Mo, *ibid.*, **17**, 695 (1945).

Reduce to Ti(III), titrate with $Fe_2(SO_4)_3$, KCNS indicator (v.), Chap. 15; Bischoff, *Z. anal. Chem.*, **130**, 195 (1950).

Zr, Hf:

Sep. by ion exchange, Chap. 8.

Sep. from Al, Fe, etc. by ppt. phosphates of Zr, Hf in 2 M H_2SO_4, adding H_2O_2 if Ti present; Lundell and Knowles, *J. Am. Chem. Soc.*, **41**, 1801 (1919).

Det. as $R(SeO_3)_2$, dried at 120° (g.); binary Zr-Hf mixtures analyzed by igniting this ppt. to 1000°, weighing again as RO_2; Claassen, *Z. anal. Chem.*, **117**, 252 (1939); Willard and Hahn, *Anal. Chem.*, **21**, 293 (1949).

Th:

As $Th(OH)_4$, ppt. pH 3–6, weighed as ThO_2 (g.); Moeller et al., *Chem. Reviews*, **42**, 63 (1948).

As $Th(IO_3)_4$ in 6 M HNO_3 (g., v.), sep. from PO_4 and all cations except Ti, Zr, Hf; Meyer, *Z. anorg. Chem.*, **71**, 65 (1911); Rodden, *Analytical Chemistry of Manhattan Project*.

Ge:

Sep. by distilling $GeCl_4$, Chap. 9; Dennis and Johnson, *J. Am. Chem. Soc.*, **45**, 1380 (1923).

Ppt. by tannin in 0.5 *M* H_2SO_4, igniting to GeO_2 (g.); Davies and Morgan, *Analyst*, **63**, 388 (1938); Holness, *Anal. Chim. Acta*, **2**, 254 (1948).

Sep. by distilling $SnCl_4$, Chap. 9.

Sn:

Reduce to Sn(II) with Pb, titrate with I_2, Chap. 15; Hillebrand and Lundell, *Applied Inorganic Analysis*.

As SnO_2 (g.), ppt. pH 2.

Pb:

As PbO_2, electrolytically (g.), Chap. 5; Shrenk and Delano, *Ind. Eng. Chem., Anal. Ed.*, **3**, 27 (1931).

As $PbSO_4$ (g.), Chap. 2; A.S.T.M., *Chemical Analysis of Metals*.

As $PbCrO_4$, dissolved in acid and det. by KI and thiosulfate (v.); Scott, *Standard Methods*.

By dithizone, from cyanide-citrate mixture at pH 7.5 (c., micro) Chap. 6; Hubbard, *Ind. Eng. Chem., Anal. Ed.*, **9**, 493 (1937); Bambach, *ibid.*, **11**, 400 (1939).

GROUP V

N:

As N_2, by combustion, Chap. 9; Niederl and Niederl, *Micromethods*.

As NH_4^+ (v.) Kjeldahl method, Chap. 9; Bradstreet, *Chem. Reviews*, **27**, 331 (1940).

Nitrates, reduce to NH_4^+ by Devarda alloy, Chap. 15.

Nitrites, by hypochlorite (v.), Chap. 15; Kolthoff and Stenger, *Ind. Eng. Chem., Anal. Ed.*, **7**, 79 (1935).

Nitrogenous bases, by titration with $HClO_4$ in glacial acetic acid, Chap. 13.

P:

As $MgNH_4PO_4$, ppt. at pH 9.5, weighed as $Mg_2P_2O_7$ (g.), Chaps. 2, 4.

H_3PO_4, titration with base, (v.), Chaps. 13, 20; Calamari and Hubata, *Ind. Eng. Chem., Anal. Ed.*, **14**, 55 (1942). Sep. from metallic ions by ion exchange, Chap. 8; Helrich and Rieman, *Anal. Chem.*, **19**, 651 (1947).

H_3PO_3, by excess I_2 at pH 7 and back titration (v.); Van Name and Huff, *Am. J. Sci.*, 1918, p. 91.

As:

Sep. as AsH_3 or $AsCl_3$, Chap. 9; Biltz, *Z. anal. Chem.*, **81**, 82 (1930).

As(III) by I_2 (v.), Chap. 15.

As(V) as $MgNH_4AsO_4$, weighed as $Mg_2As_2O_7$ (g.). By reduction of arsenomolyb-
dic acid to molybdenum blue (c., micro), Chap. 7.

Sb:

Sep. as $SbCl_3$, Chap. 9; Hubbard, *Ind. Eng. Chem., Anal. Ed.*, **13**, 915 (1941).

Sb(III) by I_2 or $KBrO_3$ (v.), Chap. 15; Kolthoff and Sandell, *Quantitative Inorganic
Analysis.*

Sb(V) by Rhodamine B (c., micro); Maren, *Anal. Chem.*, **19**, 487 (1947).

Bi:

As metal, by electrodeposition (g.), Chap. 5; A.S.T.M., *Chemical Analysis of
Metals.*

As BiOCl at pH 2.5 (g.); weigh as such or convert to Bi_2O_3; Hillebrand and
Lundell, *Applied Inorganic Analysis.*

By dithizone, with cyanide at pH 2 (c., micro), Chap. 6; Hubbard, *Ind. Eng.
Chem., Anal. Ed.*, **11**, 343 (1939).

V:

As vanadate, by $FeSO_4$ in 5 M H_2SO_4 (v.), phenanthroline indicator; North, *U. S.
Geol. Survey Bull.* **950**, 83 (1946).

As V(IV), from vanadate by SO_2 reduction, titrate with $KMnO_4$ or $Ce(SO_4)_2$ (v.),
Chaps. 12, 15; Furman, *J. Am. Chem. Soc.*, **50**, 1675 (1928).

By H_2O_2, as pervanadic acid (c.); Weissler, *Ind. Eng. Chem., Anal. Ed.*, **17**, 695
(1945).

By phosphovanadotungstate (c.), Chap. 7; Wright and Mellon, *Ind. Eng. Chem.,
Anal. Ed.*, **9**, 251 (1937).

Nb:

Sep. from Ta, by tannin, weighing as Nb_2O_5 (g.), Chap. 6; Schoeller, *Analysis of
Rarer Elements.*

By reduction with Zn to Nb(III), titrating with $KMnO_4$ (v.); Knowles and
Lundell, *J. Res. Nat. Bur. Standards*, **42**, 405 (1949).

Ta:

See Nb.

GROUP VI

O:

In organic compounds, sep. as CO, det. by liberation of I_2 from I_2O_5 (v.), Chap. 9;
Aluise et al., *Anal. Chem.*, **19**, 347 (1947).

H_2O_2, peroxy compounds: by $KMnO_4$ (v.), or $TiOSO_4$ (c.).

S:

In organic compounds, sep. as SO_2, det. as H_2SO_4 after reaction with H_2O_2, Chap. 9; Niederl and Niederl, *Organic Quantitative Microanalysis.*

Sulfate, as $BaSO_4$ (g.), Chaps. 2, 3; by $BaCl_2$ (v.), Chap. 18; Sheen and Kahler, *Ind. Eng. Chem., Anal. Ed.,* **8**, 127 (1936).

Sulfite, by I_2 (v.), Chap. 15.

H_2S, by I_2 (v.), Chaps. 9, 15; by metal salts, conductometrically (v., micro), Chap. 20.

Se:

Sep. from Te, etc., by distilling $SeCl_4$, Chap. 9; Lenher and Smith, *Ind. Eng. Chem.,* **16**, 837 (1924).

Det. as Se (g.), by reduction with SO_2 or hydroxylamine; Scott, *Standard Methods.*

Se(IV) and Te(IV) individually in mixtures, by $CrSO_4$, (v., potentiometric), Lingane and Niedrach, *J. Am. Chem. Soc.,* **70**, 1997 (1948).

Te:

Sep. and det. in mixtures; see Se.

Det. as Te (g.), by reduction of acid solutions with hydrazine and SO_2; Scott, *Standard Methods.*

Cr:

As Cr(VI), by excess $FeSO_4$ and back titration (v.) Chap. 15; Willard and Young, *Ind. Eng. Chem., Anal. Ed.,* **6**, 48 (1934) (in presence of V).

As Hg_2CrO_4 (g.); Dupuis and Duval, *Anal. Chim. Acta,* **3**, 345 (1949).

As CrO_4^- (c.); A.S.T.M., *Chemical Analysis of Metals.*

Mo:

Sep. from W, by H_2S pptn. from formate buffer; ignite at 500° and weigh as MoO_3 (g.); *J. Am. Chem. Soc.,* **60**, 640 (1938); see W, below.

By α-benzoin oxime in acid solution at 5° (g.), Chap. 6; Knowles, *J. Res. Nat. Bur. Standards,* **9**, 1 (1932).

As $PbMoO_4$ (g.); Schoeller, *Analysis of Rarer Elements;* Bonardi, *U. S. Bureau of Mines, Bull.* **212**, p. 108.

By reduction with Zn to Mo(III) and titration with $KMnO_4$ (v.).

W:

Sep. from Mo by cinchonine; ppt. tungstate in 1 N HCl, ignite at 750° and weigh as WO_3 (g.); A.S.T.M., *Chemical Analysis of Metals;* Grimaldi and Davidson, *U. S. Geol. Survey Bull.* **950**, p. 135 (1946).

By α-benzoin oxime (g.); see Mo; Yagoda and Fales, *loc. cit.*

U:

Sep. as nitrate by ether, Chap. 9; Hecht and Grunwald, *Mikrochemie*, **30**, 279 (1943).

U(VI) by oxine (g. or v.) Chap. 6; Rodden, *Anal. Chem.*, **21**, 327 (1949), reduced to U(IV) by zinc, titrated with $Ce(SO_4)_2$ (v.), Chap. 15; Rodden, *loc. cit.*

GROUP VII

F:

Sep. by distillation as SiF_4, Chap. 9; Huckaby, *Anal. Chem.*, **19**, 154 (1947).

As PbFCl, pptd. at pH 4.6 (g. or v.); Hoffmann and Lundell, *J. Res. Nat. Bur. Standards*, **3**, 581 (1929); Kaufman, *Anal. Chem.*, **21**, 582 (1949).

By $Th(NO_3)_4$ (v., semi-micro), Chap. 18; Rowley and Churchill, *Ind. Eng. Chem., Anal. Ed.*, **9**, 551 (1937).

By $AlCl_3$ (v.), Chaps. 19, 20; Geyer, *Z. anorg. Chem.*, **252**, 42 (1943).

Cl:

As AgCl (g.), Chaps. 2, 3.

By $AgNO_3$ (v.), Chap. 18; neutral solution, dichlorofluorescein indicator; acid solution, thiocyanate indicator plus excess Fe; Swift et al., *Anal. Chem.*, **22**, 306 (1950).

By $Hg(NO_3)_2$ in acid solution (v.), Chap. 19; Kolthoff and Sandell, *Quantitative Inorganic Analysis*.

Hypochlorite and chlorite, by KI in dilute sulfuric acid and thiosulfate titration (v.), Chap. 15.

Chlorate, by $TiCl_3$ or $CrCl_2$ (v.), Chap. 15; by excess $FeSO_4$ in 6 N H_2SO_4 and back titration (v.); Williams, *Ind. Eng. Chem., Anal. Ed.*, **17**, 533 (1945).

Br:

As AgBr (g.).

By $AgNO_3$, eosin or thiocyanate-Fe indicator, Chap. 18.

By displacement of Br_2 with Cl_2 (c.).

I:

As AgI (g.).

By $AgNO_3$, eosin indicator, pH 3, Chap. 18.

In presence Cl or Br, by $KMnO_4$ (v., potentiometric); Hahn, *Z. anorg. Chem.*, **195**, 75 (1931).

Mn:

Mn(II), by $KMnO_4$ in presence of pyrophosphate (v., potentiometric), Chaps. 7, 15; Lingane and Karplus, *Ind. Eng. Chem., Anal. Ed.*, **18**, 191 (1946).

By persulfate oxidation to MnO_4^- followed by titration with $NaAsO_2$, Chap. 15; A.S.T.M., *Chemical Analysis of Metals.*

As $MnNH_4PO_4$, weighed as $Mn_2P_2O_7$ (g.).

As MnO_4^- (c.), using persulfate, periodate or sodium bismuthate for oxidation.

Re:

As $(C_6H_5)_4AsReO_4$ (g.); Willard and Smith, *Ind. Eng. Chem., Anal. Ed.*, **11**, 305 (1939).

GROUP VIII

Fe:

As Fe_2O_3, ppt. at pH 4–5 (g.).

By cupferron or neocupferron in 1 N HCl, sep. from Al, PO_4; weigh as Fe_2O_3; good for traces (g.); Chap. 6.

As Fe(II), by $KMnO_4$ or $Ce(SO_4)_2$, (v.), Chap. 15. By orthophenanthroline (c., micro), Chap. 7, 17.

As Fe(III), by $TiCl_3$ (v.), Chap. 15.

Co:

Electrolytic (g.), Chap. 5; special conditions, see Brophy, *Ind. Eng. Chem., Anal. Ed.*, **3**, 363 (1931).

By 1-nitroso-2-naphthol, weighing as Co_3O_4 (g.), sep. from Ni, Chap. 6.

By anthranilic acid (g.), drying at 110–290°, Chap. 6; Duval, *Anal. Chim. Acta*, **5**, 71 (1951).

By 1-nitroso-2-naphthol-4-sulfonic acid (c.), Chap. 6.

Ni:

By dimethylglyoxime or cycloheptanonedioxime at pH 8 (g. or c.), Chap. 6; v., Chap. 20.

Electrolytic (g.), Chap. 5.

By titration with KCN in NH_3 solution (v.), Chap. 19.

Platinum metals, general:

See Schoeller, *Analysis of Rarer Elements*, also Gilchrist and Wichers, *J. Am. Chem. Soc.*, **57**, 2565 (1935).

Pd:

By dimethylglyoxime in 0.1 N HCl, Chap. 6; Wunder, *Z. anal. Chem.*, **52**, 101, 660, 740 (1913); Beamish and Scott, *Ind. Eng. Chem., Anal. Ed.*, **9**, 460 (1937).

Pt:

As $(NH_4)_2PtCl_6$ (with Ir, g.); Schoeller, *loc. cit.*, also *Analyst*, **55**, 550 (1930).

APPENDIX III

Tables of data

TABLE I

IONIZATION CONSTANTS OF ACIDS AND BASES AT 25°C
(Thermodynamic constants are quoted where available.)

Acid or base	Formula	Ionization constant	
Acids:			
Acetic.................	CH_3COOH		1.8×10^{-5}
Arsenic................	H_3AsO_4	K_1	5.6×10^{-3}
		K_2	1.7×10^{-7}
		K_3	$3 \ \times 10^{-12}$
Arsenious..............	H_3AsO_3	K_1	$6 \ \times 10^{-10}$
		K_2	$3 \ \times 10^{-14}$
Benzoic................	C_6H_5COOH		6.7×10^{-5}
Boric..................	H_3BO_3		5.8×10^{-10}
Butyric (*n*-)...........	C_6H_5COOH		1.5×10^{-5}
Carbonic...............	H_2CO_3	K_1	4.3×10^{-7}
		K_2	5.6×10^{-11}
Chloroacetic...........	$CH_2ClCOOH$		1.5×10^{-3}
Chlorobenzoic (*p*-).......	$C_6H_5ClCOOH$		1.0×10^{-4}
Chromic...............	H_2CrO_4	K_1	1.8×10^{-1}
		K_2	3.2×10^{-7}
Citric.................	$C_3H_5O(COOH)_3$	K_1	8.7×10^{-4}
		K_2	1.8×10^{-5}
		K_3	4.0×10^{-6}
Formic................	$HCOOH$		1.8×10^{-4}
Hydrazoic..............	HN_3		2.6×10^{-5}
Hydrocyanic...........	HCN		7.2×10^{-10}
Hydrofluoric............	$H \cdot HF_2$		7.4×10^{-4}
Hydrogen sulfide........	H_2S	K_1	9.1×10^{-8}
		K_2	1.2×10^{-15}
Hypochlorous...........	$HOCl$		3.5×10^{-8}
Iodic..................	HIO_3		1.7×10^{-1}
Malonic...............	$CH_2(COOH)_2$	K_1	1.4×10^{-3}
		K_2	2.0×10^{-6}

TABLE I (CONTINUED)

Acid or base	Formula	Ionization constant	
Nitrous................	HNO_2		4.5×10^{-4}
Oxalic.................	$(COOH)_2$	K_1	6.5×10^{-2}
		K_2	6.1×10^{-5}
Periodic...............	H_5IO_6	K_1	2.3×10^{-2}
		K_2	4.4×10^{-9}
Phenol.................	C_6H_5OH		1.3×10^{-10}
Phosphoric.............	H_3PO_4	K_1	7.5×10^{-3}
		K_2	6.2×10^{-8}
		K_3	4.8×10^{-13}
Phthalic...............	$C_6H_4(COOH)_2$	K_1	1.3×10^{-3}
		K_2	3.9×10^{-6}
Salicylic...............	$C_6H_4(OH)COOH$	K_1	1.1×10^{-3}
		K_2	3.6×10^{-14}
Selenious...............	H_2SeO_3	K_1	2.4×10^{-3}
		K_2	4.8×10^{-9}
Succinimid.............	$(CH_2CO)_2NH$		3.3×10^{-10}
Succinic...............	$(CH_2COOH)_2$	K_1	6.4×10^{-5}
		K_2	2.7×10^{-6}
Sulfuric...............	H_2SO_4	K_2	1.0×10^{-2}
Sulfurous..............	H_2SO_3	K_1	1.7×10^{-2}
		K_2	6.2×10^{-8}
Tartaric...............	$(CHOHCOOH)_2$	K_1	9.6×10^{-4}
		K_2	2.9×10^{-5}
Bases:			
Ammonia..............	NH_3		1.8×10^{-5}
Aniline................	$C_6H_5NH_2$		3.8×10^{-10}
Anthranilic acid.........	$C_6H_4NH_2COOH$		1.4×10^{-12}
Ethylenediamine........	$(CH_2NH_2)_2$	K_1	1.0×10^{-4}
		K_2	2.0×10^{-7}
Hydrazine..............	N_2H_4	K_1	3.0×10^{-6}
Hydroxylamine..........	NH_2OH		1×10^{-8}
Morphine..............	$C_{17}H_{19}O_3N$		7.4×10^{-7}
Piperidine.............	$C_5H_{10}NH$		1.6×10^{-3}
Pyridine...............	C_5H_5N		1.4×10^{-9}
Quinoline..............	C_9H_7N		6.3×10^{-10}

TABLE II

SOLUBILITY PRODUCTS AT 25°C

(Thermodynamic constants are quoted where available)

Salt	Solubility product	Salt	Solubility product
AgCl	1.6×10^{-10}	FeS	4×10^{-19}
AgBr	3.3×10^{-13}	Hg_2SO_4	6.2×10^{-7}
AgI	8.5×10^{-17}	Hg_2Cl_2	1.1×10^{-18}
AgCNS	1.2×10^{-12}	HgI_2	3.2×10^{-29}
AgOH	1×10^{-8}	MgF_2	7.3×10^{-9}
$Ag \cdot Ag(CN)_2$	2.2×10^{-12}	$Mg(OH)_2$	5.5×10^{-12}
Ag_2CrO_4	9.0×10^{-12}	$MgNH_4PO_4$	2.5×10^{-13}
BaC_2O_4	3×10^{-7}	$Mn(OH)_2$	5.5×10^{-14}
$BaCrO_4$	1.1×10^{-10}	MnS	1×10^{-16}
$BaSO_4$	1.0×10^{-10}	PbI_2	9×10^{-9}
CaC_2O_4	2.0×10^{-9}	$PbSO_4$	2×10^{-8}
$CaSO_4$	6×10^{-5}	$PbCrO_4$	2×10^{-14}
$CaCO_3$	4.8×10^{-9}	PbS	5×10^{-28}
CaF_2	3.4×10^{-11}	$SrSO_4$	2.9×10^{-7}
CdS	1.4×10^{-28}	SrC_2O_4	6×10^{-8}
CoS	3×10^{-26}	$SrCrO_4$	3.6×10^{-5}
CuCl	1.8×10^{-7}	TlCl	2.7×10^{-4}
CuI	1.1×10^{-12}	TlCNS	2.2×10^{-4}
CuCNS	4×10^{-14}	ZnS	4.5×10^{-24}
CuS	4×10^{-38}	$ZnNH_4PO_4(100°C)$	1×10^{-16}

TABLE III

OXIDATION-REDUCTION POTENTIALS AT 25°C

(Adapted from E. H. Swift, *Introductory Quantitative Analysis*, New York, Prentice-Hall, 1950)

Reaction	Standard potential, volts	Formal potential, volts
$F_2 + 2e \rightarrow 2F^-$	2.88	
$S_2O_8^- + 2H^+ + 2e \rightarrow 2HSO_4^-$	2.05	
$Ag^{++} + e \rightarrow Ag^+$		1.91 (1 M HNO$_3$)
$H_2O_2 + 2H^+ + 2e \rightarrow 2H_2O$	1.77	
$Bi_2O_5 + 10H^+ + 4e \rightarrow 2Bi + 5H_2O$	1.7	
$MnO_4^- + 4H^+ + 3e \rightarrow MnO_2 + 2H_2O$	1.59	
$HClO + H^+ + 2e \rightarrow Cl^- + H_2O$	1.50	
$Ce^{++++} + e \rightarrow Ce^{+++}$		1.7 (1 M HClO$_4$)
		1.44 (1 M H$_2$SO$_4$)
$PbO_2 + 4H^+ + 2e \rightarrow Pb^{++} + 2H_2O$	1.47	1.63 (1 M H$_2$SO$_4$)
$MnO_4^- + 8H^+ + 5e \rightarrow Mn^{++} + 4H_2O$	1.45	
$ClO_3^- + 6H^+ + 6e \rightarrow Cl^- + 3HO$	1.45	
$HAuCl_4 + 3e \rightarrow Au + H^+ + 4Cl^-$		1.4 (1 M HCl)
$Cl_2 + 2e \rightarrow 2Cl^-$	1.36	
$Cr_2O_7^- + 14H^+ + 6e \rightarrow 2Cr^{+++} + 7H_2O$	1.3	
$Tl^{+++} + 2e \rightarrow Tl^+$	1.25	0.77 (1 M HCl)
$MnO_2 + 4H^+ + 2e \rightarrow Mn^{++} + 2H_2O$	1.24	
$O_2 + 4H^+ + 4e \rightarrow 2H_2O$	1.23	
$H_2SeO_4 + 2H^+ + 2e \rightarrow H_2SeO_3 + H_2O$	1.2	
$IO_3^- + 6H^+ + 5e \rightarrow \frac{1}{2}I_2 + 3H_2O$	1.19	
$Br_2 + 2e \rightarrow 2Br^-$	1.07	
$2ICl_2^- + 2e \rightarrow I_2 + 4Cl^-$	1.06	
$VO_2^+ + 2H^+ + e \rightarrow VO^{++} + H_2O$	1.00	
$HNO_2 + H^+ + e \rightarrow NO + H_2O$	0.98	
$ClO^- + H_2O + 2e \rightarrow Cl^- + 2OH^-$	0.94	
$NO_3^- + 3H^+ + 2e \rightarrow HNO_2 + 2H_2O$		0.92 (1 M HNO$_3$)
$2Hg^{++} + 2e \rightarrow Hg_2^{++}$		0.90 (1 M HClO$_4$)
$Cu^{++} + I^- + e \rightarrow CuI$	0.85	
$Ag^+ + e \rightarrow Ag$	0.80	0.23 (1 M HCl)
$Hg_2^{++} + 2e \rightarrow 2Hg$	0.80	0.28 (1 M KCl)
		0.67 (1 M H$_2$SO$_4$)
$Fe^{+++} + e \rightarrow Fe^{++}$	0.78	0.70 (1 M HCl)
		0.68 (1 M H$_2$SO$_4$)
$H_2SeO_3 + 4H^+ + 4e \rightarrow Se + 3H_2O$		0.75 (1 M HClO$_4$)
$SbCl_6^- + 2e \rightarrow SbCl_4^- + 2Cl^-$		0.76 (4 M HCl)
$O_2 + 2H^+ + 2e \rightarrow H_2O_2$	0.69	
$Hg_2SO_4 + 2e \rightarrow 2Hg + SO_4^-$	0.62	

TABLE III (CONTINUED)

Reaction	Standard potential, volts	Formal potential, volts
$MnO_4^- + e \rightarrow MnO_4^=$	0.6	
$H_3AsO_4 + 2H^+ + 2e \rightarrow H_3AsO_3 + H_2O$		0.58 (1 M HCl)
$I_3^- + 2e \rightarrow 3I^-$	0.54	
$MoO_3 + 4H^+ + e \rightarrow MoO^{+++} + 2H_2O$	0.5	
$Cu^{++} + 2Cl^- + e \rightarrow CuCl_2^-$	0.46	
$VO^{++} + 2H^+ + e \rightarrow V^{+++} + H_2O$	0.34	
$UO^{++} + 4H^+ + 2e \rightarrow U^{++++} + 2H_2O$	0.4	
$Fe(CN)_6^\equiv + e \rightarrow Fe(CN)_6^\equiv$	0.36	0.72 (1 M H_2SO_4 or $HClO_4$)
$Cu^{++} + 2e \rightarrow Cu$	0.34	
$BiO^+ + 2H^+ + 3e \rightarrow Bi + H_2O$	0.31	
Normal calomel half-cell		0.282
$AgCl + e \rightarrow Ag + Cl^-$	0.222	
$SbO^+ + 2H^+ + 3e \rightarrow Sb + H_2O$	0.21	
$S_4O_6^= + 2e \rightarrow 2S_2O_3^=$	0.17	
$S + 2H^+ + 2e \rightarrow H_2S$	0.17	
$Sn^{++++} + 2e \rightarrow Sn^{++}$		0.14 (1 M HCl)
$HSO_4^- + 3H^+ + 2e \rightarrow SO_2 + 2H_2O$	0.14	0.07 (1 M H_2SO_4)
$TiO^{++} + 2H^+ + e \rightarrow Ti^{+++} + H_2O$	0.04	
$2H^+ + 2e \rightarrow H_2$	0.00	
$Pb^{++} + 2e \rightarrow Pb$	−0.12	−0.29 (1 M H_2SO_4)
$Sn^{++} + 2e \rightarrow Sn$	−0.14	
$N_2 + 5H^+ + 4e \rightarrow N_2H_5^+$	−0.17	
$Ni^{++} + 2e \rightarrow Ni$	−0.23	
$V^{+++} + e \rightarrow V^{++}$	−0.26	
$Co^{++} + 2e \rightarrow Co$	−0.28	
$Tl^+ + e \rightarrow Tl$	−0.34	−0.55 (1 M HCl)
$Cd^{++} + 2e \rightarrow Cd$	−0.40	
$Cr^{+++} + e \rightarrow Cr^{++}$	−0.4	
$Fe^{++} + 2e \rightarrow Fe$	−0.44	
$Se + 2H^+ + 2e \rightarrow H_2Se$	−0.5	
$H_3PO_3 + 2H^+ + 2e \rightarrow H_3PO_2 + H_2O$	−0.59	
$Cr^{++} + 2e \rightarrow Cr$	−0.6	
$Zn^{++} + 2e \rightarrow Zn$	−0.76	
$Sn(OH)_6^= + 2e \rightarrow Sn(OH)_4^= + 2OH^-$	−0.96	
$Mn^{++} + 2e \rightarrow Mn$	−1.03	
$Al^{+++} + 3e \rightarrow Al$	−1.7	
$Mg^{++} + 2e \rightarrow Mg$	−1.9	
$Na^+ + e \rightarrow Na$	−2.71	
$Ca^{++} + 2e \rightarrow Ca$	−2.88	

APPENDIX IV

Answers to problems

Chapter 2, page 28:

4. 0.31 by ideal law; 0.42 by extended equation.
5. 10.70 mg./l.; 2.33 mg./l. in pure water.
7. Ionic strength of sat. AgCl: 1.255×10^{-5}.
8. Ionic strength of sat. Ag_2CrO_4: 4.11×10^{-4}, neglecting the slight hydrolysis.
9. 1.015.

Chapter 4, page 56:

1. 6×10^{-5} mm.   6. By 20°C.
7. $CaSO_4$; $BaSO_4$; $Fe_2(SO_4)_3$.

Chapter 5, page 82:

1. 1610 sec.
3. -0.097 volt on hydrogen scale, ignoring cuprous ions.
4. Reduction to $Cu(NH_3)_2^+$.   5. $+0.496$ volt.
6. Zinc: -0.91 volt; hydrogen: -0.989 volt.

Chapter 6, page 109:

1. (a) 0.38 microgram.   (b) 3.1 microgram.   Equilibrium constant is 2.9.
5. (b) 7.55 mg.

Chapter 9, page 175:

1. 114 mg.

Chapter 11, page 197:

1. 0.78 volt; 0.19 volt.   2. 0.39 volt; 0.00 volt.
3. 1.9×10^8; 0.03% unreduced.   4. 0.002%; 1.34 volt.
5. 0.168 volt.   6. 1.0×10^{-12}.
13. (a) 1.1×10^3; (b) 8.7%; (c) 0.10 volt; (d) to CuCl; (e) 1.4×10^{-4}.
14. 1.2×10^{-3} M. If more than this, CuCl will precipitate at start.
15. 2.0×10^{-15}.   17. (a) 0.782 volt; (b) 0.535 volt.

Chapter 12, page 222:

3. 0.354 volt, right hand positive.

Chapter 13, page 246:

1. (a) [1] 4.76, 4.81; [2] 7.21, 7.20; [3] 9.22, 8.26.
   (b) [1] 9.24, 8.21; [2] 6.79, 5.82; [3] 4.78, 4.76.
2. (a) 25°, 8.87, 5.11, 6.99, 4.66; 60°, 8.41, 4.64, 6.54, 4.76.
   (b) 25°, 5.13, 8.89, 7.01, 9.34; 60°, 4.61, 8.38, 6.48, 8.26.
3. 8.06 at 25°.   4. 4.57.
5. (a) 8.35, 0.97×10^5, 0.245% error;
   (b) 9.35, 0.97×10^4, 2.45% error;
   (c) 3.40, 540, 44% error.

6. (a) pH 8.26, 4.76, 7.93; $\dfrac{1}{b}\dfrac{db}{d\mathrm{pH}}$, 1.6×10^{-3}.

   (b) pH 11.13, 5.28, 9.26; $\dfrac{1}{b}\dfrac{db}{d\mathrm{pH}}$, 4.8×10^{-4}.

7. 6.47; 0.087.
12. (a) about 10.8; (b) 7.31, for formation of NH_4HCO_3;
   (c) $\dfrac{1}{a}\dfrac{da}{d\mathrm{pH}} = 0.058$.
13. (a) 8.31 at first, 4.27 at second endpoint;
   (b) 3.3% at first, 1.14% at second endpoint.

Chapter 14, page 275:

1. pK, 7.91.

Chapter 17, page 345:

1. 3.75% error.   2. -0.125 volt; -0.153 volt.

Chapter 18, page 365:

2. Cl^-, 0.0224 M; Br^-, 0.0121 M; error, 0.5%.

Chapter 19, page 379:

2. 2.1×10^{-9}.
4. (a) 2.6×10^{-8}, 1.3×10^{-8}; assumption incorrect.
   (b) 4.38×10^{-12}, 6.25×10^{-7}; 0.034 ml. *Note:* $[CN^-] = 2[Ag(NH_3)_2{}^+]$.
5. 0.04% error.

Author index

Subject index